# Pigments for Paper

A Project of the
Coating Pigments
Committee of TAPPI's
Coating & Graphic Arts
Division

Task Group Chairman
John E. O'Shea

Edited by
Robert W. Hagemeyer

Atlanta, GA

TAPPI PRESS
Technology Park/Atlanta
P.O. Box 105113
Atlanta, GA 30348-5113 U.S.A.



ISBN 0-89852-064-9
TP 0102B062
*Printed in the United States of America*

**Library of Congress Cataloging-in-Publication Data**

Pigments for paper/edited by R.W. Hagemeyer
p. cm.
Includes bibliographical references.
ISBN 0-89852-064-9
1. Paper coatings--Additives. 2. Pigments. I. Hagemeyer, Robert W.
TS1118.F5P52 1997 96-54592
676'.235--dc21 CIP

# Dedication

Trailblazer, a pioneering leader in one's field of expertise, aptly describes Robert W. Hagemeyer and the role he has played in advancing paper coating technology. To formally recognize Bob's many contributions and more than 40 years of service to the industry, this book is dedicated to him.

Bob Hagemeyer broke ground in the pigment particle packing area in the mid-1950s, when very little was known about the subject. Heading up a committee, Hagemeyer spent the next 10 years investigating theories about particles. Producing a series of papers, the fourth and final report indicated that chemical composition is probably more important than particle shape in controlling particle packing. These investigations are considered the cornerstone of the work and applications that followed. He is responsible for rejuvenating the "on-site" manufacturing of precipitated calcium carbonates (PCC) and prodding the industry into alkaline papermaking.

Bob is the author of numerous papers on PCC, coated papers, and related technology. He has participated as editor and/or author of chapters in Pulp and Paper Chemistry and Chemical Technology Series, the Pulp and Paper Manufacture Joint Textbook series, and the six previous editions of this text. His role in these developments have earned him the title "Mr. Calcium Carbonate."

As one of the founders of TAPPI's Coating and Graphic Arts Division, Bob Hagemeyer has the singular reputation of having attended every annual conference since its inception in 1949. The wall in his study is covered with numerous awards, including the Division's technical award, which he received in 1974, and numerous Certificates of Appreciation for his many contributions to the Coating and Graphics Arts Division over the years.

In 1971, TAPPI bestowed the distinguished rank of "Fellow" upon Bob Hagemeyer. In 1985, TAPPI recognized his loyal service to the Association by awarding him TAPPI's Distinguished Service Award.

Ten years later in 1995, TAPPI awarded him its highest honor, the prized Gunnar Nicholson Gold Medal Award, for his relentless drive for almost a half century to disseminate ideas and information throughout the industry. Bob stands alone in the history of TAPPI as the only individual to have received both the Distinguished Service Award and the Gold Medal.

Therefore, it is with a great deal of respect for Bob Hagemeyer's pioneering spirit and unwavering commitment to the coating field that we dedicate this work.

**The Coating Pigments Committee**
John E. O'Shea
*Task Group Chairman*

# Preface

*Pigments for Paper* represents an effort to provide, in one volume, basic information on paper pigments, per se, as well as performance data on all applications for pigments in paper products. Previous texts have been more performance oriented focusing on the use of pigments either in paper coating or paper filling. It is hoped the increased emphasis on pigment technology in this text will enable the reader to better understand the intrinsic properties of these materials and, in turn, their potential for use in new applications. The information presented is basic in nature and should be of value to everyone concerned with the use of pigments in paper. The book can serve as an introductory text as well as a practical reference for anyone involved in these technical areas.

The first chapter presents general information on the history and various technical facets of paper coating, while the second chapter provides similar coverage on paper filling. Subsequent chapters deal with the individual pigments. The format used for the latter chapters is as follows:

A. Introduction
B. Historical Background
C. Product Description
    1. Principal Classes
    2. Methods of Manufacture
    3. Chemical and Physical Properties
    4. Handling, Storage, and Mixing
D. Reasons for Use
    1. Paper Coating
        a. Optical Properties
        b. Printing Properties
        c. Typical Formulations
        d. Performance Data
    2. Paper Filling
        a. Optical Properties
        b. Performance Data

E. Analytical Procedures
F. Economic Factors
G. Market Statistics
H. Future Outlook

The amount of data presented varies and is somewhat dependent upon the volumes used and diversity of applications for the individual pigments.

Chapter authors are individuals with broad experience and special knowledge of the particular pigment discussed. In most instances, the authors have been able to augment their own information with contributions from others working in the same pigment area. As a result, the chapters present a comprehensive and consensual treatment of the pigments and their performance in specific paper systems.

Much credit should be given to the various reviewers and others who have assisted in preparing this book. Unless one has been involved, it is difficult to appreciate the large amount of time and effort that is expended by the various volunteers in gathering and presenting the information contained in this text. The work of those listed and all other contributors is most appreciated.

**Robert W. Hagemeyer, Editor**
Norcross, Georgia

# Introduction

The first TAPPI book on pigmentary materials, Pigments for Paper Coating—Monograph 7, was published in 1948. In subsequent years expanded and revised versions appeared:Monograph 20, published in 1958; Monograph 30, published in 1966; and Monograph 38, published in 1976. The only edition of a related book on pigments, Paper Loading Materials—Monograph 19, was printed in 1958. The difference in the apparent amount of literary effort expended on paper coating pigments versus paper filling pigments is indicative of the relative importance attached to the use of pigments in these respective paper applications.

With the advent of alkaline papermaking the situation has changed markedly for several reasons. The most significant factor is the increasing pressure for conservation and improved utilization of fibrous raw materials. While the addition of small percentages of filler pigment for fiber extension has been practiced for many years, recent advances in papermaking technology permit the use of higher percentages of filler without loss in sheet strength. Coupling the desire to conserve fiber with the opportunity to use increased percentages of filler has resulted in a sharp increase in the total demand for paper filling pigments.

The resulting favorable market outlook is prompting pigment manufacturers to put more emphasis on the development of new and improved pigments for use in the paper web. It may take several years but some feel this effort will eventually result in as diverse a group of pigments for paper filling as that presently available for paper coating. Fortunately, the two applications for pigments in paper seem to be more complementary that competitive, which bodes well for continued product development in both areas.

# Contributors

**George E. Alderfer,** PPG Industries Inc.

**William C. Atherton,** Dry Branch Kaolin Company

**James T. Brown,** Rohm and Haas Company

**Robert A. Gill,** Specialty Minerals Inc.

**Robert W. Hagemeyer,** Consultant

**David V. Healy,** OMYA Inc.

**Rabon L. Hollingsworth,** ECC International Inc.

**Ludwig Huggenberger,** Plüss-Staufer AG

**Joseph N. Ishley,** Specialty Minerals Inc.

**Mitchell H. Koppelman,** Specialty Minerals Inc.

**Femi O. Kotoye,** Dow Chemical USA

**Klaus Kramer,** Martinswerk GmbH

**Robert A. Kwoka,** Dupont White Pigment and Mineral Products

**John A. Manasso,** Dry Branch Kaolin Company

**Hans B. Neubold,** OMYA Inc.

**John E. O'Shea,** ECC International Inc.

**Paul Sennett,** Consultant

**Nikhil C. Trivedi,** Specialty Minerals Inc.

# Table of Contents

# 1.

# Pigment-Coated Paper

*Robert W. Hagemeyer*

## Introduction

The rate of growth in demand for pigment-coated paper far exceeds the rate of growth for total paper and paperboard demand. This situation, which has persisted for several decades, has provided a strong stimulus for sustained technical effort and, in turn, is responsible for the continuing development of new and improved materials, machinery and methods for the production of pigment-coated paper. This book focuses on the current state of the art related to pigments for paper.

The principal reasons for applying a pigment coating to paper and paperboard are to improve printability and appearance. In its simplest form the coating consists of a pigment plus an adhesive to bind the pigment particles both to one another and to the base paper. Pigments are the main constituents of the coating. The binders and various additives that may be included normally comprise less than 20 percent (by weight) of the coating formulation. The pigment coating provides a surface that is more uniform in appearance and more receptive to printing ink than are the uncoated paper fibers. This, in turn, both facilitates the printing process and enhances the graphic reproduction. The improvement in print quality is readily apparent, especially in image areas or when multiple colors are involved.

## History

The origin of coated paper is obscure. Historical *(1)* references indicate that efforts to coat paper with pigments were made as long as several hundred years ago. The volume of production was small, if not insignificant, as late as 1850. In the latter half of the nineteenth century, the situation changed markedly when substantial technical effort resulted in the development of mechanical methods for coating paper on a commercial scale. These early coaters used a brush to apply followed by brushes to smooth the coating before being festooned to dry.

The process was slow and relatively inefficient, but the high aesthetic appeal of the finished paper commanded the premium in price necessary to compensate for the manufacturing cost.

By 1920 pigment-coated paper was a commercial commodity with estimated consumption in the United States of about 100,000 tons, or approximately 15 percent of total printing and writing paper. The printing fidelity and attractive appearance obtained with these pigment-coated papers gave them an aura of elegance that made them desirable for corporate annual reports and for brochures advertising high-priced items such as automobiles. Weights ranged from 90 to 150 $g/m^2$ (60 to 100 lb per book ream) with most production falling in the middle of the range. The dominant pigment was coating clay imported from England while the common binder was animal glue.

During the 1930's a number of developments combined to produce a marked increase in the demand for pigment-coated paper. The application of coating on the paper machine, rather than as a separate operation, greatly reduced the cost of producing pigment-coated paper. The invention of high-speed heat-set letterpresses made high volume, low cost printing a reality. Together these developments made possible the high-volume graphic periodicals such as **Life** and **Fortune**. In 1935 pigment-coated paper consumption in the United States approximated 250,000 tons. Fifteen years later, despite a five-year plateau dictated by World War II, pigment-coated paper volume had quadrupled, topping one million tons in 1950. During the 1950s and 1960s, technical advances in coating materials and equipment fostered continuing growth so that by 1970 pigment-coated paper demand in the United States reached 3,275,000 tons, a fourteen fold increase in 35 years, which is equivalent to a growth rate of eight percent compounded annually. If a correction is applied for the substantial lowering in average basis weight during this period, the coated surface area available for printing increased at a rate in excess of 10 percent yearly. A graphic illustration of the general relationship between the introduction of new technology and the increase in coated paper volume appears in **Fig. 1-1**.

*Figure 1-1 The Impact of New Technology on Coated Paper Volume*

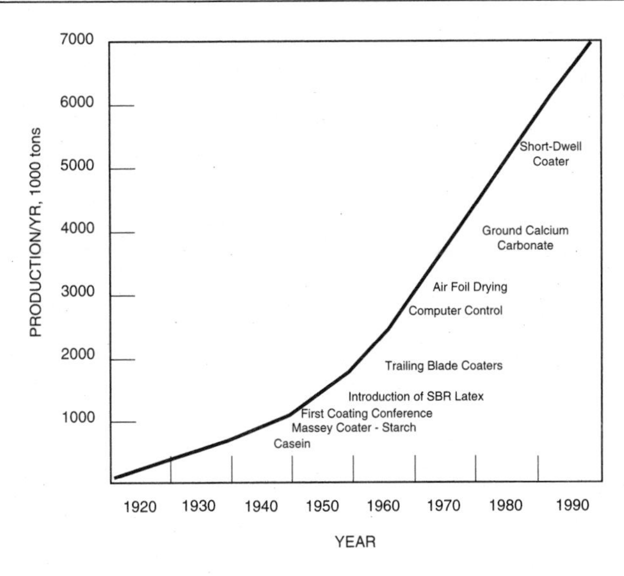


The development and use of pigment-coated printing papers has not, of course, been restricted to the United States. Considerable research, development, and production has taken place in Western Europe and Japan. In many instances the grade structure and product specifications for these countries differ somewhat from those for the United States, reflecting differences in regional availability of materials as well as in the end-use requirements of local printers and publishers. Growth in demand has fluctuated by region with changes in the respective economies and their per capita income. Since 1970 there have been a few occasions where year to year growth figures have been negative. World figures indicate a growth trend line of slightly more than four percent annually, a rate which is expected to continue into the next century. The following estimates for pigment-coated paper consumption (**Table 1-1**) and percent annual growth (**Table 1-2**) were compiled from several sources and provide a consensus forecast through 2005.

*Table 1-1 Forecast Coated Paper Production (millions of metric tons )*

| | 1990 | 1995 | 2000 | 2005 |
|---|---|---|---|---|
| **North America** | | | | |
| United States | 6,822 | 8,328 | 9,997 | 12,035 |
| Canada | 531 | 800 | 1,085 | 1,417 |
| Total | 7,353 | 9,038 | 11,082 | 13,452 |

*Table 1-1 continued*

| | 1990 | 1995 | 2000 | 2005 |
|---|---|---|---|---|
| **Europe** | 9,700 | 10,100 | 14,150 | 17,700 |
| **Japan** | 3,930 | 4,700 | 6,100 | 7,600 |
| **All other** | 750 | 1,100 | 1,550 | 2,150 |
| **Totals** | **21,733** | **24,938** | **32,882** | **40,902** |

*Table 1-2 Forecast Coated Paper Growth (percent annually)*

| | 1990 to 1995 | 1995 to 2000 | 2000 to 2005 | 1990 to 2005 |
|---|---|---|---|---|
| **North America** | | | | |
| United States | 3.8 | 3.9 | 3.8 | 3.9 |
| Canada | 8.5 | 6.3 | 5.5 | 6.7 |
| Total | 4.2 | 4.2 | 3.9 | 4.1 |
| **Europe** | 0.5 | 7.0 | 4.6 | 4.1 |
| **Japan** | 3.7 | 5.3 | 4.5 | 4.5 |
| **All other** | 8.0 | 7.1 | 6.8 | 7.3 |
| **Total** | 2.8 | 5.7 | 4.5 | 4.3 |

Based on these figures the outlook for coated printing paper is quite favorable, with an expected growth rate in excess of the paper industry average and faster than the expected growth of the general economy. Numerous factors are cited for the above average growth, with the more significant including a rising level of education, increased leisure time, and growing affluence in the developed economies. A rapid rise in literacy (**Table 1-3**) will add to the demand in the developing countries.

*Table 1-3 World Population (millions)*

| | 1970 | 1980 | 1990 | 2000 | Annual Growth (percent) 1970 to 1980 | 1980 to 1990 | 1990 to 2000 |
|---|---|---|---|---|---|---|---|
| Adults* | 1753 | 2165 | 2660 | 3117 | 2.2 | 2.0 | 1.0 |
| Literature | 1184 | 1538 | 1977 | 2400 | 2.7 | 2.5 | 2.0 |
| Illiterate | 569 | 627 | 683 | 712 | 1.0 | 0.9 | 0.4 |
| **Total** | **3663** | **4569** | **5455** | **6351** | **2.3** | **1.8** | **1.5** |

*Persons 15 years and older
Source: FAO

There is some concern that the growth of electronic communication systems will have an adverse impact on coated paper volume. Most individuals knowledgeable in the area foresee an eventual possibility for some substitution, but it is generally agreed that any major incursion into the present system is many years off. The convenience, cost, quality, and portability of hard copy afforded by coated paper will be very difficult — if not impossible — to match.

## Principal Grades

There are many different grades of coated printing papers. The two fundamental classifications are coated one side (C1S) and coated two side (C2S). The former are used primarily for labels, wrappings, and the like where only the coated surface is printed. For the United States, the volume of C1S paper represents about 10 percent of total coated paper production. The balance (C2S) is further divided into five grade categories based on brightness, fiber furnish, and gloss. Number 1 is the brightest and contains 100% chemical fiber while Number 5 is the least bright and includes a large percentage of groundwood pulp. The American Paper Institute ranks coated paper by brightness with No. 1 coated specified at a GE value of 85 or higher; No. 5 coated has a GE value of 72.9 or lower. Number 5 coated accounts for approximately 50 percent of total U.S. coated paper production and 56 percent of C2S. About 70 percent of the No. 5 C2S, also referred to as publication grade, is used for magazine publishing. Periodicals, catalogs, and commercial printing consume the remainder.

For many years the major portion of pigment coating development work has been focused on the publication grades. This emphasis is the direct result of the increase in mailing and distribution charges which prompted an industry-wide effort to lower basis weight and thus reduce the unit shipping cost. While postage rates have quadrupled, a 30 percent reduction in basis weight has offset part of the increase. This was accomplished without any degradation in print quality, thus maintaining a high impact level and preventing the loss of magazine advertising revenues to television and other media.

## Technical Considerations

At first glance, applying a pigment coating to a paper surface and its subsequent drying appears to be a rather simple, straightforward operation. It would be if quality considerations could be ignored. However, that is not the case for commercially coated paper, which must be manufactured to meet a comprehensive list of specifications that include both intrinsic and performance properties. Considering the myriad of variables involved, accomplishing this is anything but a simple task which is further complicated by the size of the equipment involved and the speed at which it must be operated. Despite many years of research and development effort, there are still many unanswered technical questions and areas wherein additional technology is needed.

Producing pigment coated paper involves many factors and functions. Important items to be considered are:

1. The choice of raw materials, i.e., base stock, pigments, and binders,
2. The color preparation procedure,
3. The rheological properties of the pigment coating formulation,
4. The method of applying the coating,
5. The drying rate,
6. The specifications and end-use requirements for the finished paper.

A brief look at the total composite coated paper provides a better understanding of the functions influenced or controlled by the individual segments and the important interactions that must be recognized and controlled.

Simplistic thinking can lead to the conclusion that the pigment coating per se is the dominant component; it provides the surface that is visible to the eye and that comes in direct contact with the printing ink. Unfortunately, the final surface is only partially controlled by the coating formulation. There are a number of additional factors that strongly influence the continuity and heterogeneity of the coated surface, the most important being the uncoated raw stock.

Since the raw stock represents approximately 70 percent of the weight and 90 percent of the volume of a C2S paper, it is easy to understand its fundamental impact on the coated surface. The situation is further complicated by the fact that the base stock is a porous mat formed by fibers of various dimensions resulting in a discontinuous surface comprised of 10 roughly equal percentages of mixed fiber and irregular void areas. Fortunately, most of the dimensions involved are microscopic; thus surface uniformity can be significantly improved by applying a pigment coating. The variability of the substrate does influence the thickness and structure of the coating layer so that some nonuniformity will still exist in the finished sheet. Some raw stock problems such as poor formation and wire marks are often accentuated by the coating layer. This is especially true at lower basis weights.

Aside from the raw stock, other factors that influence the properties and appearance of the coated sheet include the basic coating formulation, method of application, operating conditions, and finishing procedures. This combination of factors determines the inherent properties of the coating as well as its final structure and the resulting performance properties of the coated paper. Many technologists feel the key to determining and optimizing performance lies in controlling the structure of the coating layer as it exists on the finished paper.

Informal discussions on coating structure are mentioned as far back as the 1938 Minutes of the TAPPI Coating Committee. It appears the first formal investigation was instigated in May 1956 as a part of TAPPI Project 600, a study titled, "The Effect of Pigment Combination and Solids Concentration on Particle Packing and Coated Paper Characteristics". Of necessity, the work was elementary and limited by the equipment and techniques available for carrying out the work. Progress Reports *(1-3)* were presented at the TAPPI Coating Conferences of 1958, 1959, 1962, and 1964. While the study was terminated far short of its final goal, it did generate a good deal of information on the properties of pigment slips. Some of the more significant conclusions were:

1. Particle packing does influence the flow properties of pigment slips.
2. Both the shape and chemical composition of the pigment particle influence its packing tendency.
3. Poor dispersion or reflocculation results in decreased pigment packing (increased sediment volume) independent of the pigment particle shape, particle size, and chemical composition.
4. Chemical composition may be more important than particle shape in governing the packing tendencies of some pigment combinations.
5. The sediment volume for combinations of chemically similar pigments, whether physically similar or dissimilar, are directly proportional to the percentage of the component present, i.e., independent of particle shape.

By 1964, when the fourth report was presented, the number of subjects to be investigated had become too broad and complex for a volunteer group. For example, most of the studies had been limited to pigment slips. Expanding the investigation to include the various binders would have required a factorial increase in the number of systems to be investigated. Fortunately the Progress Reports had created enough interest in the subject that various individuals and organizations undertook advanced studies directed at segments related to their specific areas of interest. Much of this subsequent work is covered in a 1976 review by Lepoutre *(4)*, which summarized the published information on factors affecting coating structure. Relationships are suggested for systems with and without binder present. Some general thoughts on coating structure and properties of the finished paper are included. Lepoutre used this review as a reference point for his subsequent research studies. Work by Lepoutre and others *(5-8)* gradually led to a theory that the volume, size, and distribution of the void area is one of the more significant elements of the coating structure. A paper by Alince *(9)* supports the following hypothesis. Considering pigmented coatings as a dispersion of microvoids, the voids are the actual scattering species and their size and number determine the light-scattering efficiency. In a study of factors affecting the coating structure of lightweight coated paper (LWC), Baumeister *(10)* observed that surface coverage and rotogravure printability depend on rapid immobilization of the coating film, thus increasing coating hold-out and improving coverage of the raw stock. A subsequent study by Lee *(11)* demonstrated that pretreating paper substrates with various coagulants and flocculants hastened immobilization and significantly improved coating hold-out and, in turn, fiber coverage.

Thirty-five years of study have generated a lot of information on coating structure and the factors that influence it. There is still more to be learned, especially with regard to the relationship between coating structure and the performance properties of the finished coated paper. In the meantime, the coating technologist can profit from what has been learned thus far and should keep this subject in mind when deciding on the raw materials, equipment, and operating conditions to be used in the formulation and application of a pigment coating.

## Raw Materials

Pigment coated paper is comprised of essentially three materials: the base paper or raw stock, pigment, and binder. On a weight basis, representative percentages would be seventy, twenty-five, and five percent respectively. An approximate volume relationship would be ninety, nine, and one percent, in corresponding order. In addition, there are a number of materials such as dispersants, lubricants, and the like that are used in minor percentages.

## Base Paper

The base paper is the most important component in determining the quality of a pigment coated paper. Applying a coating tends to accentuate rather than obliterate any shortcomings of the raw stock. Base paper properties of prime importance are uniformity, formation, porosity, resiliency, strength, moisture content, brightness, opacity, finish, and surface smoothness. Furnish for the raw stock will vary and can contain from 20 to 50 percent long fiber, 40 to 70 percent short or mechanical fiber, and 5 to 20 percent pigment filler. The fiber furnish will vary with basis weight and the physical requirements for the finished paper. Both the type and source of the wood for pulping are important considerations. The large dimensions of chemical fibers from fast-growing softwood species can cause problems, especially in lightweight coated grades.

## Composition

The composition of the base paper is dependent upon the grade and end-use requirements of the coated paper. Naturally, the so-called wood-free grades should contain essentially no groundwood fiber. The percentage of long-fiber pulp is determined by the strength and the folding endurance specifications for the finished paper. The short fibers provide bulk, resiliency, and texture. They contribute to the physical uniformity of the fiber web and provide a more level surface for the coating. The pigment filler contributes to the optical properties and increases the receptivity of the raw stock for coating. A high degree of fiber bonding is desirable to minimize intrusion into the pigment coating as well as prevent picking during printing. The type and amount of sizing may vary over a wide range and is dependent upon the coating process, application solids, and intended use of the finished paper.

## Permanence

Historically, in keeping with what was the normal papermaking process, most basestock was formed under acid conditions. During the 1940s, many archival groups and libraries experienced serious problems with paper embrittlement that imperiled the life of text books and other reference works. The problem resulted from oxidation of the cellulose fibers attributed for the most part to the residuals from rosin-acid sizing. Paper formed and sized under alkaline conditions was found to be much more resistant to degradation over time. This prompted the move to neutral/alkaline papermaking conditions and the development of alkaline sizing materials. In the process it was found that adding a small percentage of residual alkaline material to the basestock is an additional safeguard that can also be helpful in acid systems. This has led to the situation where many publishers have specifications regarding the permanence of coated paper for textbooks and other archival materials.

## Porosity

Air as void area is a seldom mentioned component that represents about 50 percent of the base paper volume. The physical dimensions of the voids are an important consideration in that they determine the porosity of the raw stock and the manner in which it accepts the pigment coating. In any structure formed by discrete individual particles, the voids will range from one-tenth the size of the structuring material to several times that size, especially in fibrous systems. Thus, in a sheet of unrefined fibers, there may be voids of from less than one to more than one hundred micrometers in diameter. Fiber refining, increasing the percentage of short-fiber pulp, and the addition of groundwood substantially reduce the fibrous structure of the raw stock.

## Uniformity

Uniformity of the base paper is a prime requisite for a uniform coated surface. The density, thickness, finish, smoothness, and porosity should be as uniform as possible in both the machine and cross-machine direction. Paper that has a wild, nonuniform formation tends to absorb coating unevenly, resulting in a mottled appearance. A variation in opacity of two percent is enough to cause trouble if the variations occur within one-inch intervals. Wire or felt marks which are hard to discern on uncoated paper may be readily visible on the coated sheet.

## Finish

Finish and surface smoothness are important in controlling the even distribution of the pigment coating on the base paper. While the need for smooth raw stock is obvious, if this is achieved by excessive calendaring of a poorly formed web it can result in uneven absorption and a corresponding variation in the thickness of the coating. High spots, which become hard spots, are readily apparent. Coating raw stock should have a controlled rather than high finish to insure uniform coverage and adequate coating transfer. Many publishers have specifications regarding the shininess of coated paper for text books and other reference materials.

## Brightness

Brightness of coating raw stock would seem to be of minor importance inasmuch as the base sheet is covered by a pigmented layer. For most coated printing and writing paper, the coating film is relatively thin and the brightness of the raw stock influences the coated paper brightness. Dirt specks and foreign material will normally show through even the heaviest coatings. If low coat weights are applied, the base paper brightness should approximate that of the pigment coating; otherwise the finished sheet will often have a mottled appearance. Differences in the coating and base sheet brightness tend to accentuate any pattern, skips, or other imperfections in the coating layer.

## Opacity

Opacity of the base paper is important, especially for the lightweight coated grades. From a fiber standpoint groundwood is better for opacity than is chemical fiber. Base sheet porosity and opacity are directly related which, in some cases, may necessitate a compromise. Fillers in the raw stock help to increase opacity but at some sacrifice in strength. Naturally, opacity is a direct function of basis weight and can be a limiting factor in lightweight coated papers. Also, excessive penetration of the pigment coating into the base sheet can lower opacity.

## Pigments

As one would expect, the major component of a pigment coating is the pigment per se. There are several different generic species of coating pigments and numerous variations within each category. The dominant material by far is kaolin, also referred to as clay. Other compositions include calcium carbonate, titanium dioxide, aluminum trihydrate, amorphous silicas and silicates, satin white, talc, zinc oxide, barium sulfate, and plastic pigments. The physical characteristics and function of each of these materials will be reviewed separately in subsequent chapters.

## Future Outlook

The growth in demand for coated paper has moderated considerably from that experienced during 1935 to 1970. Nevertheless, the current outlook remains quite favorable, with demand expected to increase at 4.3% annually. This is in excess of the forecast growth rate for the total paper industry, as well as the general economy. Numerous factors are cited for the above average growth, with the more significant including a rising level of education, increasing leisure time, and growing affluence in the developing economies, as well as an increasing percentage of literate people in the growing world population. These external growth factors are being amplified by internal developments which are enabling the coated paper manufacturers to be more quality- and cost-effective. Promising trends in which pigments will play a prominent role are: further increases in coating solids, more rapid immobilization of the applied coating, and higher filler levels in the raw stock. As in the past, the manufacturers of the various pigments can be expected to come up with new or modified products tailored to meet these changing conditions. Developments such as these ensure continued growth and expansion of the markets for coated paper and a correspondingly favorable outlook.

# Literature Cited


1. Hagemeyer, R. W., *TAPPI* 43(3): 277-288(1960).
2. Hagemeyer, R. W., *TAPPI* 47(2): 74-77(1964).
3. Hagemeyer, R. W., *TAPPI* 47(10): 595-598(1964)
4. Lepoutre, P., *TAPPI* 59(12): 70-75(1976).
5. Lepoutre, P. and Rezanowich, A., *TAPPI* 60(11): 86-91(1977).
6. Borch, J. and Lepoutre, P., *TAPPI* 61(2): 45-48(1978).
7. Lepoutre, P., DeGrace, J. H., and Mangin, P. J., *TAPPI* 62(5): 33-3(1979).
8. Alince, B. and Lepoutre, P., *TAPPI* 63(5): 49-53(1980).
9. Alince, B. and Lepoutre, P., *Pulp Paper Can.* 81(10): 116-117(1980).
10. Baumeister, M.. and Kraft, K., *TAPPI* 64(1): 85-89(1981).
11. Lee, D. I., *TAPPI 1981 Coating Conference Proceedings,* TAPPI PRESS, Atlanta, pp. 143-153.

# 2.

# Paper Filling

*Mitchell H. Koppelman*

Papermakers have been introducing filler pigments into paper through the wet end of the machine as a common practice for many years. Almost all printing and writing grades of paper and paperboard contain some nonfiber (cellulosic) component, with the exception of a few linerboard grades. Perhaps the purpose of this introductory chapter should be to focus on the reasons why the various minerals, which will be discussed in subsequent chapters, have utilities in this application.

To begin with, there is not one particular or unique rationale or justification that every papermaker can quote as his or her reasons for wet-end filler introduction. The value and performance characteristics of fillers differ from paper grade to paper grade. Even for the production of the same grade specifications, it is more than conceivable that papermakers at two different mills will enunciate two different filler formulations, complete with different reasons for their selection or for the value of fillers in the grade in general.

Since the initial publication of *Pigments for Paper* in 1986, the most significant change in the direction papermakers have faced for paper filling is the arrival of the alkaline revolution on the North American continent after its inception and success in Europe.

The European front was spurred by the economic value of locally produced ground natural carbonates as a replacement for kaolin fillers, which in general were imported from kaolin producing locations such as southwest England, central France, and to a lesser degree Germany and Czechoslovakia. This presented papermakers with the opportunity to match or exceed optical performance of historic fillers at a lower cost in a more competitive environment. With time, alkaline papermaking further enhanced the return to the papermaker through a reduction in maintenance expense and fiber cost.

In 1986, in North America almost 50% of coated freesheet production was already utilizing alkaline papermaking technology, which provided value both to the papermaker and to the end user through the utilization of new ultrafine ground limestone products to enhance performance in the coating. Limited virgin ground calcium carbonate found its way into the wet end as concerns remained on wire wear, retention, prime pigment reduction, and cost effectiveness relative to kaolin clay. As a result, less than 15% of uncoated freesheet was produced under alkaline papermaking conditions in 1986.

Under acid papermaking conditions, uncoated freesheet paper grades required the use of titanium dioxide ($TiO_2$) and extender pigments to meet grade specification and customer acceptance. Filler levels were typically 8–12%, with little movement on filler for fiber substitution observed. Precipitated calcium carbonate (PCC), while not a new product, was viewed as an expensive performance enhancing filler additive, requiring shipment in dry form and a change in sizing chemistry. In 1986, one PCC supplier introduced the concept of on-site production at the paper mill, taking advantage of regionally produced raw materials, specifically local quicklime and mill provided gas and water as the three ingredients necessary to produce the product. Elimination of transportation expenses, both for supplier raw material and final product shipment, presented the papermaker with a cost effective opportunity to utilize a new pigment.

Still faced with the need to convert to the alkaline papermaking process using new or different sizing and other process chemicals, papermakers began to look closely at the performance characteristics of precipitated calcium carbonate to justify the risk of an alkaline conversion. Finding value in the $TiO_2$ and extender reduction capabilities, PCC afforded immediate cost incentive and eventually papermakers began utilizing the bulking characteristics of this pigment for value added; as such the alkaline revolution in North America began. **Figures 2-1 and 2-2** depict the conversion history for both coated and uncoated freesheet grades in North America. Conversion to alkaline papermaking technology, initially for freesheet grades and today for wood-containing papers (near neutral to alkaline conditions), has been the most significant technological phenomena relating to paper filling in the past 10 years *(1)*. Novel and improved grades of PCC and natural carbonates, new sizing chemicals and advances in application knowledge of all papermaking additives have increased the efficiency of alkaline papermaking operations, reduced the production risks associated with conversions and through filler for fiber substitution, improved paper quality, and increased market pulp availability without capital expenditure. Uncoated freesheet grades made under alkaline conditions today have average filler levels five to seven percent higher than the historic acid papers. In 1996, over 90% of total freesheet was produced under alkaline conditions, with PCC being the predominant filler of choice.

*Figure 2-1 Coated freesheet North American capacity*

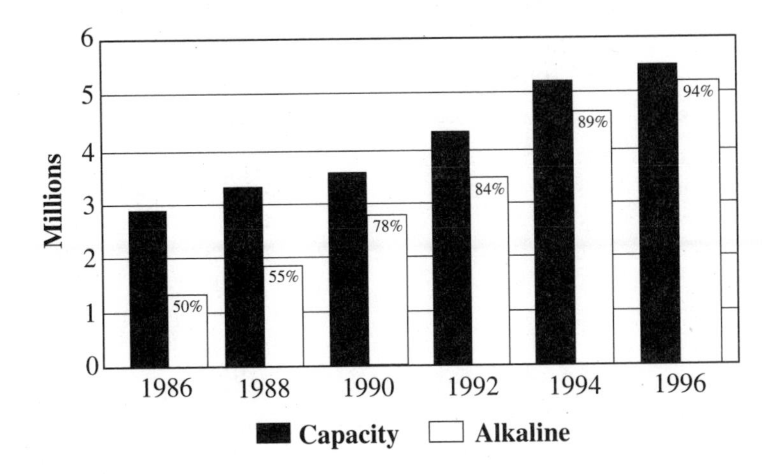


*Figure 2-2 Uncoated freesheet North American capacity*

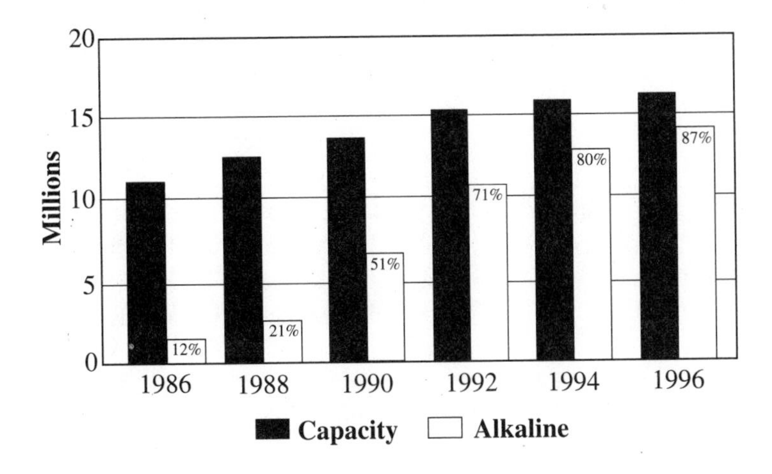


# Fiber Extension

Generally speaking, when filler pigments are added at the wet end, basis weight is maintained by reducing fiber content of the furnish or by changing machine speed. The end result of these procedures is the same: filler for fiber substitution (by weight). Bulking filler pigments have contributed to this ability, and in some applications this is the major reason for introducing filler into paper. For this purpose, filler utilization is generally defined as fiber extension. The value of fiber extension is related to the availability and cost of fiber at the mill site. An integrated mill whose paper production capability is limited by its own ability to produce fiber can literally increase both paper product and pulp mill "capacity" by making a filler for fiber substitution. With projected fiber price increases and regional fiber shortages *(2)*, we anticipate that significantly more filler pigments will be utilized in the future, citing great fiber extension as the prime reason. Currently, when fiber extension is mentioned as the reason for filler inclusion, the most economical and sometimes least optically efficient fillers are utilized. The balance of machine productivity versus fiber extension or paper quality must be considered. The bottom line value of fiber extension to the papermaker is the maintenance of grade specification with a maximized differential between delivered filler costs and fiber prices.

## Optical Improvement

A second, and perhaps more frequently cited reason for using filler pigments, is the optical improvements they can afford to a sheet of paper. In general, optical properties affected by filler for fiber substitution are opacity, brightness, and color. The degree to which each of these properties is altered is very much dependent upon the type of filler, the nature of the fiber furnish, and the basis weight of the final sheet. At basis weights of less than 40 lb/3300 $ft^2$ (60 $g/m^2$) almost all filler pigments will, upon inclusion into the web, result in increased sheet opacity. As basis weight is increased, maintenance of a constant level of filler component will result in a smaller increase in opacity, relative to an unfilled pulp sheet. At very low basis weights, a filler pigment's opacifying performance is maximized; at high basis weights, it's minimized.

The opacifying efficiency a pigment possesses in a filler application is related to its ability to scatter light at a wavelength of 572 nm. The scattering power of pigment is affected by several fundamental factors: its refractive index relative to the surrounding medium, the particle size (and/or shape), and the number of light scattering surfaces it makes available upon inclusion in the dried web. The higher the refractive index the mineral filler possesses, the greater the index of refraction of the air–pigment or fiber–pigment interface. In a filled sheet of paper, it is one of these two interfaces that offers the highest potential source for light scattering resulting in opacity. For a relative ranking of the index of refraction of these materials, consider the following:

*$TiO_2$ (rutile > anatase) >> all other common mineral fillers*
*> pulp fibers (and fines) > water >> air*

A single wavelength of light will have associated with it a single characteristic particle size which, all other factors such as shape and aspect ratio being equal, will maximize the degree to which the light is scattered and sheet opacity is generated *(3)*. This specific particle size is generally expressed in terms of a radius of a sphere. Deviation of the shape of most filler pigments from spherical geometry makes practical use of this relationship difficult. It is, however, justified to conclude that associated with every wavelength of monochromatic light there is a specific sized (or shaped) particle for every mineral filler pigment that yields maximized opacifying efficiency. Historically, most kaolin and carbonate filler pigments were polymodal in particle size (expressed as equivalent spherical diameter) and therefore possess particle size distributions; it is virtually impossible to load paper with only the specific singular particle size shown to maximize opacity. The advent of PCC, engineered (structured) pigments, and narrower distribution curve natural carbonates changed the way papermakers viewed this property. Most filler pigment suppliers will offer information relating to particle size either in the form of "% <2μm", average particle size, or pigment surface area.

## Performance Characteristics and Sheet Properties

An important factor affecting a filler's opacifying performance is the manner in which it is incorporated into the sheet structure (flocculation and coagulation chemistry). If two high indices of refraction materials are in close enough contact that pigment–air or pigment–fiber interfaces are reduced and pigment–pigment interfaces are formed, light scattering is decreased. A careful balance of charge neutralizing and flocculating chemicals in the wet end must be achieved to maximize filler retention without adverse pigment agglomeration. Additionally, for very fine particle size pigments, alum and many retention and coagulation aids often produce desirable particle agglomeration resulting in an improvement in optical efficiency.

These facts affect a pigment's ability to scatter light, which, for material of similar absorption characteristics, is related to the generation of opacity. The specific light-scattering performance of filler pigments will be discussed in the individual chapters in this book. However, to provide the reader with a generalized reference frame, on an equal weight basis, $TiO_2$ will (based on scattering coeffient data) scatter almost 10 times as much light as will refined mechanical fiber which, in turn, is about twice as efficient as moderately refined or unrefined chemical fiber. Therefore, the substitution of a small amount of $TiO_2$ for chemical fiber in a sheet will significantly increase the sheet's ability to scatter light, and, therefore, its opacity.

Most pigments used in filler applications have brightness in excess of 80% (GE). In most furnish, substitution of filler for fiber will result in an increase in the sheet's final brightness. The ability of a filler to increase sheet brightness is related to the pigment's own intrinsic brightness and the scattering efficiency of the sheet. As the fiber brightness approaches that of the filler, the increase in brightness achieved upon fiber substitution is significantly reduced.

Many papermakers historically have taken advantage in acid systems of the availability of 90%-plus GE brightness filler pigments by reducing the degree to which fiber must be chemically bleached to meet sheet specifications. Today, most mills are operating under neutral or alkaline pH conditions, and use of calcium carbonates (> 95% GE brightness) as filler pigments has afforded the papermaker new opportunities in the area of filler contribution to sheet brightness.

The specifics relating to the performance of filler pigments in sheet brightening, as well as the factors that dictate the intrinsic brightness of these pigments, will be described in the individual chapters in this book. However, it should be emphasized that, as with light scattering properties, brightness is affected by flocculation. Any flocculation process that would reduce light scattering and increase light absorption at 457 nm would appear to increase sheet brightness. It is perhaps this mechanism which results in occasional anomalies and variances in filler brightening performance expectations.

Filler pigments can also affect final sheet color or shade properties. Often it is recommended for the production of high-white grades of paper to use fillers that demonstrate low light absorption (and high reflection) characteristics throughout the spectrum of visible light. It is, though, perhaps most important to recognize that filler pigments must be considered noninert when one is discussing paper color characteristics. Some filler materials have (relatively) high light adsorption and low reflection properties at specific wavelengths. It is possible for the papermaker to use the appropriate dyes to counteract these contributions, providing filler shade properties are relatively constant. Additionally, papermakers must be aware that some dyes will tend to react with (adsorb onto) selective mineral surfaces. This can result in a significant two-sidedness shade quality problem as well as an increase in dye consumption.

The introduction of filler pigments into the paper web can also affect the caliper (thickness) of the final sheet. Broad particle-size fillers, especially in furnishes containing relatively longer unrefined fiber, often significantly reduce sheet caliper. For certain applications, such as book papers, this may be a desirable effect. Large agglomerate structure fillers may slightly reduce caliper and hence densify the sheet only to the extent of the difference in densities between pulp and filler.

Most PCC fillers, dependent upon shape and size, can actually "prop up" fibers and enhance paper bulk. This property provides a platform for fiber substitution, cost reduction, and maintenance of stiffness for end-user friendliness.

Some kaolin fillers may also tend to reduce final sheet caliper, due to tendencies for the filled sheets to be more compressible upon calendering. It is this property of the highly filled sheets, such as supercalendered papers, that can improve surface smoothness and printability. Although the term "improved printability" is often bantered around and is rather nonspecific, it is generally recognized that for uncoated printing grades correct choice of filler pigments can reduce missing dots in rotogravure, reduce strikethrough and showthrough, increase clarity of image and ink holdout in offset applications, and provide controlled ink or toner excursions for ink jet and other noncontact printing processes. These improvements may be attributed to the filler directly or to some other sheet property (such as smoothness or porosity), which in turn is affected by filler inclusion.

## Other Considerations

There are several other wet-end phenomena that may be altered when filler pigments replace fiber. Judicious choice and use of retention aids to maximize filler retention and optical efficiency often result in improved overall fines retention (and hence saveall operation). This must always be balanced by formation and strength consideration. A reason for this may be the result of improved wet-end chemistry or the ability of fiber fines to more readily heteroflocculate (with filler) rather than homoflocculate. Inclusion of filler can affect furnish drainage performance under hydrodynamic and applied vacuum conditions. This property of the filled system can be used advantageously to increase solids after the couch (maximize filler loading while maintaining web strength) and to control sheet porosity. This ability to control sheet porosity through filler utilization can be used to a paper coater's benefit to control binder penetration and rate of coating structure development.

After reading about why paper is filled with pigments, an inexperienced papermaker might be led to believe that every sheet of paper he or she may make should contain high levels of filler for fiber substitution. From this text it might appear that filler pigments can only improve sheet performance properties. Unfortunately for papermakers and pigment suppliers this is not a complete truism. Several times in this discussion the term "optimize the chemical condition in the wet end" appeared. If filler is added to furnishes where no concern is paid to this factor, wet-end operations (formation, drainage, retention), press operations (picking, web breaks), size press operations (overpenetration, breaks), coating operations (higher binder demand, pick strength), and printing performance (reduced elasticity of dry web, increased dusting, print mottle) could be adversely affected.

The price paid for the improvement in production costs, optical properties, and printing characteristics of the paper through the addition of filler is a measurable and sometimes significant loss in strength. Most paper grades with and without filler are compared at the same basis weight. Consequently, a sheet containing filler will be composed of less fiber than one without filler. Since most of the strength properties (burst, tensile, internal bond) are related to the frequency (number) of fiber–fiber bonds, reducing the total number of fibers (maintaining basis weight) has to adversely affect strength. Different fillers affect these properties to different degrees, depending somewhat on particle size or shape characteristics and the filler's specific gravity. However, much of the loss in strength associated with filler inclusion can be compensated for through the use of internal (and surface) binders such as starch, latex, natural gums, and other synthetic and natural polymers.

In summary, Bill Willets described a filler product whose characteristics would turn a paper mill into a Utopian paradise *(4)*:

1. It should have a reflectance of 100% in all wavelengths of light so that it would have maximum brightness and whiteness.
2. It should have a very high refractive index so that it would have maximum opacifying and brightening power.
3. It should be completely free from grit or extraneous matter and have a particle size distribution close to 0.3 μm, approximately half the wavelength of light.
4. It should have a slow specific gravity and be soft and nonabrasive.
5. It should be capable of imparting to paper a surface capable of taking any finish from the lowest matte to the highest gloss.
6. It should be completely chemically inert and insoluble.
7. It should be completely retained in the paper web so that there would be no loss.
8. It should be reasonable in price.

Such a perfect filler is not available.

## Literature Cited


1. Skrocki, C. A., et al., 1993 Publishing and Printing Papers Conference, *The Alkaline Revolution: Improved Publishing And Printing Papers Through The Use Of Fillers.*
2. Hagemeyer, R. W., *TAPPI JOURNAL*, 66(3): 71 (1983).
3. Sawyer, R. H., *J. Applied Physics*, 13(10): 596 (1942).
4. Willets, W. R., in *"Paper Loading Materials,"* Monograph No. 19, TAPPI PRESS, Atlanta, 1958, p. 5.

# 3.

# The Dispersion of Pigments for Paper Coating

*J. V. Robinson, Nathan Millman, and J. B. Whitley*
*(Editorial comments by Rabon L. Hollingsworth)*

Some things are as basic to papermaking as air, water, and fiber. The principles of pigment dispersion for paper coating as presented in Chapters 15 and 16 of TAPPI Monograph 28 fall into that category. For that reason, it was decided to include that work as originally presented with little modification.

The symptoms of the state of dispersion of pigments are seen at all stages in the processes of preparing coating color and of coating paper. While the pigments are being kneaded or mixed, the changing state of dispersion is manifested in the changing fluidity of the mixture. In the coating color the state of the dispersion of the pigments is manifest in the viscosity of the color. And the gloss and smoothness of the paper, and freedom from projecting particles, reflect the state of dispersion of pigments at the time the coating was laid on the paper. These characteristics are matters of common experience in the coating of paper, and it is well known that they correlate with the manner in which the pigment is treated, particularly with regard to the type of equipment in which it is mixed with water, dispersing agents, and the other ingredients of the coating color, and also with the solids content of the mixture while it is being mixed.

This chapter describes an underlying basis common to many dispersion processes. Emphasis is placed upon processes in which a dry, or nonfluid, pigment is put into a slurry.

## Basic Concepts of Dispersion

Properties essential to description of a pigment, in addition to its chemical composition, are the size and arrangement of its particles. The description of the particles may be simple or complex. In the case of particles that remain unattached, each separate from the others, the properties that determine the behavior are particle shape, which may be describable as crystalline form and habit, and particle size distribution. This, however, is the exceptional case. Usually the particles will be attached to one another, and there is no limit to the varieties of ways they may be assembled. They may be grouped in clusters of a few or many individual particles, more or less tightly packed together. To the description of individual particles is added the number of particles in the cluster, the density of packing in the cluster, the arrangement of the particles in the cluster, surface smoothness of the cluster, the mobility, or lack of it, of the particles in the cluster, and the resistance to breaking or rearrangement of the cluster. The process of dispersion is considered to be the disruption of clusters of pigment particles.

The clusters may be held together by chemical deposits at the points of contact of the particles, giving the clusters a strength almost equal to that of single particles of the same size. Or the particles may be held together loosely, as though attracted together by magnetic or gravitational forces, so that an applied force will disturb and break particular arrangements. The term "disaggregation" is applied to the disruption of clusters of particles that are held together by deposits at their points of contact, as by cement. Once the particles are broken apart, the bonds will not be re-formed, and the process of disaggregation is therefore irreversible. The term "deflocculation" is applied to the disruption of particles that are held together more loosely, as though by magnets. Such bonds, broken by an applied force, will re-form when the force is removed. The process of deflocculation is therefore reversible. The term "disagglomeration" is a generic one, and includes both deflocculation and disaggregation.

Preventing the re-forming by flocculation of particle clusters is not a mechanical problem but a chemical one. The prevention of flocculation is accomplished by bringing into the pigment system chemicals that act at the surfaces of the particles to make them mutually repellent. The use of chemical dispersing agents is an essential part of the dispersion process, efficiently using mechanical energy and lowering the viscosity of the pigment slurry. The relation between the chemical and mechanical aspects of dispersion is this: mechanically applied forces disrupt the particle clusters, while chemical dispersing agents prevent the reversible rebuilding of particle clusters (flocculation). The chemical action of dispersion must be preceded by mechanical disruption of the particle clusters.

A coating color consists of a suspension of pigment particles in a fluid medium. It is important to note that the adhesive and all other dissolved materials are considered a part of the fluid in which the pigment is suspended. Thus, starch and latex are in such a state of mobility and are properly considered a part of the fluid. The adhesive profoundly affects the viscosity of the coating color but does so solely because of its effect upon the viscosity of the fluid portion of the suspension; it has a small or negligible effect upon the particle interaction. Similarly, coating additives are a part of the fluid component, and it is the viscosity of the fluid that they modify. This is in contrast to the usual conception of a coating color as consisting of water and nonvolatile solids.

The water-adhesive fluid acts as a lubricant between particles and enables them to slide over each other much more easily than would be possible if they were dry. If the fluid is insufficient to fill all the void spaces, there will be dry solid particles sliding over each other, and the consistency will be that of a viscous paste or damp powder. By reducing the void volume, for example, by dispersing the pigment particles to eliminate aggregates or flocs, the same amount of fluid will be sufficient to fill the void spaces, furnishing a lubricating film of fluid between all the particles.

Such a transition is shown in **Fig. 3-1**, representing the separation (deflocculation and disaggregation) and rearrangement of a few enlarged particles in the presence of a limited amount of water. The diagram is intended to illustrate in two dimensions the type of process which, occurring in three dimensions, accounts for a change in consistency in a pigment-water mixture from a damp powder to a viscous liquid, with no change in composition *(2,3)*.

*Figure 3-1 Separation and rearrangement of particles in water*

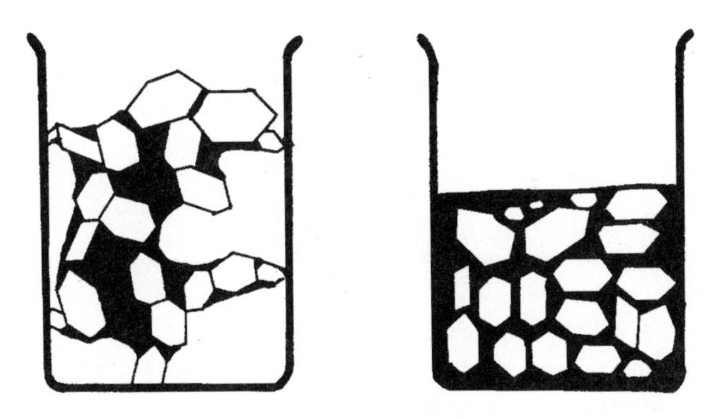

The mechanical interaction between particles that occurs during dispersion, and that relates dispersion to viscosity, is controlled by the volume concentration of the pigment. The volume concentration of the pigment is related to the weight concentration through the density of the pigment, but general expressions applicable to all pigments can only be made in terms of volume concentration. For this reason, charts showing volume concentration are not specifically marked, but charts showing weight concentration must identify, or indicate the density of, the specific pigment.

# Sediment Volume

The sediment volume is the volume that the pigment occupies when the particles are resting against one another, as shown in **Fig. 3-2**. If the particles are stuck together, and therefore cannot settle into void spaces, the sediment volume will be large. If the particles are separate, they will arrange themselves within a smaller space, and the sediment volume will be low. If the pigment-liquid mixture is to have the properties of a fluid suspension, the voids between particles and clusters of particles must be filled with liquid, and additional liquid must be present to suspend the particles and separate them from each other. By this concept, the sediment volume is related to the flow behavior of a pigment-liquid mixture. Furthermore, the process of dispersion of an agglomerated pigment may be considered to be the process of reduction of the sediment volume.

*Figure 3-2 Sediment volume of a mixture equals void volume plus solids volume*

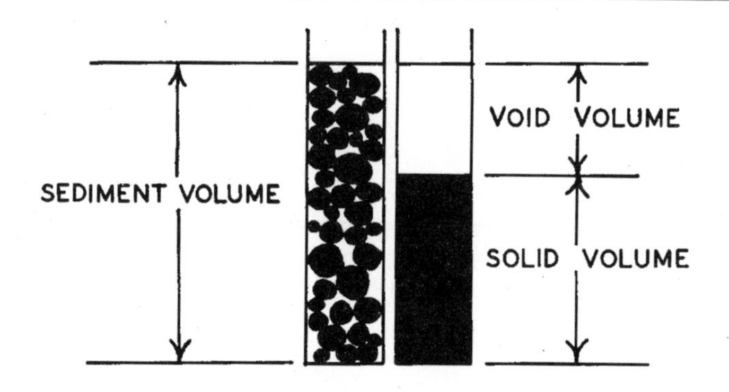


Relative sediment volume (sediment volume per unit volume of solids) is completely independent of particle size, although affected by the ratios of particle dimensions and proportions present. A high relative sediment volume of very small particles is an indication of a high degree of particle agglomeration, just as it is with large particles.

The term "sediment volume" is used because sedimentation from a suspension is the most obvious way to determine the volume that will be occupied by the pigment when the solid particles are as close together as they can get without changing their agglomerate structure. In a determination of sediment volume, the suspended pigment settles to the bottom of the containing tube, under the influence of either gravity or centrifugal force, forming a sharply demarcated sediment under a clear supernatant liquid. If the supernatant liquid is decanted from the sediment, the sediment will have a certain composition, which may be expressed as "percent solids", and this will be the composition at which there is just enough liquid present to fill exactly the void spaces between and within the particle agglomerates. The same "sediment" condition may be reached in a process of dispersion, in which there is no change in composition but the void space is decreased until the liquid present, initially insufficient, equals in volume the void volume. The volume relationship found in a sediment is thus identical to a unique point in the dispersion of a pigment in the presence of a limited quantity of liquid.

Considering the case of a sediment, an algebraic relationship exists between the relative sediment volume and the solids content. The assumptions are that there is no swelling of the pigment by the liquid, that the volume of liquid present is just that required to fill the spaces between the particles, and that the particles or clusters of particles are resting against each other. The "solids" refers to the solid pigment, and does not include material that may be dissolved in the liquid. With these limitations, the following equations are true:

$$S = (1/d_s - 1/d_L) + 100/(d_L)(\%\ solids) \quad (1)$$

$$S' = (1 - d_s/d_L) + 100\ d_s/(d_L)(\%\ solids) \quad (2)$$

$$S' = d_s S \quad (3)$$

$$S'V = 1 \quad (4)$$

$$V = (\%\ solids)/d\ /\ (100 - \%\ solids)/d_L + (\%\ solids)/d_s$$

where

| | | |
|---|---|---|
| S | = | specific sediment volume = (sediment volume)/(weight of solid) |
| S' | = | relative sediment volume (RSV) = (sediment volume)/(volume of solid) |
| $d_s$ | = | density of the solids |
| $d_L$ | = | density of the liquid |
| % solids | = | 100 (weight of solid)/(weight of solid + weight of liquid) |
| V | = | (volume of solid)/(volume of solid + volume of liquid) |
| 100 V | = | solid as percent by volume. |

The simple relationship between relative sediment volume and volume concentration, under the conditions of a sediment, may be seen by considering **Fig. 3-3**. By further definition, the volume concentration V is the ratio of the volume of solid to the volume of the solid plus the volume of the liquid. Figure 3-3 shows that the volume of the solid is 1, and the total volume is the relative sediment volume S', therefore, forming the two definitions: V = 1/S' or S'V = 1, or S' = 1/V.

*Figure 3-3 When volume of solid is unity, sediment volume equals relative sediment volume*

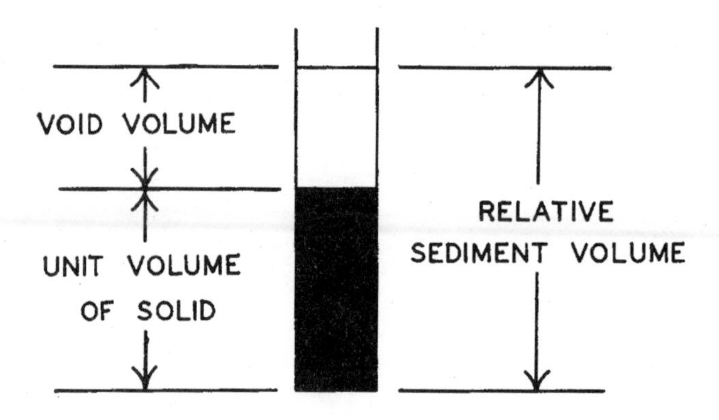


## The Dispersion Diagram

This special case, namely, that of the packed sediment and the relationship S' = 1/V, establishes a reference line for expressing the degree of dispersion of a pigment.

To visualize the reference line for dispersion, a graph may be plotted as shown in **Fig. 3-4**, in which relative sediment volume is the ordinate and percent by volume is the abscissa. Plotted logartithmically, as shown, the function S' = 1/V becomes a straight line, with a negative slope. To refer the condition of a particular pigment-liquid mixture to the graph, the relative sediment volume of the pigment and the volume concentration of the pigment in the mixture must be known. Note that the volume concentration V, or the percent by volume 100V, is computed from the relationship V = (volume of solid)/(volume of liquid + volume of solid), and that the volume of included air, if any, is ignored.

The line in Fig. 3-4 plotting S' = 1/V is called the "packed sediment line," since the relationship is true only for a sediment, as defined above. All points below the packed sediment line are descriptive of pigment-liquid mixtures in which liquid is present in excess of that required to fill the void volume between particles, and the mixture is a suspension. The greater the distance below the packed sediment line, the more fluid and less viscous will be the suspension that a point represents. All points above the packed sediment line are descriptive of pigment-liquid mixtures in which the void space between particles is greater than the volume of water present. The void volume not filled with water will be filled with air. Such pigment-liquid mixtures are not fluids at all in the ordinary sense, since there is no continouous liquid phase.

*Figure 3-4 Relation between relative sediment volume, per cent of pigment by volume, and physical behavior*

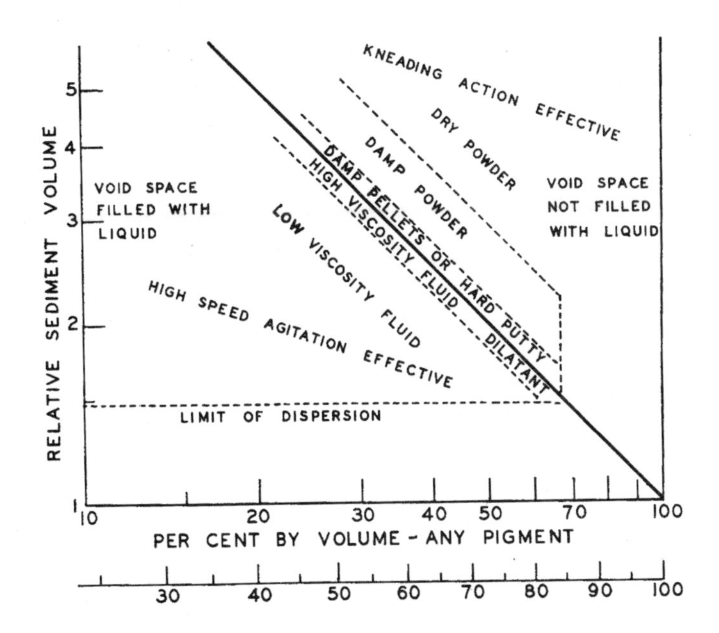


Another property of the graph is that each point on it represents a flow behavior, or viscosity, since S' and V are determining parameters for the viscosity of a pigment suspension in any given liquid, in the same manner as for spheres (4,5). The packed sediment line is the dividing line between fluids and nonfluids, and sequences of the change of flow characteristics are indicated on the graph.

Starting in the upper right corner with a dry powder, a decrease in solids, or a decrease in relative sediment volume, or both, causes the mixture to become wetter and wetter, passing through the stages of damp powder, to damp pellets or hard putty, to the packed sediment condition, then into the region of fluids. Just below the packed sediment line is the very viscous region, most often accompanied by dilatant behavior, such flow being characteristic of suspensions in which there is a very small excess of liquid over that required to fill the void spaces between the particles (3). Further decrease in either sediment volume or solids concentration progressively reduces the viscosity of the suspension.

The concept that the process of dispersion consists of reduction in the relative sediment volume of a pigment may be further elaborated by showing a typical dispersion process, charted on the dispersion diagram in **Fig. 3-5**. In this instance the process consists of adding water and chemical dispersant to dry clay until a fluid suspension is formed, and then agitating the mixture vigorously with a high-speed impeller. On the dispersion diagram, dry clay is represented on the 100% solids line, with a relative sediment volume of 3.5. The process of diluting reduces the solids content but does not change the sediment volume. This way of showing the process is not quite accurate because the volume of the dry clay is considerably greater than that of the wet, owing to bridging and electrostatic repulsion of the dry particles. However, the graph conveys the idea that no disagglomeration occurs simply as a result of diluting. Disagglomeration does occur, however, as a result of vigorous agitation of the suspension, shown on the diagram by a reduction in sediment volume from 3.5 to 2.1. This reduction in sediment volume is accompanied by a reduction in viscosity. The final value of relative sediment volume is a function more of the ease of dispersion of the pigment than of the mechanical action, because, at this low solids content, only forces of a low magnitude will reach the individual agglomerates. Strongly bound agglomerates will not be affected even by very powerful agitation, and the energy of agitation will be expended in viscous friction rather than against the suspended particles.

*Figure 3-5 Process of dispersion at low solids*

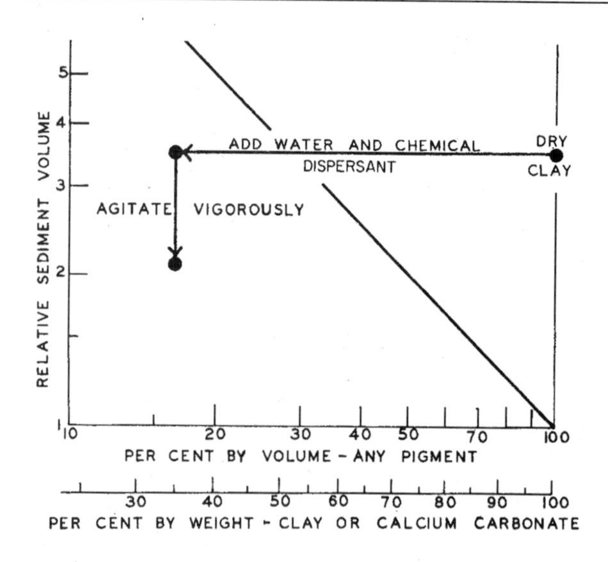


A diagram of a process of dispersion at high solids is shown in **Fig. 3-6**. Dry clay is diluted with water and chemical dispersant to a concentration of 53% by volume or 75% by weight of solids. This mixture has the consistency of damp powder. Kneading causes the particles to rub against each other, resulting in disruption of the agglomerates and reduction of relative sediment volume. When the liquid present is in excess of that required to fill the void volume, the mixture becomes fluid, and the slow-moving arms of the kneader cause little further disaggregating action. The dispersion progresses, therefore, to a point just below the packed sediment line. The final step is a dilution, and the slight rise in relative sediment volume shown is intended to suggest that flocculation took place upon dilution. Such a flocculation is commonly observed and is presumably due to a change in the stablizing layer around each particle, formed by the adsorbed dispersing agent.

*Figure 3-6 Process of dispersion at high solids, followed by dilution (solid line), contrasted to process of dispersion at low solids (broken line)*

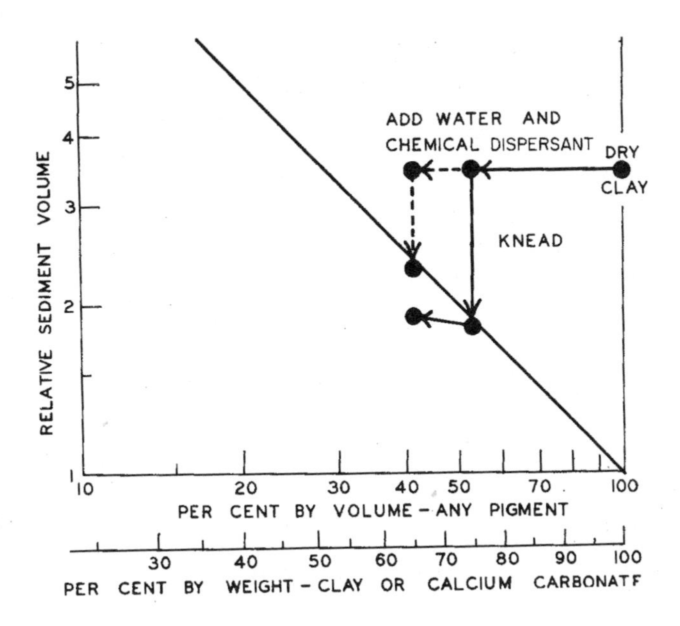


An alternative process is shown by the dashed lines in Fig. 3-6. The clay in this process was diluted to its final solids immediately, and then kneaded. The dispersion accomplished by the kneader still takes the relative sediment volume to a point just below the packed sediment line, but at the lower solids content. The clay kneaded at high solids and then diluted has a lower relative sediment volume than the clay diluted and then kneaded. The assumption from the results shown in Fig. 3-6 is that this particular clay exists in aggregates which require strong mechanical forces to disrupt them. If the clay particles were not aggregated, it is quite likely that nearly equal relative sediment volume would result from the two processes. Notice that relative sediment volume is being used as a quantitative measurement of the degree of dispersion.

The behavior diagrammed in Fig. 3-6 accounts for the lower adhesive demand of pigments dispersed at high solids, as compared to pigments dispersed at low solids. As shown by Cobb *(1)*, and confirmed many times, adhesive demand is governed by the void volume of the packed pigment, which is equal to 1 – (1/S').

Another process of dispersion is shown in **Fig. 3-7**, in which water and chemical dispersant are added to a coating grade of calcium carbonate pigment, and the mixture kneaded as before. The dispersion progresses to a point just below the packed sediment line, and more dry, undispersed calcium carbonate is added, raising both the solids and the relative sediment volume. Kneading again reduces the relative sediment volume to a point just below the packed sediment line. The processes of alternately adding dry calcium carbonate and kneading may be repeated, as indicated by the diagram, until the limit of disaggregation is reached. As the limit is approached, the points after kneading will come closer and closer to the packed sediment line. There is an irreducible minimum in relative sediment volume for each pigment sample. The purpose of repetitively kneading, raising solids, and re-kneading may be to determine experimentally this minimum sediment volume or to achieve maximum dispersion with a reduced load on the kneader arms.

*Figure 3-7 Process of dispersion by successively adding solids to achieve the limit of disaggregation and the minimum relative sediment volume*

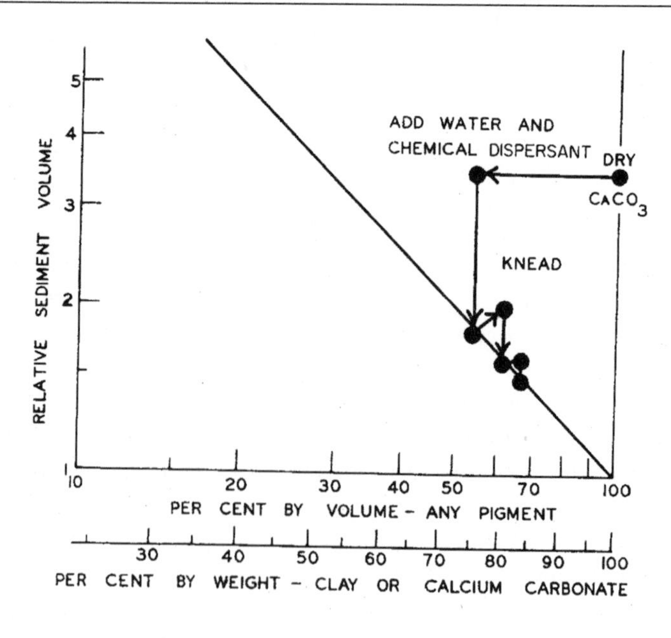

# Application of Mechanical Force to Bring About Dispersion

The dispersion of aggregates is brought about by applying a force to the aggregate that the bonds between the component particles cannot withstand. The amount of power used to effect disaggregation may not be relevant to the results achieved. Neither amount of power nor total work determines whether disaggregation occurs, but rather the force reaching each aggregate. It is frequently true that the greater the power input to a given charge, the greater the force that each aggregate will experience. An exception is the case of dilute suspensions, to which it is possible to supply high-power input, by means of high-speed agitators, without subjecting individual aggregates to forces large enought to disrupt them. The power in such a case is used to pump the fluid, and is dissipated as heat resulting from viscous work, not interparticle friction.

On the other hand, very large forces can be applied to aggregates at the expenditure of very modest power. Devices that localize the power input to a small volume are the means for such disaggregation. The edge runner, or kollergang, is such a device. Impact mills are other means of applying the principle. The colloid mill and bottom entry mixers are intended to operate on this principle, and will do so, provided the concentration of solids can be maintained high enough to make interparticle friction substantial. Even the best colloid mill will accomplish little disaggregation if the solids are so low that particle interaction is small. The gap in a colloid mill can seldom be maintained as small as the dimensions of the coating pigment particles.

Such a machine, which concentrates power on a small volume, requires a longer time to disaggregate a large volume of material than a machine that applies high power to a large volume, but given the time it will accomplish the job. By contrast, a machine that supplies low power to a large volume of material will never accomplish disaggregation, because the maximum forces that each aggregate experiences will never exceed the force required for disruption. The determining factor is power input per unit volume of material in the effective zone of the machine, with the qualification that the power be dissipated in interparticle friction, not viscous friction.

The packed sediment condition, shown by the reference line on the dispersion diagram, permits mechanical power to be applied most effectively. In this condition, any force of shear applied to the sediment causes a rearrangement of particles and an increase in volume, so the liquid within the void volume is no longer sufficient to fill it, and air–liquid interfaces are created. The surface tension of the water exerts a powerful force, pulling the particles against each other in opposition to the applied mechanical force and tending to pull the particles apart.

The action of mechanical shearing under these circumstances is somewhat similar to a squeezing action, as in a vise, which will force the particles to break apart to permit a reduction of the total volume. In the case of higher solids, in which an appreciable proportion of the void space between particles is full of air, the surface tension effect is greatly reduced, and the particles slide over each other with less interaction.

On the other hand, if there is a large volume of liquid present, the agglomerates are separated from each other, there is no surface tension effect, and the particle interaction is also small. The situation is somewhat analogous to swatting flies: each particle must be individually hit to be disagglomerated.

The dispersion diagram (Fig. 3-4) may be used as a map to generalize the application of mechanical means for dispersion, in addition to the uses already discussed. In all the area above the packed sediment line, and in that area just below it, kneading action is effective, while elsewhere below the line high-speed agitation is effective in bringing about pigment dispersion.

As the size of the aggregates decreases, it becomes increasingly difficult to provide an environment in which the aggregates will receive a force sufficient to break them. For example, if a torsional stress is to be applied to the bonded area, it must be applied through the particles on each side of the bond, and as their length decreases, the force required to achieve the same moment of torque increases. A further difficulty is encountered in reaching small aggregates with high stresses, considering that their size may be far smaller than the scratches on the surfaces of the machine parts in contact with them. The obvious means for reaching such small particles is to cause them to wear by rubbing against each other.

## Illustrative Experiments

Coating-grade calcium carbonate was dispersed in a kneader in a series of experiments in which the solids during kneading were varied. The relative sediment volume after dispersion was measured by centrifuging a sample of the suspension and measuring the volume of the sediment. The results are shown in **Table 3-1**, and in **Fig. 3-8** (solid circles). At low solids levels, the points fall below the packed sediment line, and as the solids are raised, the points come closer to the packed sediment line. The calcium carbonate was firmly aggregated, and disagregation occurred only when conditions permitted the application of maximum force to disrupt the aggregates, namely, in the condition of a packed sediment.

*Table 3-1 Effect of solids on despersion in a kneader of an agglomerated calcium carbonate (0.2% Metaphosphate dispersing agent) (7)*

| Solids at which dispersed | | Relative sediment volume |
|---|---|---|
| By weight, % | By Volume, % | Centrifugal sedimentation |
| 40.0 | 20.0 | 3.10 |
| 53.5 | 30.3 | 2.94 |
| 53.7 | 30.5 | 2.86 |
| 56.8 | 33.3 | 2.78 |
| 56.6 | 33.1 | 2.70 |
| 57.7 | 34.1 | 2.68 |
| 59.1 | 35.4 | 2.60 |
| 60.4 | 36.6 | 2.55 |
| 60.7 | 36.8 | 2.47 |
| 61.0 | 37.1 | 2.41 |
| 66.9 | 43.3 | 2.23 |
| 74.7 | 52.9 | 1.80 |
| 75.3 | 53.6 | 1.86 |
| 75.9 | 54.4 | 1.80 |
| 76.2 | 54.6 | 1.77 |
| 78.8 | 58.3 | 1.70 |
| 80.4 | 60.8 | 1.62 |
| 81.1 | 61.7 | 1.62 |
| 82.0 | 63.2 | 1.62 |
| 82.3 | 63.7 | 1.59 |

*Figure 3-8 Dispersion of three pigments*

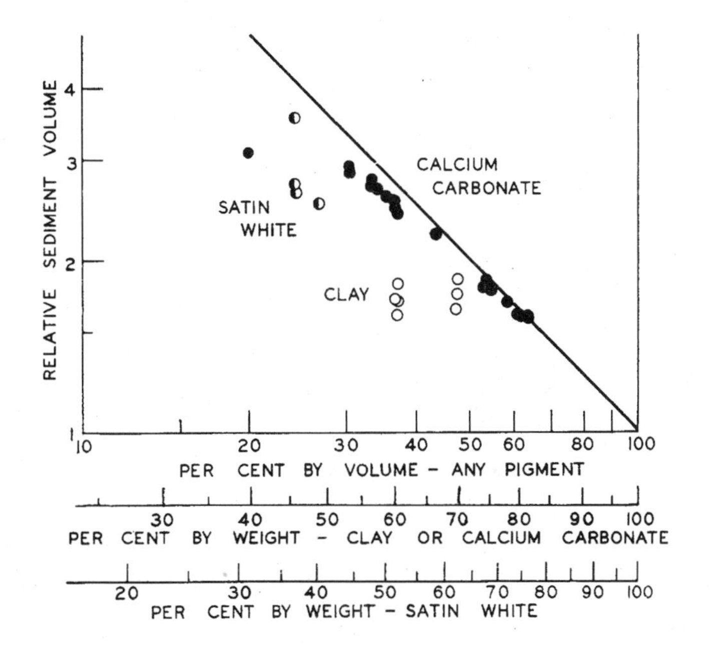

By contrast, two varieties of disaggregated coating clay were similarly dispersed in the kneader, at two solids levels, and with two levels of tetrasodium pyrophosphate dispersant. The results are shown in **Table 3-2** and Fig. 3-8 (open circles). Solids level had no effect upon the sediment volume, indicating that only a small amount of mechanical work was required to cause dispersion. Sediment volume was affected by the amount of chemical dispersant, indicating that the flocculating tendency of the particles was the factor controlling sediment volume. One could infer from the position of the points representing clay on the dispersion diagram that an increase in solids to about 76–77% by weight would bring the clay into the packed sediment condition, and kneading at this high solids content would demonstrate whether the measured lowest relative sediment volume of 1.61 was the minimum possible with this clay or whether further disaggregation could take place.

*Table 3-2 Dispersion of coating clays in a kneader (7)*

| Clay | Dispersing agent, % | Solids at which dispersed By weight, % | Solids at which dispersed By volume % | Relative sediment volume centrifugal sedimentation |
|---|---|---|---|---|
| Low viscosity, clay no. 1 | 0.35 | 70.2 | 47.1 | 1.65 |
| | 0.50 | 70.5 | 47.5 | 1.80 |
| | 0.35 | 60.4 | 36.6 | 1.72 |
| | 0.50 | 61.0 | 37.1 | 1.70 |
| Low viscosity, clay no. 2 | 0.35 | 70.4 | 47.4 | 1.75 |
| | 0.50 | 70.3 | 47.2 | 1.64 |
| | 0.35 | 61.0 | 37.1 | 1.83 |
| | 0.50 | 60.8 | 37.0 | 1.61 |

A study of the effectiveness of several dispersing agents for satin white ($CaSO_4 \cdot 2H_2O$) was made by kneading the satin white at one solids level with the various dispersants. The results are shown in **Table 3-3** and Fig. 3-8 (shaded circles). The distance of the plotted points from the packed sediment line indicates that the dispersion of satin white, to the degree represented by a relative sediment volume of 2.52, was a matter of deflocculation rather than disaggregation. The slow-moving arms of the kneader were not applying much force to the individual particles in such a fluid condition, but the best dispersing agents caused a large reduction in relative sediment volume. Evidence (not shown here) that the satin white is not substantially aggregated is that raising the solids, as by low-temperature drying, followed by kneading in the packed sediment condition, lowered the relative sediment voume to 2.0. This high relative sediment volume of satin white appears to be the result of the inability of the needlelike crystals to pack closely.

*Table 3-3 Dispersion of satin white in a kneader (7)*

| Dispersing agent, % | Solids at which dispersed By weight, % | By volume % | Relative sediment volume centrifugal sedimentation |
|---|---|---|---|
| 5% A | 36.6 | 24.2 | 2.73 |
| 5% A plus 1% B | 36.8 | 24.4 | 2.64 |
| 5% A plus 1% C | 39.6 | 26.8 | 2.52 |
| 5% A plus 1% D | 36.6 | 24.2 | 3.57 |

These experiments illustrate the points that *aggregation* may be studied by means of relative sediment volume, as with the calcium carbonate, but other factors affecting relative sediment volume are *flocculation*, as in the case of the clay, and the *intrinsic ability of the crystal particles to pack*, as in the case of the satin white.

## The Effect of Mixing Intensity on the Dispersion of Coating Pigments in Water

Many industries have the problem of dispersing pigments through some type of matrix. Such matrices as rubber and plastics can exert high disruptive forces during mastication, while the various oils and varnishes develop less shear. Water has such a low viscosity that it can produce an important shear only when violently agitated or when the visocity of the system is increased by high pigment loading. Water systems are of particular interest to the paper industry.

Dry pigments differ in their aggregative properties and, consequently, in their resistance to dispersion. Variations in the forces that bind particles into aggregates may arise from differences in chemical composition, crystalline structure, particle size distribution, nature of surface, drying methods, and the degree of cementation caused by soluble materials which may have been incompletely removed during manufacture. The inherent agglomerative properties of pigments is also a factor in restricting dispersion. These agglomerative forces are strong in such pigments as titanium dioxide and zinc oxide but quite weak in clays and talcs. Calcium carbonate falls somewhere in between.

Regardless of the type and magnitude of the forces that maintain the pigment in the form of an aggregate, this force must be exceeded if the pigment is to be dispersed. This point is emphasized in the work of Robinson (*8*). Since the magnitude of these forces is different in each material, the energy intensity factor required to produce dispersion can be expected to vary with each pigment. The purpose of this paper is to describe the behavior of the principal coating pigments in aqueous suspensions when such systems are subjected to varying mixing intensities.

## Principal Pigments Used in the Coating of Paper

The major pigment used in the coating of paper and paperboard is clay. Clay is produced in various commercial forms, depending principally on the method of drying. Such drying processes have already been expertly described by Asdell *(9)*. **Figure 3-9** illustrates a simple schematic plan of a water washing plant, showing the essential units and stages necessary for the production of coating-grade clay in its different forms. Position 1 denotes the beginning of the process. At this point the crude ore is disintegrated either by working a high concentrated nonfluid mass or by violent agitation of a fluid suspension. In either case, a deflocculated and relatively dilute clay suspension is prepared for classification. Position 2 shows a classifying unit, where fractions of the desired fineness are recovered as an overflow material. The hydroseparator pictured here is, in a sense, symbolic, since centrifuges and ordinary settling tanks are also employed. The recovered clay is chemically bleached in position 3 to remove the discoloration caused by iron compounds. In the process, the suspension is flocculated either by mineral acid or alum to condition it for filtration. Filtration of the clay takes place in position 4, usually by means of drum-type filters. The clay recovered by filtration may be dried by any of the methods shown in the diagram.

*Figure 3-9 Schematic diagram of production of coating grade clay*

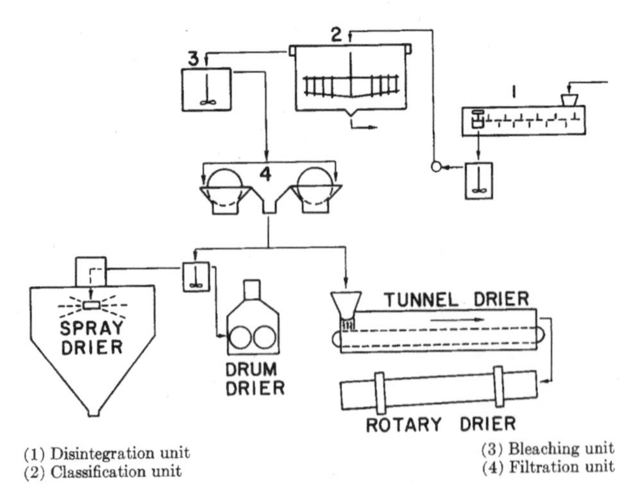

Changes in the physical forms of commercial products depend on the treatment of the filter cake and the method of drying. Two general types of coating clays are produced: undispersed and predispersed.

Undispersed clay is prepared when the filter cake, in its original plastic form, is extruded through perforated plates and the extrusions collected and dried on a screen belt moving through a tunnel dryer. Filter cake material is also dried in a rotary-type dryer, and sometimes a rotary dryer is used to supplement a tunnel dryer, as indicated in Fig. 3-9. In any case, the product is generally described as a lump acid type clay. It may be composed of rod-like pellets of one inch or more in length, or it may consist of more or less round lumps ranging in size from a maximum diameter of about one inch down to nearly a powdered state.

The predispersed clays are produced from a filter cake which is liquified by means of a suitable dispersing agent, usually polyphosphate or polyacrylate. The resulting fluid suspension is dried either by application of a thin film to heated metallic drums or by atomization in a heated chamber. The former method yields small thin flakes and the latter tiny beads or spheres. In either case, the product is commercially referred to as a predispersed clay.

Coating clay, therefore, emerges from the dryers in one of three general physical forms: the undispersed lump, the predispersed flake, or the predispersed bead type. The lump clay is sometimes pulverized and supplied as a powder, particularly where bagged shipments are involved.

While clay alone is used in many coating applications, the attainment of certain optical effects requires the use of one or more of the whiter pigments. These are generally used in combination with clay, although in some cases which require a high degree of whiteness and opacity, clay may be excluded. While a variety of such white pigments are used, finely precipitated and gound calcium carbonate and titanium dioxide are the more prominent. These pigments are generally produced in powdered form. Therefore, we deal here with a study of the dispersion properties of the different physical forms of clay just described, precipitated calcium carbonate, and titanium dioxide of the rutile type.

The coating clays used in this investigation were of medium fineness with about 80% of the particles by weight finer than 2 μ. A number of samples, several 100 lb each, were collected at each dryer over an extended production period and then blended into composites. Similar composites were prepared with the other pigments by blending several shipments of each material as received from suppliers.

# Dispersion of Pigments in General

The dispersion of pigments in aqueous systems is generally accomplished by the combined effect of chemical treatment and mechanical shear. The action of viscosity-reducing chemicals, commonly referred to as dispersing or deflocculating agents, is well defined in the extensive literature on the subject. Simply stated, such agents, acting on the surface of particles, reduce or destroy interparticle forces that cause the building of flocs or clusters, and thereby produce a condition of free particle movement. This action is accompanied by a drastic reduction in viscosity, making it possible to prepare free-flowing suspensions with pigment loadings which, in some cases, exceed 70% by weight. When the amount of pigment is increased sufficiently, the mixture attains a plastic state. The action of the dispersing agent, by releasing small quantities of otherwise immobilized liquid, permits the formation of a highly concentrated yet coherent mass suitable for kneading. Such a system can strongly oppose the motion of blades moving through it so the development of high shearing stresses becomes possible. Hence, pigments are mechanically dispersed either in highly fluid suspensions or in systems that are plastic in character.

# Types of Mixing Equipment

Four general types of equipment used to prepare pigment-water mixtures are illustrated in **Fig. 3-10**.

*Figure 3-10 Types of mixing equipment*

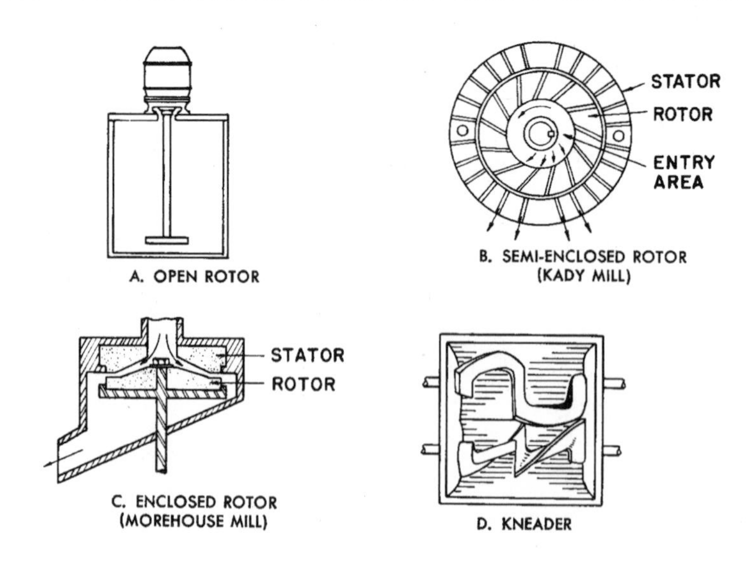

A is an open rotor machine. This is the simplest type of dispersing mechanism, and while only a single bar is pictured for illustrative purposes, these machines use rotating units of various design which may include propellers, varying shaped blades or paddles, solid disks with raised surfaces or notched edges, etc. Dispersing action is produced by the development of shearing forces between the moving agitator and the pigment fluid, and in the turbulent stream emerging from the rotor. These forces are a function of the linear velocity of the rotating element. The zone of highest energy intensity lies in the immediate vicinity of the rotation member, probably close to its most rapidly moving surfaces.

The next two mechanisms employ a design in which the rotor is either partially or totally enclosed by a static unit.

B shows a cut of the Kady mill, which employs a semi-enclosed rotor. The unit is designed to cause rapid flow of material through a slotted rotating member and through apertures in a static member that closely surrounds the rotor. This arrangement has the effect of multiplying impingement or contact areas. This apparatus consumes more power than an open rotor. Its intensive dispersing action is produced by the development of high shearing forces in the spaces between the rotor and stator, and by impingement of a high-velocity stream against the walls of the passageways in the stator.

C shows a totally enclosed rotor. Many colloid mills fall in this class. The stator and rotor are constructed of either metal or ceramic materials. The particular unit shown is a Morehouse mill, in which these parts are built of material composed of aluminum oxide particles bonded with silica frit. In any case, the fluid pigment suspension is passed through the close clearance between a static member and a rapidly revolving member. The dispersion is effected by the shear produced in the fluid system. This is another apparatus capable of intensive dispersing action. The possible energy density may be controlled by the concentration and viscosity of the pigment system and by the distance between the rotor and stator. Premixing of the suspension at some moderate speed is required prior to its admission into the mill.

The mechanisms thus far described operate on fluid systems. The apparatus shown in Fig. 3-10 D represents mixers employing slow-moving elements operating on a plastic mass. Pugmills and internal mixers using sigma and similar type blades are in this class. Since the parts move slowly, dispersion is not dependent on kinetic energy but on the direct load applied to the particle and on the very high shearing forces developed by flow within the plastic mass. In this type of mechanism, in contrast to other types of equipment, great care must be exercised to prepare a mixture that will strongly resist the motion of the mixing blades. Such factors as concentration, type and amount of dispersing agent, and volume of material in relation to blade circumference can determine the effectiveness of the dispersion. Unless these precautions are observed, the results obtained may be considerably poorer than the optimum values possible with such mechanisms.

## Description of the Experimental Equipment

This investigation employed all of the types of equipment just described.

The agitating unit using the open rotor is shown in **Fig. 3-11**. The rotating member consisted of a cross made of 1-in.-wide strips of 16-gauge stainless steel. The cross was mounted on the end of a 1-in. shaft to rotate with the thin edge of the strip leading. Three-fourths inch of the ends of each strip was turned up at a 90° angle and the vertical portion twisted through about 15° so that the leading edges were slightly closer to the shaft. This rotating unit, having a diameter of six inches, was located three inches above the center of a cylindrical container 18 in. in diameter. The liquid level was maintained at a height of 12 in., or about 13 gal of fluid. The container was jacketed for cooling to maintain a slurry termperature of not more than 35°C. High temperatures tend to reagglomerate pigment particles, particularly calcium carbonate and titanium dioxide. The speed of the rotor could be varied to provide a wide range of mixing intensities as measured by the linear velocity at the greatest radius of the rotating member. Actually, peripheral speeds ranging from about 900 to 5300 ft/min were possible. This apparatus was used as a standard, and the action of other dispersing equipment was refered to this simple unit in terms of linear speed, as will be shown in the data that follow.

*Figure 3-11 Experimental agitating unit*

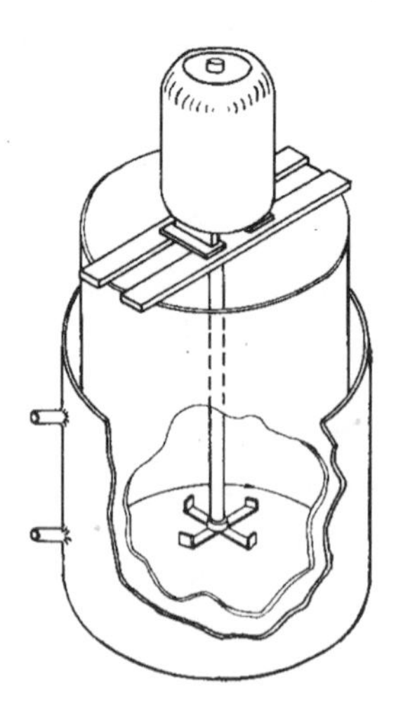

The design of the rotating unit was purely for experimental purposes. The height of the bend at the edges of each blade, as described above, was selected to permit satisfactory circulation of the material at all speeds. However, such factors as impeller design, its dimensions relative to the vessel, and volume of material in process can all affect the dispersion of the pigment and power requirements. However, for any given set of conditions, the effect obtained as a function of speed should be more or less relative to that indicated by the standard apparatus just described.

Other types of equipment were a Kady mill, Model O-20, employing the semi-enclosed rotor; a Morehouse mill, Model M, which has a totally enclosed rotor; and a Read mixer equipped with sigma blades and having a bowl capacity of approximately 10 gallons. The volume of material in process in units operating on fluid systems was kept equal to that used in the standard apparatus. The weight of pigment varied, depending on the concentration of the suspension. The amount of pigment processed in the Read mixer was maintained at a level consistent with the most desirable working characteristics of the mass. In the case of the Morehouse mill, the pigment slurry was first prepared in the standard apparatus at the lowest mixing intensity for each pigment. The entire 13 gallons of fluid were then passed through the mill once. The rate or time of flow was controlled by adjustments in the clearance between the stator and the rotor and in the feed pressure.

These mechanisms are identified here by the letters K (Kady mill), M (Morehouse mill), and R (Read kneader).

The dispersing agents used were tetrasodium pyrophosphate with clays, a modified metaphosphate glass (Calgon T) with calcium carbonate, and sodium hexametaphosphate with titanium dioxide. The dosage was controlled to produce minimum viscosity for each concentration. The amount of chemical based on the dry weight of pigment was, in most cases, 0.30% for lump clays, 0 to 0.1% for the predispersed clays, 1% for calcium carbonate, and 0.2% for the titanium dioxide. This value was determined by means of a Brookfield viscometer, using a no. 1 spindle at 20 rpm.

The degree of pigment dispersion effected by mixing intensity was determined by measuring the percentage of particles by weight coarser than 15 μ. This value was obtained by a series of sedimentation and washing steps. The effect of mixing intensity on particle packing and on the flow properties of the various suspensions was also determined.

## Effect of Time on Dispersion

The initial step in this experimental program was to determine the effect of time on dispersion at varying mixing intensities.

The energy intensity is not uniform throughout a mixing system. A rotating unit provides a zone of highest energy density surrounded by an area of much lower shearing forces. While dispersion may take place throughout the entire mixing system, depending on the size and texture of the agglomerates, optimum fineness of the entire particle system requires passage of all particles through the small volume of fluid in which maximum intensity is provided.

The concept that breaking occurs when some threshold force is exceeded does not involve the element of time. However, time becomes a factor in dispersion since time is required to bring all particles through the zone of highest energy density. Hence, for any given mixing intensity an optimum dispersion effect will be attained with time, and beyond this additional agitation under the same conditions will accomplish little. In brief, time does not compensate for a lack of intensity. Dispersion then depends on an intensity factor, which must of necessity increase as the size of the aggregate to be disrupted becomes smaller. Higher speeds raise the energy input and pass material through points of maximum intensity more frequently. This not only increases the degree of dispersion but reduces the time of processing.

An actual demonstration of these principles is presented in the following data. **Figure 3-12** shows the effect of time on the dispersion of a clay system subjected to progressively higher mixing intensities as obtained in the experimental mixer. The linear speed at the edge of the rotating member (in feet per minute) is indicated at the end of each curve. The results obtained with other mechanisms are also shown. A spray-dried clay was used in these tests and, in all but one case, the suspension contained 70% clay by weight. The exception was the experiment employing the Read kneader, in which the mixture contained about 77% clay by weight.

*Figure 3-12 Dispersion of spray-dried clay*

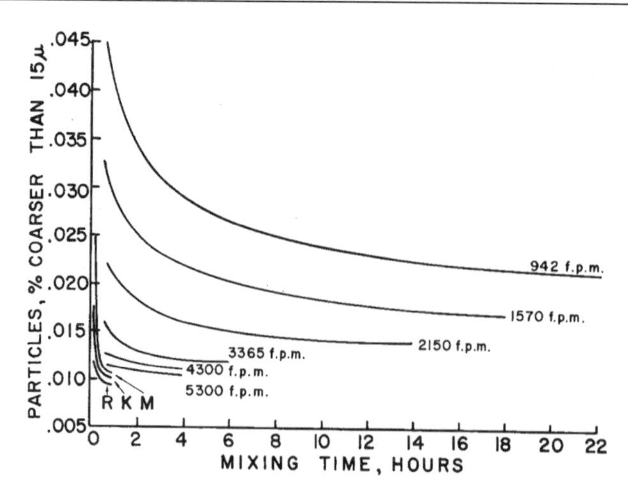

For any given mixing intensity the dispersion improves with time until some constant condition is produced. A progressive reduction in the amount of oversized particles is obtained as the intensity of mixing is increased. Higher speeds not only increase the degree of particle disintegration but greatly shorten the time of work. Mechanisms other than the standard apparatus accomplish a degree of dispersion equal to and even superior to that obtained by the standard mixer at its highest speeds. The Morehouse and Kady mills, as well as high-speed open rotors, can conceivably be employed to supplement the work of relatively slow agitators which may be used to place large volumes of material into slurry form.

Similar graphs for calcium carbonate (Purecal O) are shown in **Fig. 3-13**. In this case, suspensions containing both 70% and 75% pigment were used for fluid agitators, and a mixure composed of about 80% pigment was used in the Read machine. Although the amount of undispersed material is somewhat higher, the results follow much the same pattern as those obtained with clay.

*Figure 3-13 Dispersion of $CaCO_3$ (Purecal 0)*

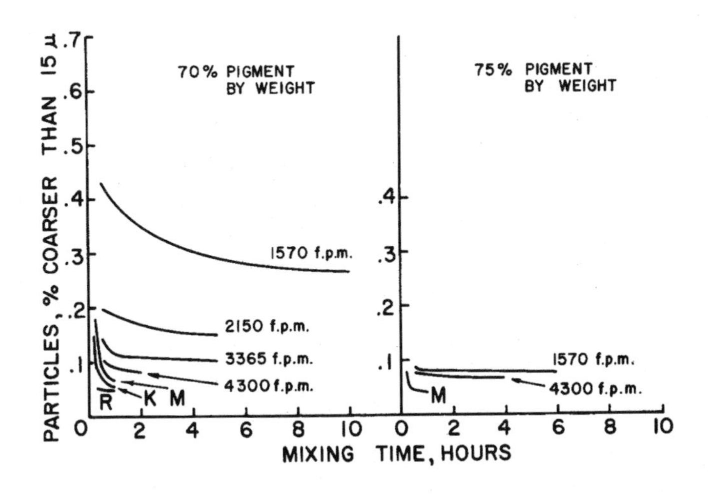


Note the effect of pigment concentration on dispersion at equal mixing speeds. For example, at a linear speed of 1570 ft/min, the final amount of undispersed particles in the 75% suspension was approximately one-fourth that remaining in the 70% suspension. A more detailed evaluation of the effect of pigment concentration will be discussed in a later section.

Graphs for rutile titanium dioxide are shown in **Fig. 3-14**. In this case, as with the carbonate, both 70% and 75% suspensions were used in mixers operating on fluid systems, and a mixture containing about 81% pigment was processed in the Read kneader. The effect was similar to that of previous pigments in fluid suspensions, but the kneader, which generally produces effective aggregate breakdown, shows an unusually high value. It is interesting, however, that this disproportionate value does not reflect, in this instance, the true state of dispersion. Other dispersion indices, such as viscosity and the degree of particle packing, indicate a position more nearly consistent with those of high-speed mechanisms.

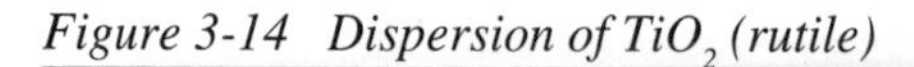

*Figure 3-14 Dispersion of $TiO_2$ (rutile)*

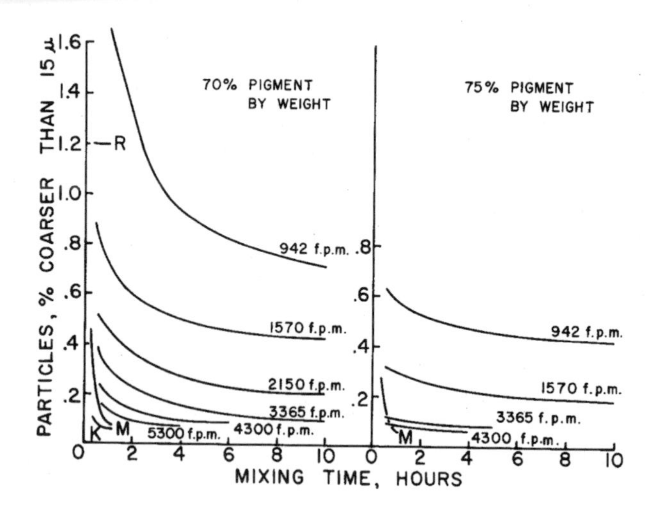


Despite this apparent favorable condition a relatively high percentage of undispersed particles was found in sedimentation tests and as rejects during screening. As far as can be determined, these aggregates appear to be remnants of undispersed pigment which adhered to kneader parts and were not assimilated by the main body of the material. This condition was not observed with other pigments and seems to be peculiar to titanium dioxide with this type of processing. This condition is eliminated when the titanium dioxide is kneaded with at least equal quantities of clay.

## Effect of Mixing Intensity on Dispersion

The foregoing data establish the optimum dispersion attainable with any mixing intensity expressed as the linear velocity of the rotating member of the standard apparatus. For example, Fig. 3-12 shows that the amount of particles coarser than 15 μ has been reduced to an approximate constant value of about 0.023% after 16 hours at 942 ft/min and to about 0.016% after 13 hours at 1570 ft/min. The lowest amounts or optimum values for all the other speeds can be found in a similar manner. If these values are now plotted against the corresponding speed of the rotating member, a curve is obtained showing the optimum values to be expected at any speed, including an extrapolation to speeds higher than obtained with the experimental unit. Such curves for various clays are shown in **Fig. 3-15**.

*Figure 3-15 Effect of mixing intensity of dispersion of clays*

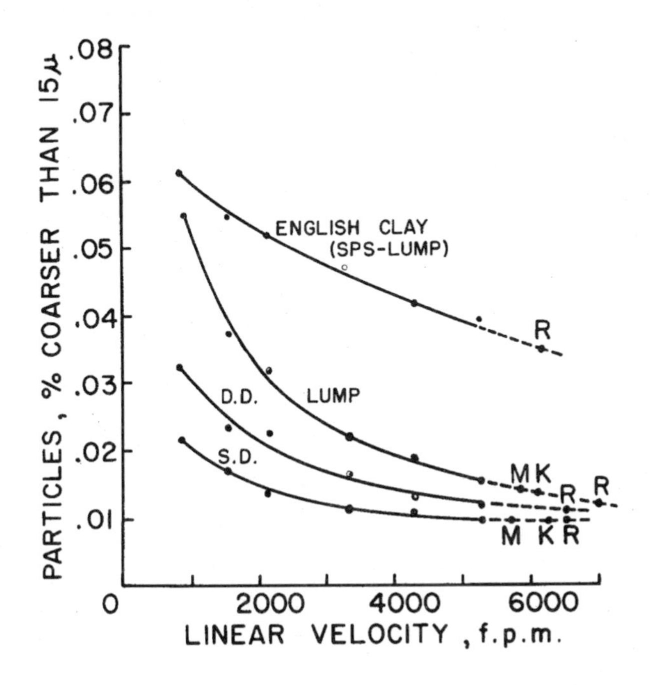


Figure 3-15 can be used to determine the relative effectiveness of other dispersing equipment in terms of the standard apparatus by simply locating the optimum dispersion value obtained with a particular mechanism on each curve and reading the corresponding linear velocity. Thus, the position of the Kady (K), Morehouse (M), and Read (R) machines with respect to the standard unit is indicated on each curve. Here, a mechanism employing slow-moving parts, operating on a plastic mass, can produce an effect that would require an approximate speed of about 6000–7000 ft/min using the standard apparatus on a fluid system.

The suspensions processed in mechanisms employing fluid systems contained 70% clay by weight for domestic products and 62% for the English clay. The plastic mixture used in the Read machine contained about 77% clay by weight for domestic clays and about 70% for the English clay.

The spray-dried (SD) clay disperses more easily than drum-dried (DD) and lump clays. The relative flatness of the dispersion curve for the spray-dried clay indicates that this material can be effectively dispersed even under moderate agitation. Dispersion differences between the three domestic clays are therefore at a maximum if the comparison is made at the lowest mixing speeds, but as mixing intensity increases, all clays, irrespective of physical form, appear to approach the same dispersion value. In fact, in many cases, the undispersed-type coating clays are preferred, since their use permits selection of a dispersing agent as well as a more precise control of its addition. Pulverization of the lump clay improves dispersion slightly at the lower speeds; however, the curves for pulverized and nonpulverized coincide at speeds in excess of about 1700 ft/min.

The English coating clay is somewhat more difficult to disperse than domestic products. This may be partly attributed to the more dilute suspensions involved. Higher concentrations were prevented due to the viscosity of the material.

The effect of mixing intensity on the dispersion of calcium carbonate and rutile titanium dioxide is similarly summarized in **Fig. 3-16**. The results for both 70% and 75% suspensions processed in fluid-type agitators are shown. Mixtures processed in the Read machine contained 80–81% pigment by weight.

*Figure 3-16 Effect of mixing intensity on dispersion of $TiO_2$ and $CaCO_3$*

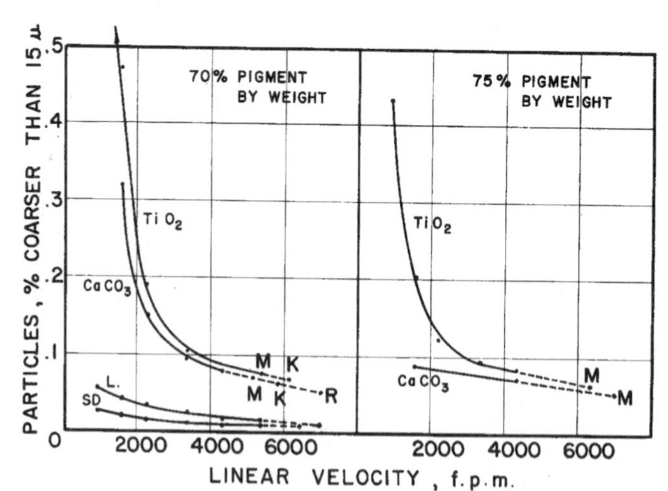


Both pigments show relatively high aggregate residue in 70% suspensions when processed at the slower speeds. However, improvement in dispersion proceeds rapidly until the speed of the rotating member reaches a linear velocity of about 3000–3500 ft/min, after which a more moderate rate of improvement is indicated.

An increase in the concentration of the suspension from 70% to 75% pigment increases the effectiveness of the slower agitators. This is particularly pronounced in the case of the calcium carbonate. In fact, the degree of dispersion obtained at 1570 ft/min is very nearly equal to that produced at the highest speeds. On the other hand, titanium dioxide, while experiencing considerable improvement as a result of increased concentration, requires the use of high-intensity equipment to attain the maximum effect.

The curves for the lump (L) and spray-dried (SD) clays shown at the bottom of Fig. 3-16 were transferred from Fig. 3-15.

## Pigment Concentration

Dispersion improves with increasing pigment concentration because of the greater shearing forces produced by the higher viscosity and increased particle interference. This is illustrated in **Fig. 3-17**, which shows the effect of pigment concentration on the reduction of aggregates obtained with spray-dried clay, calcium carbonate, and titanium dioxide. Tests were made at two different linear speeds: a slow speed and a speed of about 3400 ft/min, at which there was a sharp decline in the rate of aggregate breakdown.

*Figure 3-17 Effect of pigment concentration on dispersion*

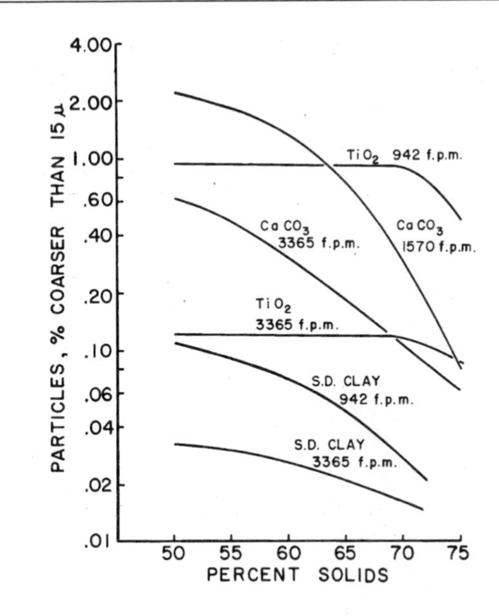

A buildup in pigment solids appears to be more beneficial to calcium carbonate than to the other pigments. For example, at the slower speed the amount of oversized calcium carbonate particles remaining in the 75% suspension was roughly 1/25th that contained in the 50% slurry. An increase in linear speed reduces this difference. For example, at a speed of about 3400 ft/min the amount of oversized particles at 75% solids is approximately one-tenth that present in 50% suspension. The dispersion effect produced with the higher speed at 50% solids is roughly equal to that produced at the slower speed at about 66% solids.

The results obtained with clay follow a similar pattern, although dispersion differences as a result of concentration are not nearly so pronounced.

The behavior of titanium dioxide appears different from the other two pigments. At both speeds no marked change in dispersion is observed until the amount of pigment by weight exceeds about 70%. Its variance from the behavior of other pigments may be largely attributed to its much higher specific gravity, or, in effect, lower pigment volume. As contrasted with clay and calcium carbonate, a much greater weight of titanium dioxide is required to increase the pigment volume concentration sufficiently to develop important interparticle shearing forces. A relationship between weight and volume for each pigment is shown in **Table 3-4**.

*Table 3-4 A relationship between weight and volume for each pigment*

| | Per cent by weight | Percent by volume | Pigment in 1 gal slurry, lb |
|---|---|---|---|
| Clay | 70 | 47.3 | 10.3 |
| Calcium carbonate | 70 | 46.8 | 10.4 |
| Titanium dioxide | 70 | 35.7 | 12.5 |
| Titanium dioxide | 79 | 47.3 | 16.6 |

## Effect of Mixing Intensity of Particle Packing and Flow Properties

The effect of mixing intensity on such properties of each pigment suspension as particle packing and flow characteristics more or less parallels the degree of dispersion as measured by the amount of oversized particles. Hence, these properties provide other methods for discerning dispersion.

# Relative Sediment Volume

The degree of particle packing was determined by a measurement of the relative sediment volume (see Appendix II), using the method taught by Robinson *(8)*. The effect of mixing intensity on relative sediment volume is illustrated in **Fig. 3-18**. The pigment suspensions were the same as those described for Figs. 3-15 and 3-16. All tests were made on suspensions containing 70% pigment by weight.

*Figure 3-18 Effect of mixing intensity on relative sediment volume*

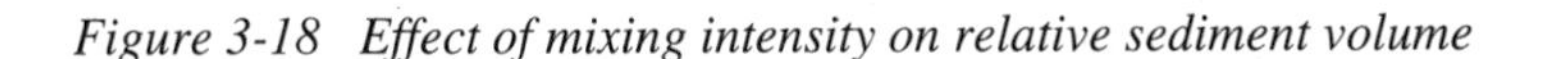

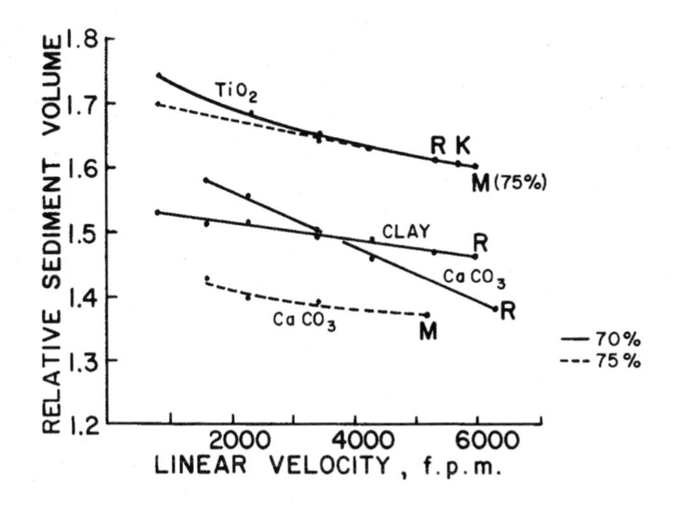


The results indicate, in all cases, that the relative sediment volume is reduced as mixing speed is increased. In general, the results indicate much the same trend as obtained with measurements of oversized particles, shown in Fig. 3-16. The exception is the value obtained with the titanium dioxide processed in the Read (R) machine, which now takes a position equivalent to that attained at a speed of about 5300 ft/min, despite its relatively high aggregate content. In the case of clay and calcium carbonate, using 70% suspensions, the results obtained with Kady (K) and Morehouse (M) mills were for all practical purposes equal to the value shown for the Read kneader.

# Flow Properties

The effect of mixing intensity on the flow properties of the pigment-water system, as measured with a Hagan high-shear viscometer, offers another interesting study of dispersion. An increase in mixing intensity reduces the resistance of the system to flow. This is due to an alteration in the pigment particle system, which reduces particle interference and causes the system to engage less liquid when subjected to shear *(10)*. These effects are illustrated in **Figs. 3-19 through 3-21**.

*Figure 3-19 Hagan rheograms for $CaCO_3$ (Purecal O), 70% pigment*

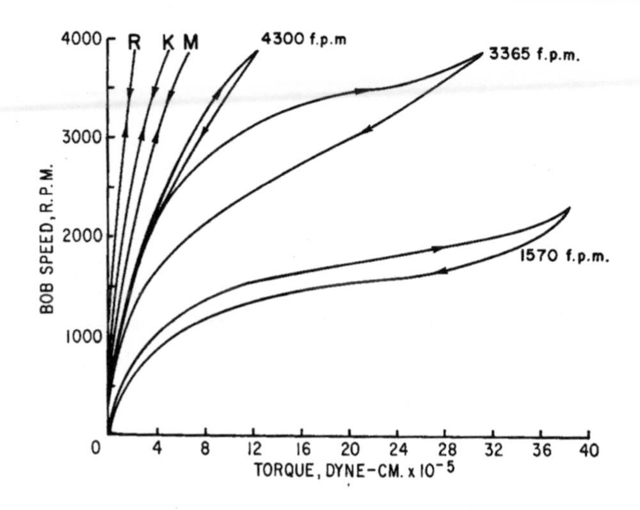


*Figure 3-20 Hagan rheograms for $CaCO_3$ (Purecal O), 75% pigment diluted to 70% for testing*

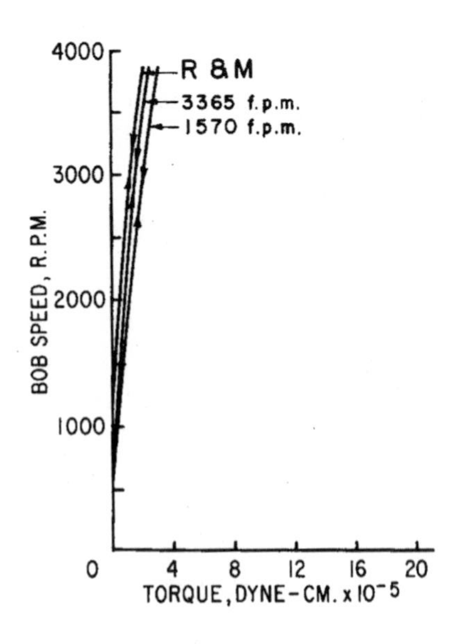

*Figure 3-21 Hagan rheograms for clay*

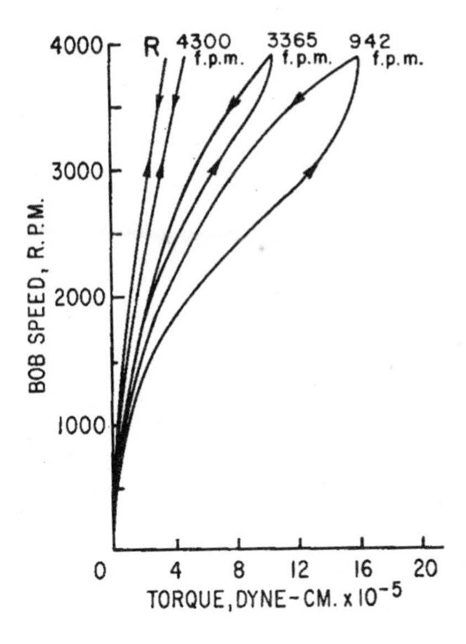


Figures 3-19 and 3-20 show the flow properties of calcium carbonate (Purecal O) as affected by varying mixing conditions. Figure 3-19 shows results for suspensions prepared at 70% pigment by weight and tested at the same concentration, Fig. 3-20 for suspensions prepared at 75% pigment but diluted to 70% pigment for testing. In both cases, the mixture processed in the Read machine, originally containing about 80% pigment, was diluted to 70% pigment for purposes of this test.

Figure 3-19 clearly demonstrates the progressive decrease in the resistance of the system to flow as the speed of the standard apparatus is increased. Other types of equipment appear to produce an even greater effect than that attained with the highest speed of the experimental unit. The rheograms of Fig. 3-20 show very nearly equal flow properties, indicating again the improved effectiveness of slower speed when the concentration of the carbonate suspension is increased to 75% pigment.

Figure 3-21 shows the effect of mixing intensity on the flow properties of a spray-dried clay. In all but the Read machine, mixtures containing 70% clay were prepared and tested at the same concentration. In the case of the Read machine, in which the processing concentration was about 77%, the mixture was diluted to 70% for this test. The results exhibit a relationship similar to that obtained with the carbonate (Fig. 3-19), although differences between the various rheograms are not a pronounced.

Similar rheograms obtained with titanium dioxide follow much the same pattern observed with calcium carbonate and clay. However, the very low viscosity of titanium dioxide in 70% suspensions allows for only minor differences between the rheograms. This is, of course, due to the much lower pigment volume concentration with the titanium dioxide as compared to the other pigments.

## Screening Efficiency

A practical aspect of the effect of mixing intensity may be found in the screening rate of the suspensions through a relatively fine screen. The rate of screening is influenced by both the viscosity of the suspension and the amount and size of undispersed particles.

It is generally customary to screen dispersed pigment-water suspensions through screens ranging from about 100 to 250 mesh. To determine relative screening efficiencies of the various suspensions in the laboratory, the time required to screen a liter of the material through a 150-mesh screen was determined. In all cases, suspensions containing 70% pigment by weight were used. The results, reported in gallons per minute, are shown in **Fig. 3-22**. The rate of screening of all pigments is greatly increased as the velocity of the rotating member is increased. The effect is considerably more pronounced with calcium carbonate and titanium dioxide than with clay. In the case of clay and calcium carbonate the results obtained with the Kady and Morehouse mills were for all practical purposes the same as the values shown for the Read kneader.

*Figure 3-22 Effect of mixing intensity on screening rate (150 mesh)*

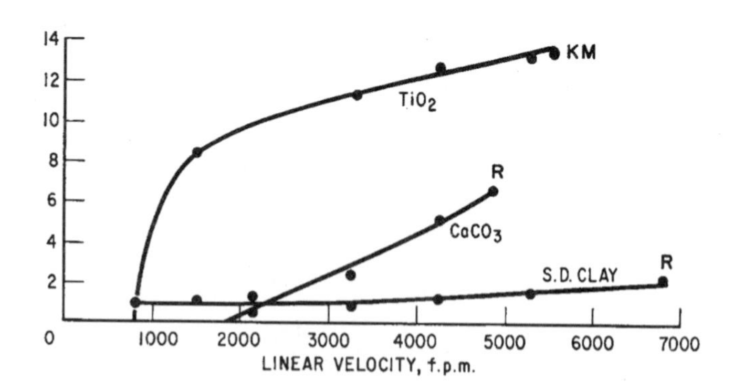


## Summary

The degree of dispersion improves as the intensity of mixing is increased. Mixing intensity can be increased by increasing the speed of the equipment, by increasing the concentration of the pigment, or by a combination of the two.

Time is a factor in dispersion only because time is required to cause all particles to flow through the zone of highest energy density.

Clays disperse under much lower mechanical forces than calcium carbonate and titanium dioxide. Spray-dried clays disperse more easily, but all physical forms of clay disperse to nearly the same degree if the mixing intensity is increased sufficiently. Titanium dioxide requires high-speed mechanisms to produce satisfactory dispersion. Calcium carbonate can be effectively dispersed at slower speeds provided the pigment concentration is held at about 75% by weight.

## Literature Cited

1. Cobb, R. M. K., *TAPPI* 41(10): 581–600(1958).
2. Daniel, F. K., *India Rubber World* 101(3): 50–52 (1939); (4): 33–37(1940).
3. Fischer, E. K., *Colloidal Dispersions*, New York, John Wiley & Sons, Inc., 1950.
4. Mattson, V. F. and Leighton, J. R., *TAPPI* 42(1):1–5(1959).
5. Robinson, J. V., *J. Physical Chem.* 53: 1042–1056(1949); 55: 455–464(1951); *Trans. Soc. Rheology* I: 15–24(1957).
6. Thompson, R. N., *"Dispersion of Coating Colors,"* In TAPPI Monograph Series No. 11, TAPPI PRESS, Atlanta, 1957.
7. Robinson, J. V., *TAPPI* 42(6): 436–437(1959).
8. Robinson, J. V. *TAPPI* 42(6): 432–438(1959).
9. Asdell, B. K., *TAPPI* 38(8): 476–481(1955).
10. Millman, N., *Paper Trade J.* 132(7): 28–32(1951).

# 4.

# Kaolin Clays

*Paul Sennett*

Kaolin clay is the most widely used pigment in paper, both as a filler, where it is mixed with the fiber before the sheet is formed, and as a coating, where it is mixed with a binder and other ingredients and applied to the surface of the sheet. In 1990, 4.2 million tons of kaolin was produced for use by the paper industry in the United States. About 65% of this was used in coating and most of the remainder in filling *(1)*.

Kaolin clay is so widely used because it is low in cost, reasonably white, and readily available worldwide. Traditionally, the major sources of paper kaolin have been the Cornwall district in England and the middle Georgia area in the United States. More recently, large quantities of kaolin suitable for paper use have become available from Brazil and Australia, while smaller quantities are obtained from other countries around the world *(2)*.

Although there is some variation in specific properties of kaolin that depends on its geographic source and method of processing, all kaolins share the following desirable characteristics:

- Inert (nonreactive and very water insoluble)
- Nontoxic
- Good color (white or nearly so)
- Fine particle size (for good opacity and smoothness)
- Easy dispersion (readily dispersed in water at high solids content)
- Platy particle shape (for good ink receptivity and print quality).

Coated paper was reportedly first made by the Chinese around 700 A.D. *(3)*. However, kaolin as a coating pigment was not used until around 1870 *(4)*. In subsequent years, kaolin use in paper has grown as finer particle, improved brightness, and grit-free clays have become available. After World War II, the demand for coated sheets with good print quality at low basis weight has markedly increased kaolin clay use. More recently, the use of calcined clay, first introduced in the late 1940s, has increased rapidly.

Kaolin clay for paper is mined and processed to make a suitable product as opposed to other paper pigments ($TiO_2$, precipitated $CaCO_3$, etc.), which are manufactured from chemical raw materials. Since kaolin producers are somewhat at the mercy of the crude kaolin deposits that they mine, the geology of the kaolin source is important because it dictates the processing scheme needed to produce a satisfactory product. In addition, the clay source influences, to some extent, the properties of the final product. A good review of geologic factors and their effect on kaolin product quality is given by Murray *(5)*.

Kaolin deposits are usually classified as "primary" or "secondary". Primary kaolins are those that have been formed by the weathering of the source rock and remain in place, frequently along with large quantities of the unweathered source rock. A notable example of primary kaolins are those of Cornwall in the United Kingdom. Secondary clays are those that have been transported away from the source rock and concentrated in deposits which may be some distance away from the parent rock. The middle Georgia kaolins in the United States are good examples of secondary kaolin.

## Product Description
## Types of Kaolin

Kaolin clays for paper may be classified in several ways:

- By the source of the crude and how it was formed (primary or secondary)
- By processing method (dry or wet)
- By use (coating or filling)
- By product characteristics (brightness, particle size distribution, etc.).

Since, to the papermaker, product characteristics are most important, they normally use these as a basis for classification. It is also useful to classify kaolins broadly as coating or filler clays, although there is frequently some overlap since coating clays are sometimes used as fillers and filler clays are used in coatings.

**Table 4-1** attempts to classify various North American kaolins according to their important properties of brightness and particle size. Also included in the table is a "slurry % solids", which gives us some idea of the clay's fluidity in water. This table is an abridged version of the Kaolin Pigment Index published by TAPPI *(6)*. Not included in this table are commercially important paper clays from sources in England, Brazil, and Australia. In general, English kaolins, like those from the United States, are available in a wide variety of particle sizes — from very fine particles for coatings to quite coarse particles for filling — as is shown in **Table 4-2**. The English clays typically are slightly more viscous than the clays from Georgia and are slightly brighter and less yellow. Most clays from Australia and Brazil are available only as a very fine particle-size product (95% less than 2μm) having good fluidity and a brightness slightly higher than domestic standard grades. Products with 90% GE brightness are currently becoming available from Brazil.

*Table 4-1 U.S. Kaolin Clays and Typical Properties*

| | Slurry, % Solids | Brightness, % | Percent < 2 μm |
|---|---|---|---|
| **Coating Clays** | | | |
| High-Brightness Coating Clays | | | |
| No. 1 (Ultrafine) | 70 | 90-92 | 95-100 |
| No. 1 | 70 | 90-92 | 90-94 |
| No. 2 | 70 | 90-92 | 80-86 |
| Regular-Brightness Coating Clays | | | |
| No. 1 (Ultrafine) | 70 | 86-88 | 94-98 |
| No. 1 | 70 | 86-88 | 90-94 |
| No. 2 | 70 | 85-87 | 78-84 |
| No. 3 | 70 | 85-86 | 73-75 |
| Delaminated | | | |
| Fine Particle | 69.5 | 87-89 | 96-98 |
| Regular | 67.5 | 87-89 | 96-98 |
| Coarse Particle | 63 | 84-86 | 45-55 |
| **Filler Clays** | | | |
| Water Washed | | | |
| Fine-Particle Premium | 70 | 84-86 | 88-95 |
| Fine-Particle Regular | 70 | 80-83 | 88-95 |
| Full Fraction | 70 | 79-86 | 50-70 |
| Delaminated | 65-70 | 88-91 | 45-55 |
| Airfloat | | | |
| Regular | NA | 79-82 | 50-75 |
| **Structured Pigments** | | | |
| Calcined, Low Temperature | NA | 80-82 | 78-84 |
| Calcined, High Temperature | 50-52 | 92-94 | 80-94 |
| Chemically Structured | Variable | Variable | Variable |

This table is a slightly modified version of TAPPI Technical Information Sheet TIS 0106-06 (issued 1988).

*Table 4-2 Typical Properties of English Kaolin Clays*

| | Slurry, % Solids | ISO Brightness,[a] % | Percent < 2 μm |
|---|---|---|---|
| **Coating Clays**[b] | | | |
| Ultrafine, High Gloss | ... | 86.5 | 93 |
| Fine | 66.5 | 85.5 | 80 |
| Coating | 68.0 | 85.5 | 74 |
| Coating | 66.0 | 83.0 | 65 |
| **Filler Clays**[b] | | | |
| Fine Filler | ... | 82.5 | 55 |
| Intermediate | ... | 81.0 | 50 |
| Intermediate | ... | 79.5 | 50 |
| Coarse Filler | ... | 79.5 | 30 |
| Coarse Filler | ... | 77.0 | 30 |

[a]ISO brightness is about two points lower than the GE brightness used in the United States.
[b]Listed in order of decreasing fineness within each group.

## Chemical Properties

Kaolin is an aluminum silicate with a layered structure of alternating alumina and silica sheets. Chemically it is represented by the formula:

$$(OH)_8Si_4Al_4O_{10}$$

This formula is frequently written as $Al_2O_3 \cdot 2SiO_2 \cdot 2H_2O$, probably because it is easier to remember. When written in this latter fashion the formula implies the presence of water as part of the structure, which is not the case. Kaolin contains structural hydroxyl groups which are liberated as water only on heating to about 500°C or higher. Published reports frequently (and erroneously) refer to "hydrous" kaolins to distinguish uncalcined kaolin from calcined products. A schematic of the kaolin structure is shown in **Fig. 4-1** *(7)*.

*Figure 4-1 Schematic diagram of the Kaolinite Structure*

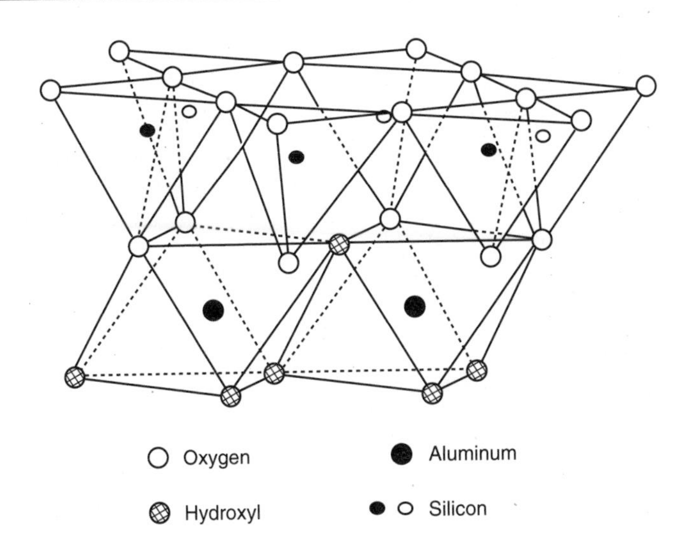


Individual kaolin crystals of fine particle size show a roughly hexagonal outline as exemplified by **Fig. 4-2**. The shape of the larger particles deviates considerably from hexagonal and depends on the geology of the deposit. The larger particles from the primary English kaolins, for example, are thin, larger diameter platelets but do not show a clear hexagonal outline. Coarse particles of some kaolins from the Georgia deposits in the United States are often described as "booklets" since they show a pronounced layer structure with gaps between the layers, much like the pages of a loosely-bound book *(8)*. **Figure 4-3** shows coarse particles from an English kaolin, while **Fig. 4-4** shows the booklets present in coarse middle Georgia clays. These booklets may be selectively ground to a finer particle size to give "delaminated" clays whose particles are of large diameter yet thin.

*Figure 4-2 Fine Particles of Kaolin from Middle Georgia*

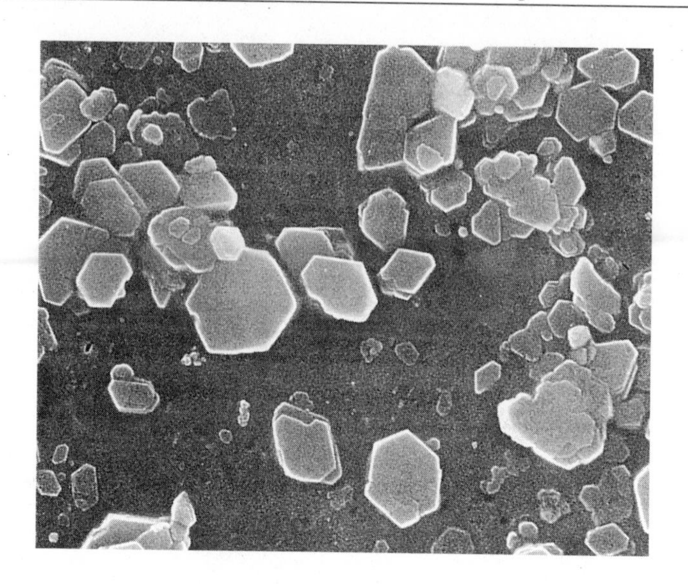

*Figure 4-3 Coarse, Platy Particles from English Kaolin*

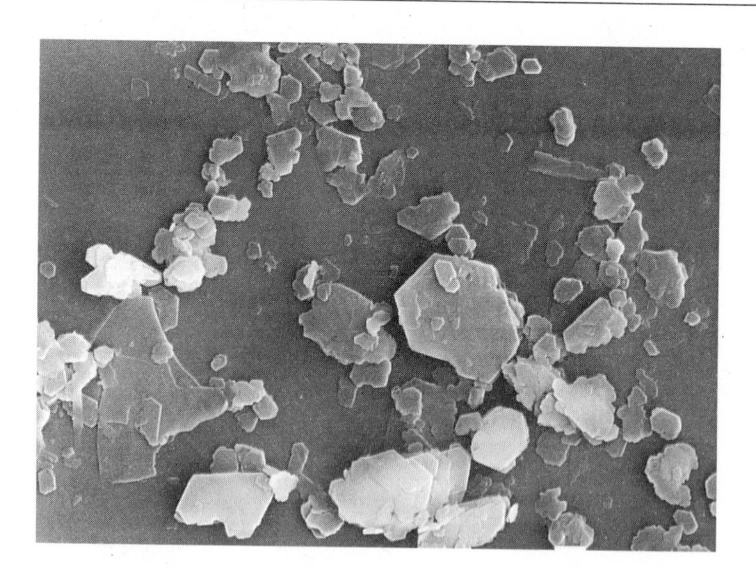

*Figure 4-4 Kaolin Booklets from Middle Georgia Crude Clay*

Although the value of kaolin clay to the papermaker rests largely on its physical properties, the chemical composition is sometimes important, especially with regard to impurities. **Table 4-3** gives representative analyses of several kaolins used in paper.

*Table 4-3 Typical Chemical Analysis*

| | U.S. No. 1 | English Coating | Brazilian Coating | Pure Kaolinite |
|---|---|---|---|---|
| $Al_2O_3$ | 38.4 | 36.8 | 38.0 | 39.8 |
| $SiO_2$ | 45.1 | 48.0 | 45.0 | 46.3 |
| $TiO_2$ | 1.7 | 0.06 | 1.10 | ... |
| $Fe_2O_3$ | 0.5 | 0.61 | 1.9 | ... |
| CaO | 0.1 | ... | ... | ... |
| MgO | 0.1 | 0.18 | ... | ... |
| $K_2O$ | 0.1 | 1.10 | 0.10 | ... |
| $Na_2O$ | 0.2 | ... | 0.10 | ... |
| Ignition Loss | 13.8 | 13.3 | 13.8 | 13.9 |

In Table 4-3, ignition loss represents weight loss at 1000°C, which is mostly the loss of structural hydoxyl groups as water. Small amounts of organic material, if present, will also contribute to the weight loss. Other than $Al_2O_3$, $SiO_2$, and ignition loss, the other elements in the analysis are from mineral impurities present in the crude that are not removed during processing or are residues from processing chemicals. Although the crude ores may contain a fairly large number of accessory minerals, most of these are removed in wet processing. Dry processing is less efficient in removing mineral impurities but no chemical additives need be used.

Anatase $TiO_2$ is ubiquitous in middle Georgia kaolin crudes and is a major discoloring impurity. Although pigmentary titanium dioxide is white, the naturally occurring material contains a small amount of iron (2-5% expressed as $Fe_2O_3$) which gives it a dark brown color that lowers the brightness of the product *(9)*. A number of processes for improving the brightness of kaolins are based on the removal of discoloring anatase *(10)*.

## Physical Properties

The major physical properties of kaolins that dictate their suitability for paper applications are particle size and shape, the distribution of particle size and shape, color, brightness, and viscosity in water at high solids.

**Particle Size.** It has long been known that, in general, finer particle kaolins give higher gloss in coatings, lower viscosity at higher shear rates, higher opacity (up to a point; extremely fine kaolins become transparent), higher brightness, and a greater loss in sheet strength when used as a filler. Historically, particle size has been measured by sedimentation methods based on Stokes' law and "percent less than 2 μm equivalent spherical diameter" used as a single number measurement of particle fineness, as given in Table 4-1. This provides a convenient method of expressing particle size but does not take into account the distribution of particle sizes present nor particle shape, both of which are important in predicting kaolin performance.

As an example of how size distribution may vary, **Fig. 4-5** shows the particle-size distribution of two kaolins, both having a sedimentation diameter of 92% less than 2 μm. Obviously, the "% less than 2 μm" does not adequately describe the particle size of the kaolin. All kaolins have an extremely wide distribution of particle size. For example, a No. 2 coating clay can contain particles as fine as 0.05 μm and as coarse as 5 μm — a 100 to 1 ratio between the finest and coarsest particles. As a practical matter, the clay having the wider distribution of size gives slurries of lower viscosity. A narrower distribution, on the other hand, gives a bulkier coating of higher opacity and improved print quality.

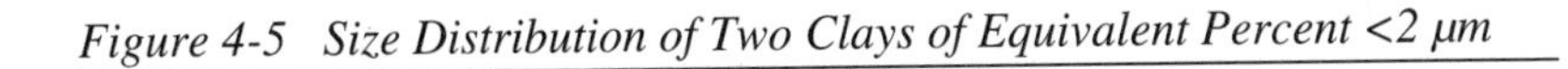

*Figure 4-5 Size Distribution of Two Clays of Equivalent Percent <2 μm*

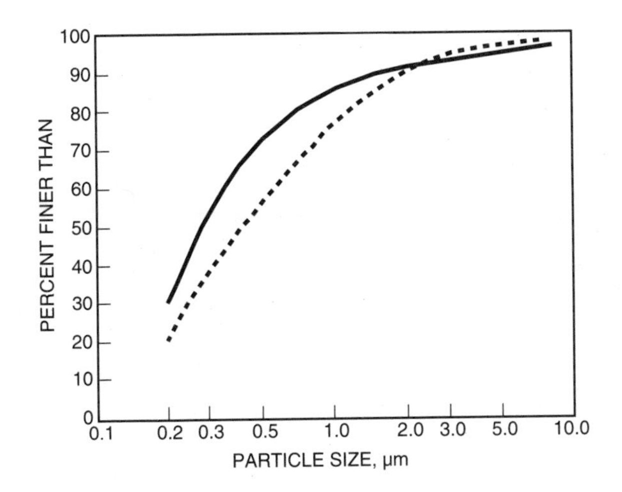


**Particle Shape.** In addition to particle size distribution, particle shape is also important. Platier particles (those with a higher ratio of diameter to thickness, or "aspect ratio") tend to give higher viscosity slurries but better coverage of the paper fibers when used in coating. This is especially true at lighter coating weights *(11, 12)*.

**Brightness and Color.** Brightness is a measure of the blue reflectance of a packed sample of the dried and pulverized kaolin powder and is a good single-number measurement for near-white clays that do not vary much in color. A system for measuring the brightness of paper and clays was first developed in the early 1930s. A commercial instrument for brightness determination was manufactured by the General Electric Co. and first marketed to the paper and pigments industry about 1935 *(13)*. Instruments that measure the blue reflectance according to this system are still being used in the United States. The resulting measurement is still often referred to as "GE brightness" although the tester was last manufactured by General Electric over 35 years ago. The brightness values given in Table 4-1 are "GE" brightness values.

Since clays do vary to some degree in color, there is an increasing trend toward measuring color, not just brightness. The complete description of the color of a sample requires three numbers. Several systems are available for expressing color *(14)*, but in the paper and pigments industry the "L,a,b" system is commonly used:

L = the total reflectance in the range of wavelengths to which the eye is sensitive
a = a measure of the red-green coloration (+a = red, -a = green)
b = a measure of the blue-yellow coloration (+b = yellow, -b = blue).

Numerous instruments are available for color measurement. The paper industry in the United States has used the "Hunter" L,a,b system *(15),* but the 1976 CIE L*,a*,b* system *(16, 17)* is being increasingly used, especially outside the United States.

**Viscosity.** Experience has shown that the viscosity of clay in water, provided that it is properly dispersed, relates to the viscosity of the coating formulation; i. e., a clay that gives a low viscosity in water will generally give a coating formulation of low viscosity. In most cases, a coating formulation having the lowest possible viscosity at the highest solids is desirable for good runnability at high speeds.

The viscosity of clay/water slurries and coating formulations at high solids is, as is the case with most suspensions of fine-particle solids in liquids, a function of the shear rate at which the viscosity is measured. Thus, when reporting viscosity, not only should the viscosity of the suspension be reported but also the shear rate at which it is measured.

Traditionally the viscosity of clays and coatings is measured at low shear with the Brookfield viscometer, while measurements at higher shear are measured using the Hercules viscometer *(18).* Over the years many studies of viscosity have been made using the Hercules to evaluate the effect of viscosity on runnability and sheet quality; however, in recent years, viscometers capable of higher shear rates have become increasingly available and are being used in coating studies *(19-21).* Higher-shear viscosity should relate more closely to coating behavior on the machine since very high shear rates are developed on modern high-speed coaters.

An important variable in viscosity is the percent solids of the slurry. **Figure 4-6** shows the effect of solids on Hercules viscosity for a fine-particle coating clay.

*Figure 4-6 Hercules Viscosity of Delaminated Clay*

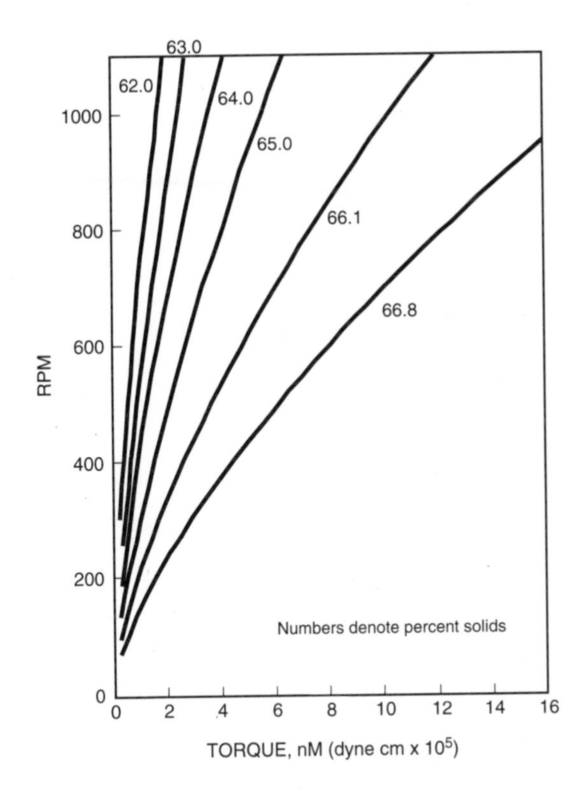


## Wetting and Dispersion

All kaolins are readily wet with water so that wettability of kaolins, unlike, say, that of talc, is probably not an important consideration in obtaining low viscosity, although little data is available.

There are two aspects of dispersion: the mechanical part, where dry clay is added to water and, with appropriate mixing, a uniform suspension is produced, and the chemical part, where suitable chemical agents are added to give the lowest possible viscosity. Although the mechanical part is important, the chemical part is more so and controls the viscosity of the final product. "Dispersion" is an ill-defined term. In the kaolin and paper industries it is generally used to mean "deflocculation" although, strictly speaking, it is defined as the process of making a uniform suspension of a solid in a liquid and does not require that the solid be deflocculated *(22)*. However, in this chapter we will conform to custom and use the term "dispersion" to mean "deflocculation".

Optimum dispersion for a given clay is considered to be the point where, as a result of dispersant addition, the particle charge (or zeta potential) is at a maximum as the result of dispersant addition *(23)*. It is not easy to determine this point rapidly and reliably in the laboratory so a more practical method is to determine viscosity at low shear as a function of dispersant addition as shown in **Fig. 4-7**. Figure 4-7 (from Ref. 27) shows the effect of the addition of tetrasodium pyrophosphate (TSPP) to a clay that has not previously been dispersed. As dispersant is added, viscosity decreases rapidly to a minimum and then slowly increases. The minimum in this curve is taken as the optimum dispersant level. When dispersant comparisons are made, not only is the minimum viscosity important but also the amount of dispersant required to reach the low viscosity.

*Figure 4-7 Effect of TSPP on 70% Solids Viscosity*

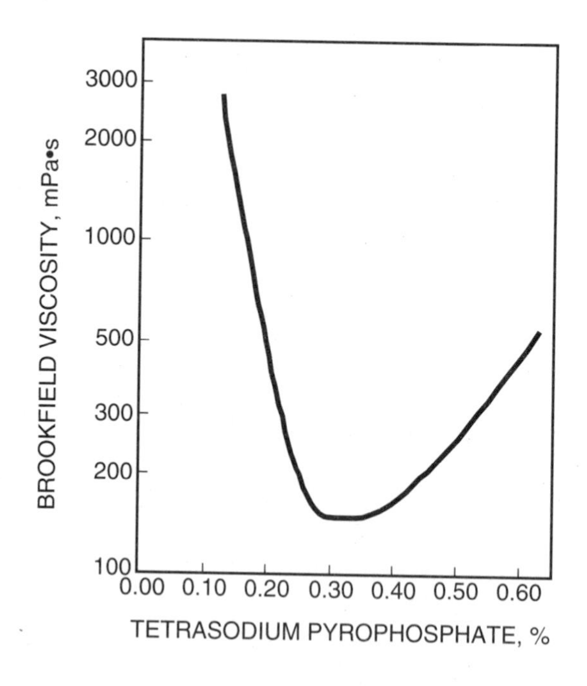

# Clay Physical Properties Data
# Particle-Size Distribution

**Figure 4-8** gives particle-size distribution curves for some of the commonly used paper clays and shows the wide range of particle-size distributions available. These curves were determined by sedimentation *(24),* so they give no indication of particle shape. Tables 4-1 and 4-2 give the "percent less than 2 μm" for some commonly used American and English kaolins.

*Figure 4-8 Sedimentation Particle-Size Distribution of Representative Kaolins*

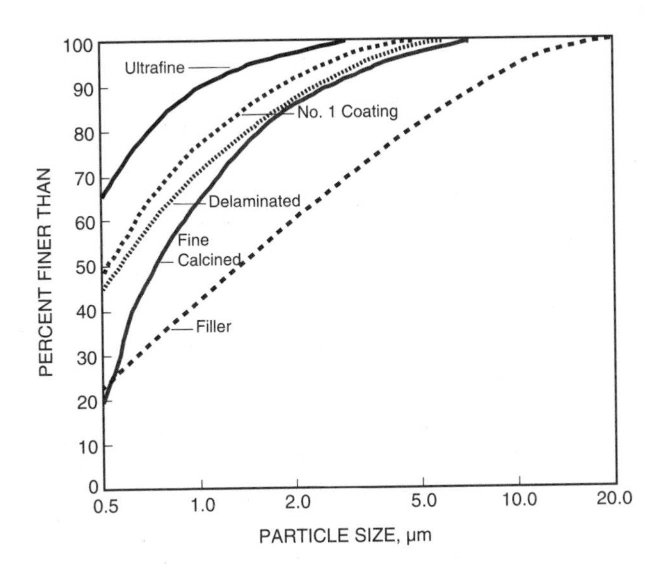


## Particle Shape

As stated previously, particle shape is important because it strongly affects the coating and filling properties of the pigment. The aspect ratio (the ratio of platelet diameter to thickness) varies with the source of the crude kaolin, the particle size, and whether or not it has been mechanically delaminated during processing. The determination of aspect ratio is difficult because it is carried out by measurements on electron micrographs. Since all commercial kaolins have a broad distribution of sizes, a large number of particles must be measured.

Recently a technique has been developed for measuring the "shape factor", which shows promise as a rapid method for comparing the particle shape of various pigments *(25)*. Further, the aspect ratio of kaolins varies with particle size, especially for U.S. kaolins that have not been delaminated.

**Figure 4-9** (from Ref. 11) shows the variation in aspect ratio of kaolins from Georgia as a function of particle size. Obviously, no single number for aspect ratio will adequately describe a given kaolin since the aspect ratio changes with particle size. There is also a pronounced difference between regular clays and delaminated clays since the delamination process has selectively ground the thicker particles so that only thinner particles remain.

*Figure 4-9 Change in Particle Shape with Size*

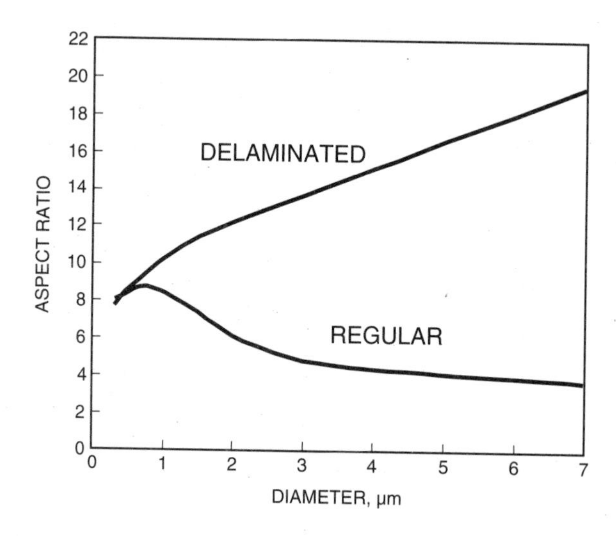


## Viscosity

As pointed out earlier, one of the important characteristics of kaolin that makes it of value in coatings is that high-solids aqueous slurries may be readily made. Viscosity of kaolin slurries is influenced by a number of factors. In addition to the solids content, as illustrated in Fig. 4-6, and the state of dispersion, illustrated by Fig. 4-7, other factors affecting viscosity are particle-size distribution, particle shape, the presence of mineral impurities, and the ionic environment surrounding the kaolin particles.

Particle-size distribution is important because of particle packing characteristics. Other things being equal, a kaolin with a wider size distribution will have a lower viscosity than a kaolin of equivalent median size but with a narrower size distribution. Presumably the smaller particles can fit between the larger ones and give better packing so that higher solids can be reached before the viscosity becomes intolerably high *(26)*.

Particle shape is important because of the dynamics of the fluid suspension. Under shear, the platy kaolin particles tend to rotate in the surrounding liquid. As the solids level is increased, particles get closer together and come into contact with each other. This contact interferes with free rotation and leads to a higher viscosity. For this reason, platy particles such as those in delaminated clays tend to interfere with each other at lower solids than the less platy particles of conventional kaolins *(27)*.

The presence of mineral impurities can also affect viscosity. Although coarse-particle minerals are removed in wet processing, finer, clay-sized particles, if present in the crude kaolin, can be carried through to the final product. Smectite (montmorillonite) is sometimes found in kaolin deposits and, if present in the kaolin product, even in small amounts, can increase the viscosity markedly *(28)*. To prevent the higher viscosity that would result from the presence of smectite in kaolin products, crudes containing smectite are avoided.

The ionic environment of kaolin suspended in water also influences viscosity. The presence of increasing amounts of soluble salts gives higher viscosities, especially at low shear rates. For this reason, manufacturers who produce kaolin by the wet process make every effort to minimize the quantity of soluble salts in the final product.

# Method of Manufacture

## Wet Processing

By far the largest tonnage of kaolin used in the paper industry is wet processed or "water washed". The wet process is used because it allows removal of mineral impurities and over-size kaolin particles, chemical bleaching to improve brightness, blending of different crudes to maintain product uniformity, and size fractionation to give kaolin products having specific desirable properties for use in a given application.

A simplified schematic of wet processing of kaolin is given in **Fig. 4-10**. (This schematic, although modeled after the wet process used in middle Georgia, is generally applicable with only minor modification to the wet processing used for kaolin deposits in other parts of the world.) Wet processing of kaolin has been described in detail by Murray *(29)*, Pemberton *(30)*, and Hill *(31)*.

*Figure 4-10 Major Steps in the Wet Processing of Kaolin*

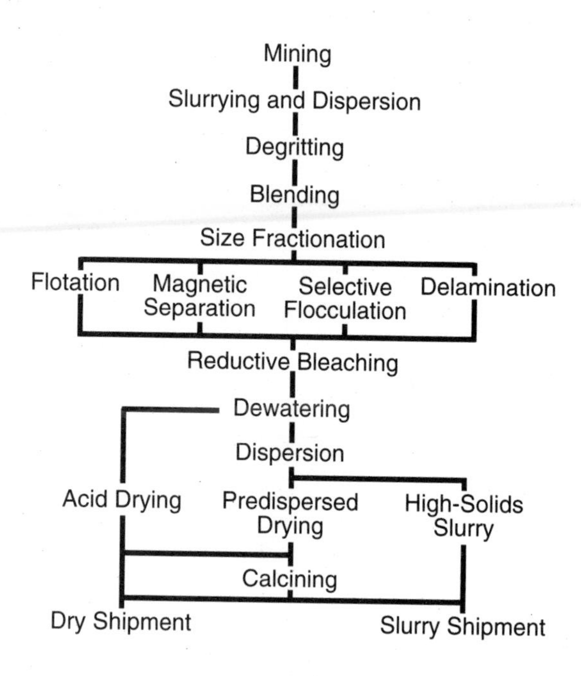


Once a clay deposit is located (by core drilling) and its quality judged satisfactory for producing paper-grade kaolin, overburden is removed using large draglines. The exposed clay is then mined with scrapers or draglines and placed in stockpiles where it is further tested. The next step is to slurry the clay with water ("blunging") using high-energy mixing along with a small amount of dispersant. This results in a fluid clay-water slurry of about 35% solids, which is subjected to degritting where coarse particle impurities and undispersed clay aggregates are removed by gravity settling, screening, or treatment in cyclones. Typically, clay from several crude sources, each with somewhat different characteristics, are blended to give a uniform plant feed so that the resulting products do not vary over a period of time. The clay slurry at this point is about 97-98% kaolin but consists of a wide distribution of particle sizes that are separated into various size fractions by high-speed centrifugation. Kaolin product properties vary considerably with particle size, so fractionation by size is an important step in making the best product for a given application.

Following fractionation, the separate grades are subjected to chemical reductive bleaching as the next step or may be subjected to other processes that improve brightness, such as flotation *(9, 10)*, magnetic separation *(32)*, and selective flocculation *(9, 33, 34)*, before this bleaching step is carried out. As noted previously, coarse-particle kaolin "booklets" may be selectively ground ("delaminated") to give finer particles of high-aspect-ratio kaolin platelets with coating and filling characteristics quite different from the undelaminated products.

The chemical bleaching step is carried out after acidification with sulfuric acid to a pH of 3 to 4 using a dithionite ("hydrosulfite") reducing agent. Zinc dithionite was the salt of choice in the past, but in recent years this zinc salt has been all but replaced by the sodium salt, $Na_2S_2O_4$. The reductive bleaching step gives an improvement in brightness of 1% to 3% and a whiteness improvement as well. It is not clear exactly why this brightness increase is obtained, although there is an oft-repeated conclusion that the brightness gain results from reduction of highly colored ferric iron to more soluble ferrous ions, which are then removed in the filtration step. It is likely that this explanation is an oversimplification because only small amounts of iron are removed (perhaps, at most, 5% of the total present), brightness improvement is obtained even if a subsequent filtration step is not carried out, and reductive bleaching and iron removal with some kaolins does not lead to a brightness improvement.

At this point in the wet processing of kaolin, the solids of the slurry has been reduced to 20% or less so that dewatering is needed to make dry or high-solids slurry commercial products. Some dewatering can be carried out in thickeners, but to obtain economically the high solids needed, rotary vacuum filters are used to raise the solids to 55% or more. This higher solids filter cake then can be dried directly to make an "acid dried" product, or redispersed and spray dried to produce a predispersed product, or redispersed and subjected to thermal evaporation or dry clay addition to make high-solids slurries suitable for shipment.

In the Cornwall district of the United Kingdom, processing follows roughly the scheme shown in Fig. 4-10. An important difference, however, is that the kaolin is washed from the source rock using a high-pressure stream of water so that the initial kaolin solids at the start of the process is only about 15%. Another difference is that filtration often is carried out using high-pressure tube or plate and frame filters. Most of the English kaolins are shipped in the nonpredispersed (acid) form. Australian and Brazilian wet processed kaolins are treated similarly to those from middle Georgia.

## Dry Processing

Dry processing of kaolin is considerably simpler than wet processing *(35)*. Dry processing or "air-floating" of kaolins is carried out by selecting the appropriate crude, drying, crushing, pulverizing, and air classification to remove oversize particles. Some air floated grades are slurried at 70% solids for convenience in shipping and handling. In this case the addition of a small amount of dispersant is required to obtain a low viscosity. Dry processing is considerably less costly than wet processing. Air floated products are, in general, less uniform in product quality because of crude variability and limited opportunities for blending, of lower brightness, and higher oversize particle content than water washed kaolins. Most air floated kaolins used by the paper industry are used as fillers.

## Handling, Transportation, and Storage

### Handling

Kaolin clay pigments are available as dry products in bulk or bags or as dispersed slurries in water. Slurries are available at 50% to 70% solids, depending on the particular grade of clay. Not all grades are available in all forms.

**Table 4-4** summarizes the advantages and disadvantages of the various physical forms of kaolin.

*Table 4-4 Physical Forms of Commercial Kaolin Products*

| Form | Advantages | Disadvantages |
|---|---|---|
| Dry Bulk | Can Air Convey | Potential for Dust |
| | Unlimited Storage Stability | Opportunity for Contamination |
| | No Costly Packaging | Need to Reslurry |
| Dry in Containers (Paper Bags, Big Bags) | Unlimited Storage Stability | More Costly Packaging |
| | Convenient for Low Use Rate | Possible Dust on Makedown |
| | | Need to Reslurry |
| Slurry | Easy and Rapid Handling by Pumping | Higher Delivered Price (Cost of Transporting Water) |
| | No Makedown Needed | Limited Storage Stability |
| | No Dust | Bactericide Required |
| | Smaller Storage Volume Than Dry | Stirred Storage Required |

## Transportation

All grades of kaolin may be transported by the usual methods used for bulk commodities of fine particle size; the choice is dictated by costs, volume of use, handling equipment at the mill, distance from the source, etc. Dry bulk shipments may be made in trucks, rail cars, or ships. Sparger cars often are used for calcined products. Slurries of predispersed kaolins are shipped domestically by truck and rail, although overseas shipments of slurry have been made on an experimental basis.

## Storage

Dry clay may be stored in bulk silos or in bags for an indefinite period of time provided that it is kept dry and free of contamination. Slurry kaolin, however, is not stable for more than a few months. The slurry contains a small amount of organic matter and nutrients which can promote bacterial growth leading to odor and dispersion problems. No kaolin dispersant has been found that will give a stable kaolin slurry indefinitely; eventually slurries will thicken due to dispersant loss from decomposition and bacterial action. As clay slurries are stored for substantial time periods, a gradual viscosity increase from dispersant decomposition is noted. The addition of small amounts of additional dispersant will usually lower the viscosity to near the original value.

Although a slurry of fine-particle kaolin can be stored for some time without agitation, it is usually recommended that mild agitation of the storage tank be provided. Coarser-particle kaolins have a greater tendency to settle over time. Coarse-particle and calcined kaolin slurries frequently contain an additive that retards settling by slightly increasing the viscosity of the aqueous phase.

# Reasons for Use

## Coatings

Kaolin clay is used in coatings because it improves the optical and print properties of the sheet. It can be used as the sole pigment or blended with other pigments to obtain specific sheet properties that cannot be obtained with kaolin alone. For example, titanium dioxide is often blended with clay to improve brightness and, especially, opacity, although at a higher cost. When precipitated calcium carbonate or calcined kaolin is blended with kaolin, a higher brightness and opacity is obtained, but usually the solids of the coating formulation must be reduced if the amount of the carbonate or calcined clay exceeds a few percent. Ground calcium carbonate is sometimes blended with kaolin clay to reduce gloss, improve brightness, and, in some cases, reduce cost. Ground calcium carbonate, unlike the precipitated product, does not lead to a viscosity increase and, in some cases, allows higher-solids coating formulations to be run.

## Performance of Kaolins in Coatings

The data in this section attempts to illustrate how different kaolins affect the properties of the finished sheet of paper. In most cases, laboratory formulations are used that contain only the necessary ingredients of pigment and binder, with few additives (if any). Commercial practice may include additives such as defoamers, added dispersants, biocides, water retention aids, starch insolubilizers, etc.

**Table 4-5** compares the performance of several clays on a sheet designed to be printed by the offset process. The data shown were obtained in the laboratory on sheets coated on the wire side at 8 g/m$^2$. The uncoated stock had a basis weight of 36 g/m$^2$, a brightness of 65.8%, and an opacity of 79.9%. The formula used consisted of 100 parts clay, 8 parts starch, 8 parts styrene-butadiene latex, and 0.5 parts calcium stearate. The coatings were adjusted to a pH of 8 with ammonium hydroxide and coated at 57% solids. The sheets were calendered through four nips at 88 kN/m (500 pli) and 60°C.

*Table 4-5 Regular-Brightness Clays in Lightweight Offset Coatings*

| | Ultrafine | No. 1 | No. 2 | Regular Delaminated | Full-Fraction Filler |
|---|---|---|---|---|---|
| Brightness, % | 80.0 | 81.8 | 80.5 | 82.3 | 81.3 |
| Opacity, % | 80.0 | 81.8 | 81.4 | 82.2 | 80.3 |
| Gloss, % | 49.0 | 48.0 | 43.0 | 47.0 | 25.0 |
| Print Gloss, % | 61.0 | 62.0 | 59.0 | 64.0 | 55.0 |
| K&N Ink Ads.* | 20.0 | 21.0 | 21.0 | 21.0 | 24.0 |

*Brightness Drop, %

To obtain the best balance of properties against pigment cost, only the No. 1, No. 2, and the delaminated kaolins (or blends of these) would be used in lightweight coatings. The ultrafine kaolin could be used to give a slight gloss improvement at the expense of opacity, while use of the coarse filler clay reduces both gloss and opacity.

**Table 4-6** gives the data for the same clays but in a formulation designed for rotogravure printing. The uncoated stock had a basis weight of 36 g/m$^2$, a brightness of 65.9%, and an opacity of 80.0%. The formula here contained 100 parts clay, 7 parts starch, 4 parts styrene-butadiene latex designed for rotogravure printing, and 0.5 parts calcium stearate. These coatings also were adjusted to a pH of 8 with ammonium hydroxide and coated at 57% solids to give a coating weight of 8 g/m$^2$. The calendering conditions were the same as those used for the offset formulation.

*Table 4-6 Regular-Brightness Clays in Lightweight Rotogravure Coatings*

| | Ultrafine | No. 1 | No. 2 | Regular Delaminated | Full-Fraction Filler |
|---|---|---|---|---|---|
| Brightness, % | 81.7 | 82.8 | 82.6 | 83.7 | 82.1 |
| Opacity, % | 81.6 | 82.6 | 82.5 | 83.7 | 82.1 |
| Gloss, % | 48.0 | 46.0 | 40.0 | 46.0 | 31.0 |
| Heliotest* | 56.0 | 64.0 | 62.0 | 71.0 | 62.0 |

*Millimeters to 20th missing dot.

As with the offset formulation, the primary pigments used for this grade are the No. 1, No. 2, and delaminated clays. For rotogravure printing, coarser particle grades, usually delaminated grades, are sometimes used. This is especially true in Europe *(36)*.

**Table 4-7** illustrates the performance of four representative kaolins on a heavier weight, coated wood-free sheet. The formulation used in this case was 100 parts clay, 4 parts starch, 12 parts styrene-butadiene latex, 0.5 parts calcium stearate, and 0.5 parts melamine-formaldehyde resin (as a starch insolubilizer). The coating was applied with a blade to obtain a coating weight of 13 g/m$^2$. After coating and drying, the sheets were calendered through four nips at 88 kN/m and 60°C. The uncoated stock had a basis weight of 82 g/m$^2$, an opacity of 90%, and a brightness of 83%.

*Table 4-7 Performance of Representative Kaolins in Coated Wood-Free Offset*

| Sheet Property | Ultrafine | No. 1 Regular Brightness | No. 2 Regular Brightness | Delaminated Regular Brightness |
|---|---|---|---|---|
| 75° Gloss, % | 68.0 | 65.7 | 61.9 | 64.2 |
| Opacity, % | 92.8 | 92.7 | 92.7 | 92.7 |
| Brightness, % | 78.2 | 80.9 | 78.7 | 80.8 |
| Sheffield Porosity | 48.0 | 30.0 | 23.0 | 12.0 |
| Sheffield Smoothness | 22.0 | 25.0 | 21.0 | 21.0 |

*Table 4-7 Performance of Representative Kaolins in Coated Wood-Free Offset*

| | | | | |
|---|---|---|---|---|
| K&N Ink Absorption | 12.0 | 10.0 | 9.0 | 7.0 |
| IGT Pick | 32.0 | 57.0 | 61.0 | 62.0 |
| Offset Print Gloss, % | 90.0 | 95.0 | 91.0 | 90.0 |

Typically, the finest kaolin gives the highest sheet gloss. The opacity obtained with all clays is essentially the same, while brightness varies with the grade of clay used. The brightness of the sheets coated using the No. 1 and delaminated kaolins is equivalent, while that obtained through the use of the ultrafine and No. 2 clays is lower. The lower brightness from the latter clays reflect their lower pigment brightness. The porosity is highest for the ultrafine kaolin and progressively lower for the No. 1 and No. 2 grades. The delaminated clay has the lowest porosity of all, which results from its platy particle shape. Ink absorption correlates with porosity, the more porous coatings absorbing a greater quantity of ink. Binder demand, as measured by IGT pick, also decreases as we go from finer to coarser particles. Print gloss is greatest for the No. 1 clay, while the other three clays give essentially equivalent values.

As with other paper grades, the choice of kaolin for coated wood-free grades is very dependent on the desired properties of the finished sheet as well as the cost of pigment. Often, high-brightness kaolins as well as titanium dioxide are used in this grade.

## Rheology and Runnability

Viscosity measurements of pigment slurries and coatings are routinely determined at a wide range of shear rates, but the results are not always meaningful in terms of runnability on a high-speed coater. Runnability in this case is the ease of applying thin coatings at high speed and high solids without streaks, scratches, skips, paper breakage, blade "weeping", or other problems that might be associated with the viscosity characteristics of the coating formula. Since, as a general rule, paper coatings are applied at as high a solids as possible (to minimize drying costs as well as improve coated sheet properties through rapid immobilization of the coating layer), viscosity under high shear rates is especially important. Assuming a uniform gap between the coating blade and the paper surface, shear rates in excess of $10^6$ $s^{-1}$ must be tolerated by the coating formulation. The coating also must be fluid at low shear rates as well so it flows under any shear rate to which it might be subjected *(37)*. **Table 4-8** (adapted from Ref. 20) summarizes the shear rate ranges that a coating formulation encounters during the coating operation.

*Table 4-8 Shear Rate Ranges for the Coating Operation*

| Operation | Storage and Handling | Coating Pan | Under the Blade | After Coating |
|---|---|---|---|---|
| Shear Rate, $s^{-1}$ | $< 10^3$ | $10^4$ | $10^6$–$10^7$ | < 1 |
| Residence Time | Long (hours) | Undefined | Ext. short (μs) | Short |
| Viscometer used | Rotational | Rotational | Capillary | Rotational |

Although clay water slurries that are fluid at the highest solids (70-71% in some cases) usually give coating formulations that are also fluid at high solids, there are enough exceptions to this rule that the viscosity of the coating color itself should also be determined as an aid in predicting its runnability. Even though the kaolin may be the major ingredient in the formulation, the viscosity contribution of binders and additives frequently overshadows the viscosity contribution of the clay. Further, although the clay may be dispersed to its minimum viscosity in water, once the other ingredients of the coating formulation are added it may be less well dispersed. Often it is necessary to add additional dispersant to the coating formulation.

Coating formulations usually have a yield point but then become less viscous at increasing shear rates. In some cases thickening has been observed (dilatancy) at high shear rates, and this has been correlated with poor runnability on the coater. Other things being equal, coatings probably run best that have the lowest viscosity at the highest solids and have a decreasing viscosity as shear rates are increased.

The relationship between viscosity and runnability is the subject of active investigation, both from the theoretical *(38-40)* and practical *(19, 41-43)* point of view.

## Optical Properties

The optical properties of gloss, brightness, and opacity are strongly affected by the specific clay used. Other variables such as type and amount of binder, calendering conditions, coating weight, etc. all contribute to the finished sheet optical properties, but if these are held constant some generalizations concerning the effect of various kaolins on opticals can be made.

Gloss is controlled by the surface smoothness of the sheet, and even the coarsest-particle clays will give a smoother surface than can usually be obtained on an uncoated sheet. As particle fineness of the clay increases, gloss also increases. For the highest gloss in coated paper or board, the finest particle-size kaolins are used. Not only must the kaolin be of fine particle size, it also must be free of oversize particles since only a few oversize particles at the surface of the coating can decrease gloss markedly.

Brightness also increases with particle fineness, but many clays have been processed by flotation or other means to improve brightness. For example, a No. 1 grade is available in a "regular" brightness version as well as a "high" brightness version, as shown in Table 4-1. The high-brightness version has a pigment brightness three or four points higher than the regular-brightness product, although both clays have the same particle-size distribution, so they give equivalent gloss at the same coating weight. Delaminated kaolins have a higher brightness than kaolins of equivalent particle size that have not been subjected to the selective grinding process. This brightness improvement comes about because the grinding process gives particles of better scattering power, so the improved opacity obscures the discoloring effect of residual mineral impurities. The brightness of the product kaolin also tends to depend somewhat on the source of the kaolin. For instance, a fine-particle coating clay from Brazil or England is slightly brighter than its counterpart from the middle Georgia area.

Opacity, like gloss and brightness, is also a function of particle size and, at least for regular- and high-brightness clays, improves as particles become finer in size. There is a limit to the opacity improvement with increasing fineness, however. Extremely fine kaolin particles are too small to scatter light effectively, so they contribute little to opacity. An ultrafine No. 1 clay, for example, would give a lower opacity than the slightly coarser No. 1 grade. It is possible to remove some of the ultrafine, more or less transparent particles from the clay to give a product of improved opacity *(44)*.

## Coating Structure

In coatings, opacity and brightness are a complex function of pigments, binders, and voids in the coating. Pigments themselves provide opacity because of their light scattering ability which, as noted above, varies with particle size. Opacity is also highly dependent on the presence of voids in the coating since these voids are effective themselves in giving opacity by light scattering *(45)*. Since paper coatings are not applied in a layer thick enough to completely obscure the basestock, the properties of the underlying sheet also have an effect on coated sheet properties.

Pigments themselves may be structured so as to provide additional light scattering voids in a coating. For example, very-fine-particle kaolin, which contributes relatively poorly to opacity, may be calcined by heat treatment at 550-1000°C to give a thermally structured product containing many internal voids which enhance the opacity contribution of the pigment *(46-48)*. More recently, "chemically structured" pigments based on uncalcined clay have been developed *(49-51)*. Although the structure of these pigments is not as durable as that of the thermally structured products, they do provide an improvement in coating properties over that obtained by the use of regular kaolins. Thermally and chemically structured pigments are discussed in more detail in Chapter 5.

The binder used to bond the kaolin pigment to the paper surface also affects the gloss, brightness, and opacity of the finished sheet. As a general rule, when the binder amount is lower than that required to reach the critical pigment volume concentration (the point at which sufficient binder is present to fill the voids between the particles), the less binder present, the greater the gloss, brightness, and opacity *(52, 53)*. Since paper coatings almost always are formulated below the critical pigment volume concentration, the amount of binder used is an important factor in determining the properties of the finished sheet. Economics are also important here. Since the binder is more expensive than kaolin pigments, coating formulations are made using the smallest amount of binder that gives sufficient bonding of the pigment to the sheet that will allow the paper to withstand the rigors of handling and printing.

## Printing

The coating pigments and binders and their method of application not only influence the optical properties of the coating but also the response of the sheet to printing. All kaolins have an ink-receptive surface and give a uniform surface on which to print.

Historically, there have been three major printing processes: rotogravure, letterpress, and offset. The clay and binder used for coating the sheets is dictated somewhat by the process by which the sheet is to be printed. Some generalizations may be made to assist in the choice of clay to be used:

- Letterpress requires a coating with controlled ink absorption and a fair degree of pick resistance. The gloss, opacity, and brightness obtained is a function of the clay pigment used and the coating weight. Number 2 coating clays and delaminated clays are widely used for this application. At lighter coating weights, delaminated clays are preferred because of their good coverage of the substrate.
- Offset, like letterpress, also requires controlled ink absorption and pick resistance. In addition, because the sheet becomes damp during the printing process, a degree of water resistance is required. Water resistance is obtained by the appropriate choice of binder and the use of additives. The particular clay used, like that for sheets intended for letterpress printing, is dictated by coating weight and the need for gloss, brightness, and opacity.
- Rotogravure printing does not require that the clay be as well bonded to the sheet as in letterpress and offset because the printing process exerts less stress on the coating and water resistance is not required. Generally, less

binder is used. Coarse kaolins, especially coarse delaminated kaolins, work well for sheets designed for rotogravure printing *(53, 54)*. Structured pigments, either thermally structured calcined clay or a chemically structured uncalcined product, often are blended with the regular clay pigments to improve print quality.

Other printing processes such as laser, ink jet, and thermal each have somewhat different requirements for pigmentation for the best printing characteristics *(55, 56)*.

## Kaolins as Fillers

Although all of the clays listed for coating use in Table 4-1 (as well as many other clays) can be used as filler clays, most clays are chosen for filler use because of specific properties. In the past, low cost has been a primary consideration in choosing a clay for filler use, however, with the advent of thermally structured clays and, to a lesser extent, chemically structured clays, cost has been less of consideration because of the major property improvements that the structured pigments provide. (Structured kaolin-based pigments are discussed in Chapter 5.)

This section describes briefly only the use of uncalcined ("hydrous") and unstructured kaolins as filler pigments; comparisons with structured pigments are given in Chapter 5.

**Table 4-9** compares the properties imparted to a sheet by several clays used as fillers. In this handsheet study *(57)*, comparisons were made in a light weight directory paper at 36g/m$^2$ and at a 6% filler level. At a constant filler level, 6% in this case, all of the fillers improve brightness and opacity. The degree of brightness improvement reflects the brightness of the filler used while the opacity improvement is a function of the scattering power of the pigment.

Since all filler pigments weaken the sheet somewhat, a more realistic comparison is made in **Table 4-10** where opacity and brightness are compared at constant strength, in this case at a burst index (burst strength per grammage) equal to 1.0. Here it can be seen that the different clays affect sheet strength differently and the brightness and opacity imparted by the different clays at a constant sheet strength may differ from that obtained when comparisons are made at a fixed filler level. The data in Tables 4-9 and 4-10 are for a fairly low brightness sheet; if the sheet were of higher brightness the brighter clays (No. 2 coating, standard and coarse delaminated) would give a greater brightness improvement than the less bright filler and air float.

**Figure 4-11** shows brightness and opacity of a brighter sheet as a function of filler loading for two clays, a regular water washed filler and a coarse delaminated clay. Although the coarse delaminated and the water washed filler are of about the same brightness (84.8 and 84.5 respectively), the delaminated kaolin gives a greater brightness and opacity improvement.

*Table 4-9 Comparison of Properties of 36 g/m² Directory Paper*

| | At 6% filler level | | |
|---|---|---|---|
| | Brightness | opacity | % clay |
| Unfilled | 56.5 | 80.7 | - |
| No. 2 coating | 59.7 | 82.8 | 4.9 |
| Standard delaminated | 59.5 | 82.6 | 4.7 |
| Coarse delaminated | 59.4 | 82.3 | 7.1 |
| Full fraction filler | 59.2 | 81.7 | 8.7 |
| Regular air float | 58.8 | 81.7 | 5.8 |

*Table 4-10 Comparison of Properties of 36 g/m² Directory Paper*

| | At burst index = 1 | | |
|---|---|---|---|
| | Brightness | % clay | Opacity |
| Unfilled | - | - | - |
| No. 2 coating | 59.1 | 5.1 | 82.6 |
| Standard delaminated | 58.8 | 5.3 | 82.4 |
| Coarse delaminated | 59.8 | 7.3 | 82.8 |
| Full fraction filler | 60.3 | 9.0 | 82.3 |
| Regular air float | 58.7 | 5.5 | 81.6 |

*Figure 4-11 Brightness and opacity of a 36 g/m² sheet as a function of filler loading.*

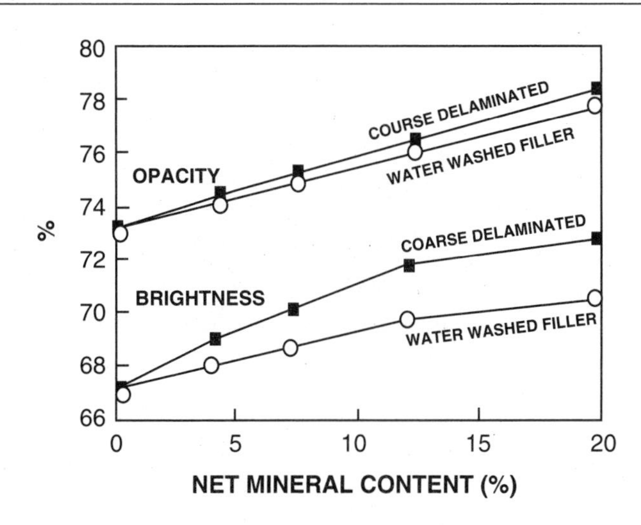

## Engineered Pigments

Most kaolin clays contain a significant portion of ultra-fine particles that do not effectively scatter light. The removal of these particles by mechanical processes can produce an improved product *(44)*. Pigments that attain improved performance solely through mechanical manipulation are referred to as engineered pigments.

Engineered pigments are of controlled particle morphology, size, and particle-size distribution. Many of the basic kaolin processing unit operations such as grinding, screening, and centrifugation are utilized for the production of a controlled shape or size distribution. The delamination process, for example, can be defined as an engineering operation performed to alter the product morphology by increasing the aspect ratio of the separated plates compared to the unground booklet. Similarly, screening and centrifugation remove selected portions of a pigment's particle-size distribution and affect binder demand and gloss.

The unit operations used in the production of an engineered pigment depend more on the desired product than special crude characteristics or blends. Most kaolin products can be considered to be engineered because their particle size is controlled at a certain size (2 μm) by centrifugation, grinding, and screening. For the purpose of this discussion, however, an engineered pigment will be defined as one having a controlled particle size over the entire size distribution range. This often results in the use of only selected products from multiple centrifugation steps. For example, a No. 1 type clay might be made using a fine fraction from a crude blend and then reducing the ultrafine level by using a coarse fraction from a second centrifugation. The resultant material will be similar to a No. 1 clay at 2 μm but contain many fewer particles below 0.25 μm. Such a material offers good glossing with low binder demand and enhanced print gloss as a result of the low ultrafines content. The low fines level creates a coating with special packing characteristics having a lower density and small air voids that give better light scattering and therefore improved optical properties to the coated sheet. The distinctive pore sizes formed can improve print quality by allowing ink vehicle penetration while controlling pigment penetration for good leveling and enhanced print gloss. Ching *(58)* illustrates the advantages seen in using an engineered pigment in lightweight coating (LWC) applications. The data in **Table 4-11**, from Ching's study, is for an 8-g/m$^2$ coating applied to a 35-g/m$^2$ stock using a laboratory high-speed coater.

*Table 4-11 Properties of Engineered Pigments in LWC Applications*

| | Engineered Pigment | No. 2 Kaolin | Delaminated Kaolin |
|---|---|---|---|
| Brightness, % | 70.9 | 68.5 | 70.0 |
| Opacity, % | 81.6 | 78.7 | 80.1 |
| Gloss, % | 55 | 52 | 55 |
| Roughness, PPS, µm | 0.9 | 1.1 | 0.9 |
| Heliotest, mm | 72 | 42 | 74 |

Many of the newest structured pigments use engineering techniques in combination with thermal or chemical structuring.

## Analytical Procedures

Clay manufacturers all use a wide variety of test methods to control such properties of clays as brightness, color, particle size distribution, low and high shear viscosity, abrasion, sieve residue and moisture content. Although these tests may be company specific, various organizations such as TAPPI, ISO, and ASTM have published referee methods that are frequently used for specifying the properties of the final product *(59)*. In addition to the referee methods, TAPPI has also published "Useful Methods" that can also be used for clay testing *(60)* and "Technical Information Sheets" that contain physical property data *(61)*. For most paper clays, it is the physical properties that are important rather than the chemical composition.

**Table 4-12**, from references 59-61, lists various TAPPI methods and information sheets that are applicable to kaolins. Where available, related or equivalent ISO and ASTM methods have been listed.

*Table 4-12 Test Methods Applicable to Kaolin*

| | TAPPI Method | Related or Equivalent ISO | Method ASTM |
|---|---|---|---|
| **Referee Methods** | | | |
| Brightness of (Diffuse) | T 534 | 2469 | B259 |
| Brightness (45/0 deg.) | T 646 | 246, 2470, 368 | B 259 |
| X-ray Analysis of Paper and Related Products | T554 | | |
| Viscosity of Coating Clay Slurry | T648 | 5351 | |
| Particle Size Distribution of Coating Clay | T649 | | |
| Sampling of Fillers and Pigments | T 657 | | C 322 |
| pH of Filler and Pigment Slurries | T 667 | 6587, 6588 | D 1208, E 70 |
| Free Moisture in Fillers and Pigments | T 671 | 287, 638, 5270 | |
| Screen Residue | T 681 | | |
| Accelerated Test for Viscosity Stablility | T 697 | | |
| **Useful Methods** | | | |
| Abrassiveness of pigments and fillers | UM 603 | | |
| Brightness of powdered materials | UM 605 | | |
| Amount of coating on mineral coated paper | UM 542 | | |
| Mineral constituents (qualitative) coated paper | UM 470 | | |
| **Technical Information Sheets** | | | |
| Physical data of hydrous clay water slurries | TIS 0106-02 | | |
| Guidelines for reporting of SQC data for pigments | TIS 0106-04 | | |
| Kaolin clay pigment index | TIS 0106-06 | | |
| Physical data of calcined kaolin-water based suspensions | TIS 0106-09 | | |

## Economic and Market Factors

Kaolin clay's long use in paper coating and filling results from its low cost, wide availability and its ability to impart desirable qualities to a sheet of paper. No other pigment is available that gives such a wide range of desirable properties to paper at such a reasonable cost although other pigments can be better in certain applications. Among pigments that compete with kaolin are calcium carbonate (both precipitated and ground), talc, gypsum, precipitated silicas, precipitaited aluminum silicates, precipitated alumina, barium sulfate, plastic pigments, and satin white. All of these can be used either as the sole pigment or blended with clay, the final choice depending on the final sheet properties desired and the pigments cost at the mill.

## Differences in World Use

In North America, kaolin clays are the most widely used coating and filling pigments although in recent years there has been a dramatic increase in calcium carbonate usage. With abundant, low-cost supplies from the kaolin sources in middle Georgia, there has been less incentive to find alternate pigments than in other parts of the world where kaolin is not locally available and must be shipped long distances.

Calcined kaolin is also widely used, both as an ingredient in coating for improved brightness, opacity, and print quality and as a filler. In both these applications the calcined clay may be used to extend the more costly titanium dioxide or as an opacifier and to improve brightness in its own right. In neutral or alkaline sized sheets, lower cost, on-site manufactured precipitaited calcium carbonate has proved to be a strong competitor to calcined clay. Calcined kaolins are also being increasingly used in newsprint where not only do they contribute to brightness and opacity but also absorb the ink vehicle and prevent show-through.

In western Europe, where the largest amount of kaolin for paper comes from the Cornwall district of the U. K. or is imported from the United States or Brazil, ground calcium carbonate, which is produced locally, has long been used in substantial quantities in coating. Talc and gypsum are also being increasingly used as paper pigments since, being produced nearby, they can be lower in cost than kaolin.

In Japan, which has no significant source of kaolin of its own, clays from the United States, England, Brazil and Australia are widely used for paper coating. Ground calcium carbonate, available locally, is also used to a considerable extent with kaolin in coatings, often up to 30% level.

Most of the less developed countries have no local, high quality coating clay so that it must be imported. Many countries do however, have local clays that can be used as fillers. Since, in many cases, the machines are slower than those of the more developed countries, the need for high solids, low viscosity, coating clays is not as great.

## Future Outlook

It is anticipated that the used of kaolin and calcined kaolin will increase modestly over the next few years. Kaolin from sources other than the United States and the Cornwall district of England will become increasingly important. The trend toward improved sheet quality and lighter coating weights will put greater demands on kaolin producers for lower cost products that will meet these needs. It is expected that competitive pressure from fine-ground and precipitated calcium carbonate will increase as carbonate producers improve their products and as more paper mills switch to an alkaline or neutral sized system.

## Impact of Developing Technologies

The continued push at paper mills for higher productivity will keep the pressure on kaolin producers to manufacture products that give the desired sheet properties when coated at high solids and high speeds, i.e., low viscosity kaolins that, when incorporated into the coating formula, give good runnability. All of these desirable properties, of course, should be obtained at lower cost.

The growth of non-impact printing methods should fuel the development of clays to be used as fillers and coatings for sheets designed for these newer types of printing. It may well be that the current clay products are not the best ones for obtaining the optimum sheet and print quality for these grades.

The continued development of improved thermally and chemically structured kaolins, hybrid pigments such as structured kaolin-titanium dioxide, catonic kaolins and other new products should be anticipated. Research by kaolin producers may well lead to "interactive" kaolins which may be used at high levels as fillers without significant loss in sheet strength

*The assistance of William Atherton, especially in the area of engineered pigments, is gratefully acknowledged.*

## Literature Cited

1. Virta, R. L., "Clays, Annual Report 1990", U.S. Bureau of Mines, April 1992.
2. Loughbrough, R., *Ind. Minerals* (10): 51-69(1993).
3. Wheelwright, W. B., *The Paper Industry and Paper World* (12): 936-940(1942).

4. Rice, J. C. and Hudson, E. F., *American Paper Ind.* (5): 49-56(1966).
5. Murray, H. H., "Clay", in *Pigments for Paper* (R. W. Hagemeyer, ed.), TAPPI PRESS, Atlanta, 1984, pp. 95-143.
6. TAPPI Technical Information Sheet TIS 0106-06 "Kaolin Clay Pigment Index", TAPPI PRESS, Atlanta, 1993.
7. Gruner, J. W., *Z. Krist.* 83: 75-88(1932).
8. Olivier, J. P. and Sennett, P., *Clays and Clay Minerals* 21: 403-412(1973).
9. Sennett, P. and Young, R. H., "Current Problems in Beneficiation of Kaolin Clay", in *Beneficiation of Mineral Fines, Problems and Research Needs*, AIME, 1979.
10. Jameson, M. P. and Sennett, P., "The Removal of Mineral Impurities from Kaolin Using Flotation", AIME Symposium *"Advances in Coal and Mineral Processing using Flotation"*, AIME, 1990.
11. Morris, H. H., Sennett, P., and Drexel, R. J., *TAPPI* 48(12): 92A-99A(1965).
12. Gunn, F. A. and Morris, H. H., U.S. pat. 3,171,718 (March 2, 1965).
13. "Pigments, Opacity and Color Symposium", Technical Association Papers, Series XVII, No. 1, TAPPI PRESS, Atlanta, June 1934, p. 131.
14. TAPPI Test Method T 1209 rp-87, "Identification of Instrumental Color or Color-Difference Measurement", TAPPI PRESS, Atlanta, 1992.
15. TAPPI Test Method T 524 om-86, "L.A.B Colorimetry of White and Near-White Paper and Paperboard", TAPPI PRESS, Atlanta, 1992.
16. Robertson, A. R., *Color Res. App.* 2(1): 7-11(1977).
17. Jordan, B. and O'Neill, M., *Pulp Paper Can.* 88(10): 109-113(1987).
18. TAPPI Test Method T 648 om-88, "Viscosity of Coating Clay Slurry", TAPPI PRESS, Atlanta, 1992.
19. Tsuji, A., Nitta, J., Sasagawa, Y., and Nojima, N., *Tappi J.* 73(9): 163-168(1990).
20. Ramthun, J., Wallpott, G., and Rahlwes, D., *Woch. fur Papierfab.* 13: 542-546(1988).
21. Kurath, S. F. and Larson W. S., *Tappi J.* 73(9): 235-241(1990).
22. *Dispersion of Powders in Liquids* (G. D. Parfit, ed.), Elsevier, London, 1969.
23. Sennett, P. and Olivier, J. P., *"Electrokinetic Effects in Kaolin-Water Systems, I., The Measurement of Electrophoretic Mobility",* Clays and Clay Minerals, Proc. of the 15th Conf., Pittsburgh, Pergamon Press, N.Y., 1967.
24. Sennett, P., Olivier, J. P., and Hicken, G. K., *TAPPI* 57:(6): 92(1974).
25. Slepetys, R. A. and Cleland, A. J., *Clay Minerals* 28: 495-508(1993).
26. Bundy, W. M. and Ishley, J. N., *App. Clay Sci.* 5: 397-420(1991).
27. Millman, N., *TAPPI* 47(11): 168A-174A(1964).
28. Ianicelli, J. and Millman, N., *"Relation of viscosity of kaolin-water suspensions to montmorillonite content of certain Georgia clays", Clays and Clay Minerals, Proc. of the 14th Natl. Conf.,* 347-354 (1966) Pergamon Press, NY.
29. Murray, H. H., *Interceram.* 31(3): 196-197(1983).
30. Pemberton, M. J., *Ind. Chem. Bull.* (12): 21-28(1983).
31. Hill, B. F., *AustMM Bull. and Proc.* 293(2): 51-57(1988).
32. Ianicelli, J., *IEEE Trans. on Magnetics*, MA6-12: 436-443(1976).
33. Maynard, R. N., et al., U.S. pat. 3,371,988 (March 5, 1968).
34. Olivier, J. P., et al., U.S. pat. 3,432,030 (March 11, 1969).
35. Murray, H. H., *Interceram.* 30(2): 108-110(1982).
36. Baumeister, M., *Pulp Paper Can.* 90(3): 106-111(1989).
37. Ramthun, J., Wallpot, G., Reif, L., and Rahles, D., *TAPPI 1989 Coating Conference Proceedings*, TAPPI PRESS, Atlanta, pp. 27-35.

38. Saita, F. A. and Scriven, L. E., *TAPPI 1985 Coating Conference Proceedings*, TAPPI PRESS, Atlanta, pp. 13-21.
39. Pranckh, F. R. and Scriven, L. E., *TAPPI 1988 Coating Conference Proceedings*, TAPPI PRESS, Atlanta, pp. 217-238.
40. Aidun, C. K., *Tappi J.* 74(2): 213-219(1991).
41. Gane, P.A.C., McGenity, P. M., and Watters, P., *Tappi J.* 75(5): 61-73(1992).
42. Triantafilopoulos, N. and Grankvist, T., *TAPPI 1992 Coating Conference Proceedings*, TAPPI PRESS, Atlanta, pp. 23-36.
43. Roper, J. A. and Attal, J. F., *Tappi J.* 76(5): 55-61(1993).
44. Bundy, W. M., Manasso, J. A., and Berberich, J. P., U. S. pat. 5,085,707 (Feb. 4, 1992).
45. Lepoutre, P., *Prog. in Org. Coatings* 17: 89-106(1989).
46. Proctor, W. J., U.S. pat. 3,014,836 (Dec. 26, 1961).
47. Sennett, P., *Sci. Geol. Mem.* 89: 71-79(1990).
48. Lepoutre, P., Pauler, N., Alince, B., and Rigdahl, M., *J. Pulp Paper Sci.* 15(5): J183-J185(1989).
49. Bundy, W. M. and Harrison, J. L., *Clays and Clay Min.* 34: 81-86(1986).
50. Pratt, R., U.S. pat. 4,738,726 (April, 1988).
51. Nemeh, S. N., U.S. pat. 4,767,466 (Aug., 1988).
52. Weber, R. E., *Tappi* 43(10): 833-836(1960).
53. Sennett, P., Massey, H. L., and Morris, H. H., *TAPPI 1983 Coating Conference Proceedings*, TAPPI PRESS, Atlanta, pp. 17-22.
54. Baumeister, M., *TAPPI 1980 Coating Conference Proceedings*, TAPPI PRESS, Atlanta, pp. 11-22.
55. Borch, J., *Trans. of the 10th Fundamental Res. Symp. held at Oxford: Sept. 1993, Products of Papermaking, Vol.1* (C. F. Baker, ed.), Pira Intl., Leatherhead, Surry, UK, 1993, pp. 209-236.
56. Wilken, R., Weigl, J., and Baumgarten, H. L., *TAPPI 1991 Coating Conference Proceedings*, TAPPI PRESS, Atlanta, pp. 27-37.
57. Negele, A. R. and House, L. W., *Pulp Paper Can.* 90(8): T291-296(1989).
58. Ching, B., *TAPPI 1995 Coating Conference Proceedings*, TAPPI PRESS, Atlanta, pp. 419-433.
59. Bohanan, C. T., *TAPPI 1992 Process and Product Quality Conference Proceedings*, TAPPI PRESS, Atlanta, pp. 1-10.
60. *TAPPI Test Methods 1994-1995*, TAPPI PRESS, Atlanta, 1994.
61. *TAPPI Useful Methods: 1991*, TAPPI PRESS, Atlanta, 1991.
62. *TAPPI 1993-1994 Technical Information Sheets*, TAPPI PRESS, Atlanta, 1993.
63. Hollingsworth, R. L., Jones, J.P.E., and Bonney, C., *TAPPI 1983 Coating Conference Proceedings*, TAPPI PRESS, Atlanta, pp. 9-16.

# 5.

# Structured Pigments

*William C. Atherton, John A. Manasso, and Paul Sennett*

## Structured and Engineered Pigments

Kaolin clays may be "structured" or aggregated into larger particles that give improved coating and filling properties than those obtained by using an unstructured kaolin. Kaolin, even the coarser particle grades, contains a significant quantity of very fine particles that do not scatter light effectively and hence give lower opacity than optimum sized particles. These ultra-fine particles can be selectively aggregated into larger particles to enhance light scattering. The aggregation may be carried out either thermally, i.e., by calcining at a temperature in the range of about 550°C to 1100°C *(1, 2)*, or chemically, where chemical treatment is used to bind the smaller particles together *(3-5)*. In either case, the aggregation of fines creates somewhat larger particles that have a significant void volume, which carries through into the paper coating and gives an opacity increase and, in some cases, a brightness increase. Structured pigments also increase the bulk of the coating because of their greater pore volume, which generally results in improved print quality.

## Thermally Structured Pigments

Structuring by heat treatment (calcination) to sinter the particles together dates from the 1940s. At that time it was found that heating a kaolin to about 1000°C gave a product of improved whiteness and imparted an improved opacity to sheets when used in coatings and as a filler. Unfortunately, the product was more abrasive than the uncalcined clay and could only be slurried at a maximum of about 50% solids due to its high viscosity. In subsequent years the increased abrasivity of the original calcined product has been overcome to a large extent by improvements in calcining technique and the proper selection and processing of the calciner feed.

Calcined clays are prepared from a carefully pulverized, fine-particle kaolin that is specially prepared to give the desired pigment properties after heat treatment. The kaolin is heated above 1000°C (or to 700-800°C if a metakaolin product is desired) in large multiple-hearth or rotary kilns. After calcination, the clay is cooled and pulverized. The product is shipped dry in bags, sparger cars, or as a slurry after the addition of water and a dispersant. Traditionally the product is shipped as a 50% slurry, although several rheologically improved grades can be shipped at 60% solids.

The calcination step dehydroxylates the clay (the structural hydroxide groups are removed as water vapor) and converts the kaolin to a noncrystalline aluminum silicate. An electron microscope shows us that the very smallest particles present in the feed have been aggregated into larger particles. The individual clay platelets do, however, retain some of their roughly hexagonal shape. Although the calcination slightly lowers the refractive index (contrary to several published reports) from an average value of 1.58 to 1.56, the thermal structuring of the fine particles into larger aggregates containing many voids gives a product of much better opacifying efficiency than any uncalcined kaolin. The physical properties of a fully calcined product used for paper coating and filling are shown in **Table 5-1**.

*Table 5-1 Characteristics of Calcined Kaolin*

|  |  |
|---|---|
| Brightness, % | 93 |
| Particle Size | |
| Percent <2 μm | 88 |
| Percent <1 μm | 68 |
| Median Size, μm | 0.7 |
| Surface Area, $m^2/g$ | 17 |
| Specific Gravity | 2.69 |
| Refractive Index | 1.56 |
| Slurry pH | 6.0 |
| Viscosity, mPa·s at 50% solids | 250 |

The low-temperature calcined clay (or "metakaolin") is similar to the higher-temperature calcined kaolin except that it is slightly less abrasive, depending on particle size, and lower in brightness. It is somewhat lower in cost than the high-temperature material, so its use is indicated in lower-brightness filler applications like newsprint.

Because of its good brightness and opacity, calcined kaolin has been used as a replacement for higher cost titanium dioxide. Fine-particle calcined clay suitable for use in paper sells for 20-25% of the cost of titanium dioxide but will not replace titanium dioxide on a part for part basis. In coating and filling applications where titanium dioxide can be at least partially replaced, about two pounds of calcined clay is necessary to replace one pound of titanium dioxide. This "two for one" rule is only a generalization; actual performance will vary with the system. Fine-particle calcined clay is also used in systems that contain no titanium dioxide to improve brightness, opacity or print quality of the sheet.

**Table 5-2** illustrates the performance of fine-particle calcined clay when used as a partial replacement for $TiO_2$ in offset coating where the primary pigment is a 90% brightness No. 1 coating clay. In this comparison, the binder used is 10 parts oxidized starch with six parts SBR latex. The coatings were made at 12 $g/m^2$ on an 84% brightness sheet and calendered through three nips at 88 kN/m and 60°C. The data show that the calcined clay can replace half of the titanium dioxide without affecting sheet properties.

*Table 5-2 Fine-Particle Calcined Clay as an Extender for $TiO_2$*

| | | |
|---|---|---|
| Parts No. 1 90% Brightness Clay | 90 | 90 |
| Parts $TiO_2$ | 10 | 5 |
| Parts Fine-Particle Calcined Clay | 0 | 5 |
| Brightness, % | 80.4 | 80.1 |
| Gloss, TAPPI 75° | 57 | 59 |
| Opacity, % | 91 | 91 |
| IGT Pick, VVP | 41 | 40 |
| Print Gloss, % | 57 | 57 |

Calcined clay use has been shown to be beneficial in improving rotogravure print quality, especially at low coating weight. Successful high-speed rotogravure printing depends largely on two factors, bringing the sheet into good contact with the ink-filled printing cells and wicking the fluid ink out of these cells onto the paper surface. Incorporation of calcined clay into the coating formulation fulfills both these requirements. It increases the coating's bulk and therefore its ease of finishing, and it adds an abundance of fine internal pores that result from the calcination process. The effect of calcined clay on rotogravure printability is demonstrated by data in **Table 5-3** *(6)*, which indicates a significant improvement in rotogravure printability with the addition of up to 15 parts of calcined clay.

*Table 5-3 Effect of Calcined Clay on Rotogravure Printability*

| Formulation | Heliotest Rating |
|---|---|
| Control: 50% Delaminated/50% No. 2 | 5.0 |
| 48% Delaminated/48% No. 2/4% Calcined | 3.5 |
| 46% Delaminated/46% No. 2/8% Calcined | 3.0 |
| 42.5% Delaminated/42.5% No. 2/15% Calcined | 2.5 |

When used as fillers, the thermally structured clays also permanently impart a high degree of opacity and brightness by increasing light scatter. This is in contrast to brightness gains achieved through increased pulp bleaching, i.e., lower light absorption, which is reversible with time and exposure to ultraviolet light. In addition, the pore size and pore volume of the thermally structured clays promote good ink vehicle absorption with good ink pigment holdout to prevent strikethrough. Both low- and high-temperature calcined clays are increasingly being used in newsprint because of their ability to limit ink penetration into the sheet, as well as for brightness and opacity improvement.

**Figure 5-1** compares the filled sheet opacity obtained by using high-temperature calcined clays with that obtained with several other commonly used fillers. **Figure 5-2** is a comparison of the sheet brightness obtained with the same clays. These data *(7)* were obtained on 36-g/m² directory paper.

*Figure 5-1 Effect of Various Clays on Filled Sheet Opacity*

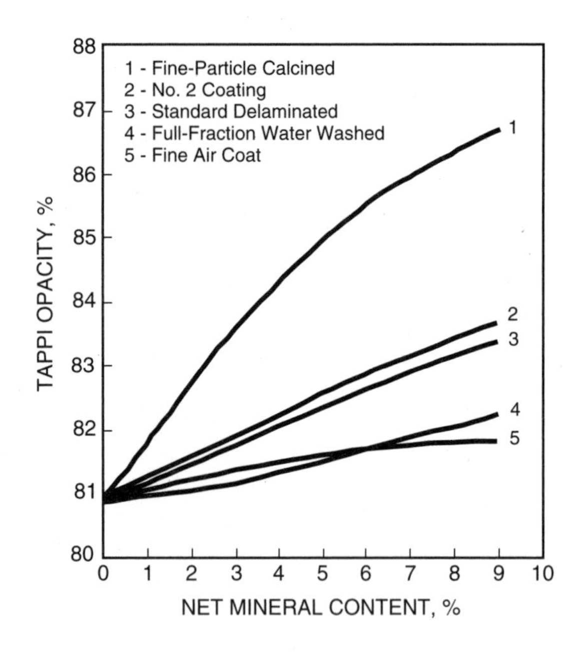

*Figure 5-2 Effect of various clays on filled sheet brightness*

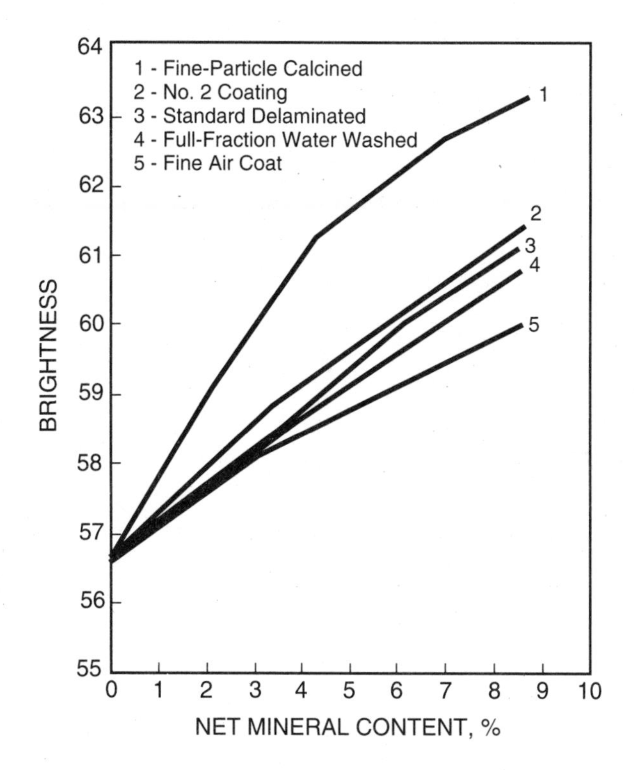


As with any filler, the addition of calcined clay weakens the sheet because it interferes with fiber bonding so, to be truly meaningful, optical property comparisons should be made at constant strength. For example, if we look at the opacity at constant strength (in this case the burst index, which is the ratio of the burst strength to the grammage) imparted by the five clays shown in Fig. 5-1, the thermally structured calcined clay maintains its opacity advantage (**Table 5-4**).

*Table 5-4 Comparison of Opacity at Constant Strength*

| Clay | Opacity, % |
|---|---|
| Fine Calcined, High Temperature | 84.4 |
| Regular Brightness, No. 2 | 82.7 |
| Regular Delaminated | 82.5 |
| Full Fraction, Water Washed Filler | 82.3 |
| Air Floated | 81.6 |

Burst Index = 1.00

## Chemically Structured Pigments

The commercial development of chemically structured clay pigments is more recent than that of thermally structured kaolins and development of new products in this area is continuing at a rapid pace. Chemically structured pigments are made by aggregating the finer particles through the use of chemicals, either precipitation reactions to form an insoluble binder or through the use of polymers *(3-5, 11, 14, 15)*, rather than through thermal sintering. Some chemically structured pigments have been formed by direct chemical reaction of a metal base with kaolin under hydrothermal conditions to give a family of different products by altering reaction conditions, kaolin pigments, and metal bases. Chemical structuring does not give the brightness improvement that is obtained by calcination, so the brightness of the structured pigment is the same as that of an unstructured kaolin. Chemical structuring, however, does not increase the abrasivity of the product but may increase the viscosity of the clay slurries because of the porosity and water-trapping ability of the aggregates. In some cases it appears that the strength of the aggregates formed by the chemical structuring is not as great as that obtained by thermal means, so some care must be used in pigment makedown to prevent shear-induced break up of the aggregates.

Chemically structured clays can be used like ordinary uncalcined kaolins in coatings as shown in **Table 5-5**. Here a comparison is made between a regular delaminated kaolin and a chemically structured coating product. These coatings were made in the laboratory using an offset formulation containing 100 parts pigment, 8 parts hydroxyethylated starch, 8 parts SBR latex, 0.5 parts calcium stearate emulsion, and 0.5 parts of an insolubilizer. Coatings were applied at 8 g/m$^2$ on a 36 g/m$^2$ stock. Calendering was carried out using four nips at 60°C and a calendering pressure of 70 kN/m.

*Table 5-5 Property Comparison of Chemically Structured and Delaminated Clay in Offset Coating*

| | Regular Delaminated | Chemically Structured |
|---|---|---|
| **Pigment Properties** | | |
| Brightness, % | 87.9 | 86.3 |
| Particle Size, μm | | |
| Percent <5 | 95 | 100 |
| Percent <2 | 79 | 90 |
| Percent <1 | 62 | 67 |
| Percent <0.5 | 38 | 30 |
| Surface Area, $m^2/g$ | 13 | 12 |
| **Coating Properties** | | |
| Viscosity | | |
| Percent Solids | 56.9 | 56.9 |
| Brookfield, mPa•s | | |
| 20 rpm | 2450 | 2600 |
| 100 rpm | 860 | 890 |
| Hercules[a] | 23 | 19 |
| **Sheet Properties** | | |
| Brightness, % | 67.5 | 68.1 |
| Opacity, % | 84.3 | 85.6 |
| Gloss, % | 51 | 51 |
| Print Gloss, % | 68 | 67 |
| PPS,[b] μm | 1.3 | 1.2 |

[a]Shear stress in mN·m (dyne cm x $10^5$) at 4400 rpm, "E" bob.
[b]Print-Surf smoothness, S10 backing.

Although the chemically structured pigment has a 1.6% lower pigment brightness than the delaminated clay, the sheet brightness from the use of the structured pigment is significantly improved over that obtained by using delaminated clay. The incorporation of the structured pigment into the formulation also improves opacity. These improvements probably result from an improvement in the light-scattering ability of the coating. The removal of ultrafine particles by aggregation results in a coating layer with many microvoids, formed within the aggregates themselves or resulting from the packing characteristics of the aggregates and other pigments. There is a high refractive index difference between these air voids (refractive index = 1.00) and the kaolin (refractive index = 1.58), resulting in a coating with good light scattering ability. These voids also reduce the coating's density, which improves basestock coverage and optical qualities. For maximum effectiveness, chemically structured pigments of this type should be used as the major constituent of the coating. This contrasts with thermally structured products that are effective at low concentrations.

Using chemical structuring techniques, it is possible to produce composite pigments containing more than one type of mineral particle. For example, titanium dioxide can be combined with either a calcined or uncalcined kaolin into a structured aggregate that is described as giving an improvement in brightness and opacity greater than that obtained by mixtures of the two pigments in the same ratio. The improvement in optical properties probably results from the composite pigment's improved dispersion of the titania in the coating matrix, which maximizes the coating's scattering power. Composite pigments can be produced using the structuring methods used for clay alone or by other processes.

Composite pigments are being used as $TiO_2$ substitutes in alkaline and acid wood-free filler applications. The composite pigments improve the $TiO_2$ distribution in the filled sheet. Composite pigments are being used as calcined clay substitutes in acid wood-free and wood-containing filler applications. The composite pigments have equal optical properties and lower abrasion compared to calcined clay. Composite pigments are commercially available in anionic or cationic forms. The cationic composite pigments provide higher retentions compared to anionic pigments.

## Historical Development

The evolution of non-thermally structured pigments can be traced back to 1963. Work by Rowland (U.S. pat. 3,085,894) *(8)* showed that modification of the particle size of selected clay products can result in significant improvements in optical properties in paper coatings. Utilization of the coating pigment gave improved brightness, gloss, and opacity. This pigment consisted essentially of clay particles having weight fractions of 25% to 35% less than 0.5 μm in equivalent spherical diameter and 10% to 15% less than 0.3 μm. This response was especially evident when the material was blended with calcium carbonate. The work was a continuation of his U.S. patent 2,992,936. *(9)* Examples from this patent are illustrated in **Table 5-6**, where the coating pigment consisted of either 100% clay or 70% clay/30% ground carbonate.

*Table 5-6 Influence of Particle Size Modification upon Optical Performance*

| Clay | Brightness, % | Opacity, % | Gloss, % |
|---|---|---|---|
| Control Clay | 72.6 | 91.8 | 60 |
| 70% Control/30% $CaCO_3$ | 74.5 | 89.9 | 50 |
| Experimental Clay | 73.9 | 92.3 | 63 |
| 70% Experimental/30% $CaCO_3$ | 75.4 | 92.1 | 53 |

The optical advantages for the experimental clay are quite evident. These advantages also produced equal pick strength and better ink receptivity, relative to the control clay.

A later approach to development of clays with improved optical properties was found by Bundy et al. in U.S. patent 4,076,548 *(10)* in 1978. In this work, a high-bulking clay product was produced by selectively flocculating the ultra-fine particle-size fraction in the presence of fine mica (< 150 mesh). The amount of mica was minimized to form an effective void structure. In general, this was about 0.025% to 5% on the weight of the kaolin. In addition to the mica, the kaolin was selectively flocculated to recover ultra-fine particles by using low-molecular-weight (< 1 million) organic flocculants in the presence of a mineral acid flocculant. The preferred combination of flocculants was a mixture of polyamide and citric acid, with the addition of a mineral acid for the reduction of pH to facilitate separation of the selectively flocculated clay.

To illustrate the effectiveness of the treatment, the coatings were incorporated into a coating formulation and various optical properties measured (**Table 5-7**).

*Table 5-7 Chemical Treatment of Kaolin*

| Clay | 75° Gloss, % | Brightness, % | Opacity, % |
|---|---|---|---|
| Control Clay | 56 | 72.7 | 90.6 |
| Control + Mica | 56 | 72.7 | 90.6 |
| Experimental Clay | 55 | 74.0 | 91.6 |

The data show that the combination of flocculants and mica yields the greatest improvement in opacity and brightness. Mica alone failed to yield any improvement in properties.

In later work, some of the earlier technology was utilized to produce a high-performance paper filler. This is discussed in the U.S. patent 4,943,324 of Bundy, Manasso, and Berberich *(11)*. A clay was developed that exhibited improved opacifying efficiency as a paper filler. It was comprised of a hydrous clay, consisting essentially of kaolin particles treated with an amine upon which aluminum hydroxide has been precipitated. Dating back to the earlier patent of Rowland *(9)*, the final particle-size distribution was such that 20% of this experimental clay had a particle size of less than 0.3 μm in equivalent spherical diameter and 88% to 92% was less than 2 μm. Clay brightness was 89.0%.

The clay was dispersed in water with a water-soluble dispersing agent to form an aqueous clay slurry. The slurry was subjected to delamination and partially defined to remove a significant portion of the colloidal fines. After defining and delamination, the kaolin particles were surface treated by mixing the slurry with water-soluble amine, such as hexamethylene diamine, aluminum sulfate, and mixtures of the two, while under agitation. The subsequent mixture was continually mixed to ensure an even deposition of aluminum hydroxide upon the kaolin particles formed during delamination. After treatment, the clay was subjected to leaching under standard kaolin procedures. The pH of the aqueous clay slurry was adjusted to 5.0 to cause the precipitation of aluminum hydroxide upon the surface of the clay plates. The delaminated, defined, and treated clay particles were then filtered and rinsed with water to produce the filter cake of this invention. The filter cake was dispersed or redispersed in an aqueous solution at a pH of about 8.0 for commercial use as a paper filler.

In **Table 5-8** we see that an improved paper filler can be produced with or without the surface treatment and at different particle sizes. In an uncoated free-sheet-type furnish with a polyacrylamide retention aid, the results reported in Table 5-8 were found.

*Table 5-8 Improved Filler Performance through Chemical and/or Mechanical Modifications*

| Kaolin Type | Defined | Delaminated | Surface Treatment | Opacity, % |
|---|---|---|---|---|
| Example A | X | X | No | 78.0 |
| Example B | X | X | Yes | 78.2 |
| Example C (coarse) | X | X | No | 78.0 |
| Example D (coarse) | X | X | Yes | 78.8 |
| Example E | ... | ... | No | 77.1 |
| Example F | ... | X | Yes | 77.4 |

The best opacity was exhibited by Example D. This kaolin was produced by defining, delaminating, and surface treatment in accordance with the proposed invention. It exhibited a nearly two-point higher opacity than that of a filler incorporating the base kaolin clay. In addition, a comparison of

Examples A and B to E and F illustrates the positive effect of removing the colloidal fines.

The filler described here was found to yield synergistic effects when blended with the standard hydrous clays in wood-containing papers. This is the subject of the U.S. patent 5,207,822 of Manasso, Mueller, and Di Donato *(12)*. The invention related to a kaolin composition exhibiting a high opacifying efficiency with a minimum negative effect upon paper strength. The composition can be formulated from a range of hydrous and calcined products. The uniqueness of the blend is such that, when incorporated into wood-containing paper, it gave optical properties similar to those obtained with calcined clay at equivalent loadings. This is despite the fact that the product of the invention is formulated with a calcined clay having a scattering coefficient of 2400—2600 $cm^2/g$, and a hydrous filler clay having a scattering coefficient of 1900—2100 $cm^2/g$. The resulting blend had unexpectedly been found to have a scattering coefficient of 2400—2600 $cm^2/g$. The latter is essentially the same as 100% calcined clay. An added benefit was that wood-containing paper with the blends have higher strengths than sheets with the calcined clay alone. An example of the benefits of these blends can be shown in **Table 5-9**.

*Table 5-9 Synergistic Filler Blends*

| Filler | Opacity at Sheet Brightness of 61%, 6% Loading | Breaking Length, km |
|---|---|---|
| Calcined Clay | 88.6 | 1.76 |
| Bulking Clay of pat. 4,943,324 | 87.1 | 1.89 |
| Synergistic Blend | 88.4 | 1.92 |

The synergistic blend was a 50/50 mixture of the calcined and bulking clay. Both opacity and tensile strength, as measured by breaking length, were equal to or higher than the values obtained with the individual fillers. The papermaker can thus increase loading without sacrificing strength. This example was in a 30-lb newsprint sheet formulated from a pulp furnish of 85% thermomechanical pulp (TMP) and 15% softwood kraft. The retention aid was a combination of polyethylene oxide and phenolic resin.

In an extension of the work on this defined, delaminated, and treated clay, it was disclosed in U.S. patent 5,085,707 *(13)* that treated or untreated clay performs superiorly in paper coating compositions containing either all or part of the structured clay. It was found that this clay would give improved print gloss, sheet gloss, and printability in both offset and rotogravure applications. The range of applicability was fairly broad, with a coating composition of about 40–55% of this clay and the remainder standard coating clays.

The optimum performance from the delaminated and defined product had a particle-size distribution of approximately 90% less than 2 µm and 8% less than 0.3 µm of the colloidal fraction. This particle-size distribution was such that 83% of the weight of kaolin particles fell between 0.3 µm and 2 µm.

The superior opacity and brightness of sheets containing the defined, delaminated, and treated product is show in **Table 5-10**. These are coating test results in a standard rotogravure formulation.

*Table 5-10 Quality Improvements of Rotogravure*

| Kaolin | Brightness, % | Opacity, % | Sheet Gloss, % | Rotoprintability, Missing Dots |
|---|---|---|---|---|
| Experimental | 72.2 | 90.6 | 64 | 86 |
| Commercial Delaminated | 70.3 | 89.4 | 67 | 111 |
| Commercial No. 1 Hi-Brite | 69.2 | 88.0 | 65 | 166 |
| No. 2 Hi-Brite Coating Clay | 68.7 | 88.9 | 64 | 207 |

There are significant brightness and opacity advantages for the experimental clay. Gloss was equal to or somewhat less than that of standard coating clays. Of further significance was that the experimental clay gave better rotoprintability as shown by the lower number of missing dots than the other clays.

# Literature Cited


1. Proctor, W.J., U.S. pat 3,014,836 (Dec. 26, 1961).
2. Sennett, P., *Sci Geol. Mem.* 89: 71-79(1990).
3. Bundy, W.M. and Harrison, J.L., *Clays and Clay Min.* 34:81-86(1986).
4. Pratt, R., U.S. pat 4,738,726 (April, 1988).
5. Nemeh, S.N., U.S. pat 4,767,466 (August, 1988).
6. Hollingsworth, R.L., Jones, J.P.E. and Bonney, C., *TAPPI 1983 Coating Confernece Proceedings,* TAPPI PRESS, Atlanta, pp. 9-16.
7. Negele, A.R. and House, L.W., *Pulp Paper Can.* 90(8): T291-296(1989).
8. Rowland, B.W., U.S. pat. 3,085,894(April 16, 1963).
9. Rowland, B.W., U.S. pat. 2,992,936(July 18, 1961).
10. Bundy, W.M. Beberich, J. P. and Sastre, D., U.S. pat. 4,076,548(Feb. 28, 1978).
11. Bundy, W.M., Manasso, J.A. and Beberich, J.P., U.S. pat. 4,943,324(July 24, 1990).
12. Manasso, J.A., Mueller, K. and DiDonato, S., U.S. pat 5,207,822(May 4, 1993).
13. Bundy, W. M., Manmasso, J.A. and Beberich, J.P., U.S. pat 5,085,707(Feb. 4, 1992).
14. Bundy, W.M., Beberich, J.P. and Sastre, D., U.S. pat. 4,075,030 (Feb. 21, 1978).
15. Slepetys, R.A. and Morgan, L.J., *TAPPI 1990 Coating Conference Proceedings,* TAPPI PRESS, Atlanta, pp. 227-236.

# 6.

# Precipitated Calcium Carbonate for Paper Coating

*Joseph N. Ishley*

*Editor's Note: This chapter is divided into two sections. The second section begins on page 115.*

Calcium carbonate is the chemical name for a very diverse category of physically different materials. Even though there are many variations in the physical form and uses of these products, all are chemically classified as calcium carbonate. There are two distinguishing classes of calcium carbonate: natural (obtained through mining from the ground) and precipitated (chemically synthesized). Depending on the end use, the physical or chemical properties, and possibly both, will be critical. In applications such as fluxing, neutralization, and scrubbing, the chemical properties are of the utmost importance. When used in paper as a coating pigment, the physical properties of the calcium carbonate are critical to coated sheet performance and will be the focus of this chapter. The ground calcium carbonate (GCC — filler and coating) and the precipitated calcium carbonate (filler) products used in the paper industry are discussed in other chapters of this book. Today the chemical composition of the precipitated calcium carbonate (PCC) used for coating is not a major concern, but this could change with the manufacture of new chemically modified precipitated calcium carbonate products. With the modern analytical techniques available today, it will be possible to accurately characterize the surfaces of these products. When this chapter is next rewritten, the chemical nature of the precipitated calcium carbonate surface and its effect on coated paper performance could be the primary focus.

## Historical Background

The use of calcium carbonate reaches back to the earliest days of the paper industry, but its initial impact was not seen until the first alkaline conversions during the 1960s. Prior to this time, the predominance of acid papermaking prevented the widespread use of calcium carbonate as either a filling or coating pigment. At first, the main reason for using PCC in a paper coating was to improve the brightness, color, and opacity. As paper specifications changed and became more demanding through the years, the enhanced ink receptivity and sheet gloss exhibited by PCC were of greater importance. With the discovery of improved grinding techniques, new GCC products were produced in the 1970-1980 time frame, which displaced many of the PCC coating pigments. In addition, a shortage of PCC in the late-1970s contributed to an increased usage of GCC pigments in the paper industry. From the mid-1980s to the present time, there have been new PCC pigments introduced which retained all of the previous benefits while also providing improvements in roughness, porosity control, printing properties, pigment slurry solids, coating color rheology, and coater runnability.

How a PCC performs in a coating is determined by the following: (a) particle size, (b) particle size distribution, (c) surface area, and (d) particle morphology or shape. All of these factors can influence particle packing *(1-3)*. These are the four elements over which a PCC supplier has control during the precipitation of the pigment. The chemical properties of the PCC such as surface charge, pH, and the effect of impurities have not been investigated to any great degree. The advent of new techniques, which allow for the detailed analysis of the PCC surface at the molecular level should provide much information which we hope can be related to coated sheet performance. Several articles in this area have recently been published. Eventually (probably by the year 2000), chemical treatment of the PCC surface will become the fifth element that a PCC supplier has at his or her disposal. There have been modifications and improvements to the processes and chemicals used in the dispersion of PCC pigments at high solids concentrations. Slurry stability packages for the prevention of settling during the shipment of PCC are still used in some cases. The on-site "satellite concept" (used by several PCC suppliers) has all but eliminated the need for these chemical stability packages. The PCC satellite is located at the paper mill site, and it is only necessary to pump the PCC slurry from a storage tank in the satellite to a storage tank in the mill. This process eliminates transportation costs and allows the PCC supplier to custom tailor products for the various grades of coated paper manufactured at the mill. There are currently more than 40 satellite plants located at paper mills throughout the world, and the number continues to grow. The size, shape, and amount of PCC used in a coating formulation will be dependent on the requirements for the particular grade of paper. No single PCC is suitable for all applications; many of the PCC pigments are being designed for very specific uses (an important benefit of the satellite concept). When choosing a PCC pigment for coating, cost and performance must be considered on a systems basis (cost to produce a ton of coated paper), not on a cents/pound or dollars/ton basis, so the true value of the pigment can be determined.

# Product Description

## Crystallographic Properties and Morphologies

Precipitated calcium carbonate exists mainly as either the calcitic or aragonitic crystalline polymorph. A third polymorph, called vaterite, has been prepared through synthetic precipitation processes *(4)* but is very unstable and has no commercial applications even though it has been the subject of many patents in recent years *(5)*.

The calcite form belongs to the hexagonal-scalenohedral crystal class in the hexagonal system. The number of crystal habits found in nature is quite large, but in commercial grades of PCC the rhombohedral, prismatic, and scalenohedral crystal habits are most commonly seen. There are a number of U.S. patents related to the prismatic and rhombohedral crystal habits and their uses in paper *(6, 7)*.

The aragonite form belongs to the dipyramidal crystal class in the orthorhombic system. The crystal habits normally seen with aragonite are elongated prismatic or acicular (needlelike). Aragonite is quite rare in nature due to its metastable characteristics and is found only in low-temperature deposits located near the earth's surface. The commercially available grades of aragonitic PCC are usually composed of crystals with parallel sides having a high aspect ratio (large length-to-width ratio), but many variations exist depending on the synthesis and post-synthesis processing conditions.

## Chemical Properties

From a thermodynamic perspective, calcite is the only stable form of calcium carbonate. The aragonite and vaterite are metastable and convert irreversibly to the calcite form when heated above 400°C. In a slurry, this conversion to calcite occurs at lower temperatures and under the right set of conditions can occur even at room temperature (25°C). When PCC is heated to 800-900°C, decomposition takes place with the release of carbon dioxide and the production of calcium oxide, commonly referred to as quicklime. Under very specific conditions, this decarboxylation reaction can begin at a temperature as low as 550°C. Commercial PCC pigments are typically greater than 97% $CaCO_3$ with the remainder being $MgCO_3$ (1-2%) and other minor impurities. The pH value for PCC slurries is normally in the 8.5 to 10.5 range. A higher pH would be indicative of the presence of free (unreacted) lime, but this is normally not a problem due to stringent post-precipitation monitoring and control.

## Physical Properties

The physical properties of PCC pigments differ depending on the source of raw materials, the method of preparation, post-precipitation treatments, and the intended product application. It is possible to manufacture PCC pigments having a size range that covers three orders of magnitude and a surface area range that covers two orders of magnitude. **Figure 6-1** shows typical particle size distributions for several of these pigments along with a commercially available coating grade GCC pigment. Note the narrowness of the particle size distributions for the PCC pigments compared to the GCC. Many of these PCC pigments do not have an application in the paper coating processes due to their extremely small or large particle sizes. The PCC pigments used in paper coating fall into the 0.4- to 3.0-micrometer particle size range. With this particle size range it is possible to address the requirements of paper grades ranging from matte to high gloss. The surface areas of these pigment vary from 4.0 to 13.0 $m^2/g$. **Figures 6-2 to 6-8** show a variety of calcitic and aragonitic PCC pigments and a GCC pigment which are currently used to produce coated papers. The uniformity of particle size and shape for the PCC pigments is in sharp contrast to the broadness of the size distribution and the variety of shapes exhibited by the GCC. Both crystal types have multiple indices of refraction (calcite = 1.658 and 1.486, aragonite = 1.531, 1.681, and 1.685), with aragonite having a slightly greater average index of refraction. The calcite crystal has a specific gravity of 2.71 and a Mohs' hardness in the range of 2.9 to 3.0. The respective values for the aragonite crystal are 2.93 and a range of 3.5 to 4.0 *(8)*.

*Figure 6-1 Typical $CaCO_3$ Partice Size Distributions*

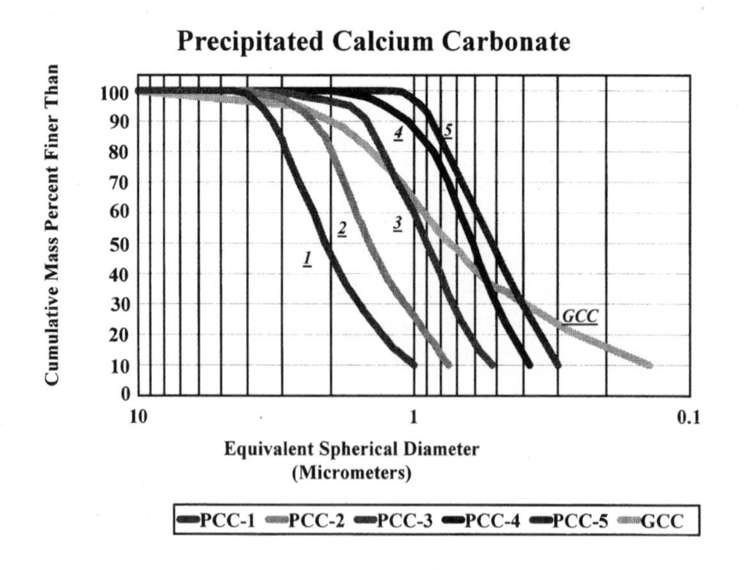

*Figure 6-2 Prismatic PCC (Calcite): Average Particle Size = 0.6 Micrometers*

The dispersant demand for the PCC pigments is quite low and tends to increase as a function of smaller size and larger surface area, as is the case with other pigments such as kaolin. These PCC coating grade pigments are available in slurries with a percent solids range of 65% to 72%. **Figure 6-9** shows the high shear Hercules rheograms for a number of PCC pigments, illustrating the variations in viscosity from one product to another. For comparison, a rheogram of a commercial coating grade GCC is included. The PCC pigment viscosity generally is higher than that of GCC. However, there tends to be only a small difference in the high shear viscosity values of the GCC and PCC when formulated into a coating color. This difference decreases dramatically as the percent solids of the coating color decreases from 68% (coated freesheet) to 55% (lightweight coated groundwood) *(9)*.

*Figure 6-3 Prismatic PCC (Calcite): Average Particle Size = 0.8 Micrometers*

## Methods of Manufacture

To manufacture PCC, high-purity limestone (95% calcium carbonate) is calcined in a kiln, producing carbon dioxide gas and calcium oxide (quicklime). It is very important that the limestone feed to the kiln be free of colored and abrasive impurities. The $CO_2$ gas is then cooled, scrubbed if necessary to remove other gaseous impurities, and stored for use in preparation of the PCC. The calcium oxide is slaked with water under very controlled conditions to yield milk of lime, a slurry of calcium hydroxide. This slurry is then coarsely screened to remove any unreacted lime or other impurities. There are a multitude of process variables that have a major impact on the slaking process and the resulting milk of lime or lime slake *(10)*. In the preparation of PCC, the purity, particle size, concentration, and temperature of the lime slake have a major effect on the physical properties of the final product.

The three methods used to manufacture PCC are shown in **Fig. 6-10**. In the lime/$CO_2$ or carbonation process, the carbon dioxide gas is bubbled through the milk of lime. The particle shape and size of the PCC are determined by precipitation conditions such as concentration, starting temperature, temperature profile, type and degree of agitation, pH, and the use of additives. Precipitation of aragonite is promoted by the presence of small amounts of other divalent cations or the sulfate anion. High temperatures, rapid precipitation, and high reactant concentrations also lead to the production of aragonite. By controlling conditions, either calcite, aragonite, or a mixture of the two pigments can be obtained. In commercial practice PCC pigments are usually only one form or the other:

$$Ca(OH)_2 + CO_2 = CaCO_3 + H_2O$$

The simplicity of the chemical equation for the overall process misrepresents the complex nature of the reaction, especially when a product with very specific physical properties is desirable. This process is the most complex of the three but is most widely practiced (almost exclusively) since it uses the most readily available and lowest cost raw materials. It is this process that is used by several PCC suppliers who manufacture products at paper mills using the on-site “satellite concept”.

*Figure 6-4 Prismatic PCC (Calcite): Average Particle Size = 1.2 Micrometers*

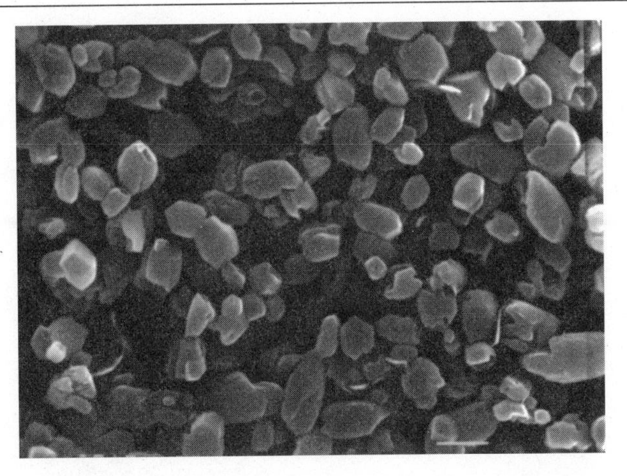

*Figure 6-5 Prismatic PCC (Calcite): Average Particle Size = 2.2 Micrometers*

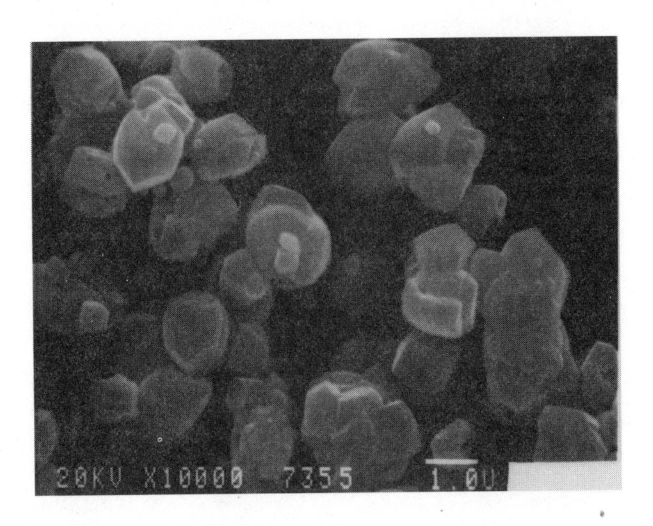

*Figure 6-6 Sherical PCC (Calcite): Average Particle Size = 3.0 Micrometers*

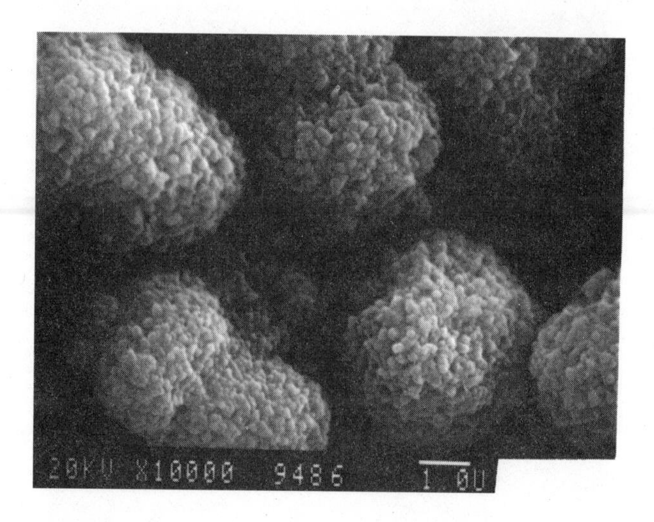


*Figure 6-7 Sherical PCC (Aragonite): Average Particle Size = 1.5 Micrometers*

*Figure 6-8 Prismatic GCC (Calcite): Average Particle Size = 0.75 Micrometers*

In the lime soda process, sodium carbonate and milk of lime react to yield sodium hydroxide and calcium carbonate. As in the prior reaction, the physical properties of the calcium carbonate product are a function of reaction conditions *(11)*:

$$Ca(OH)_2 + Na_2CO_3 = CaCO_3 + 2NaOH$$

When this process was used by alkali suppliers, the primary concern was the production of caustic soda. Because of this, a coarse calcium carbonate was precipitated, thereby simplifying the recovery of the caustic soda from the PCC filter cake. By controlling the reaction conditions, it is possible to produce many, if not all, of the morphologies that can be produced by the lime/$CO_2$ process. This, however, has a negative effect on the efficiency of the caustic soda recovery process. Before this PCC can be used in paper, it is usually necessary to neutralize the alkali content by treatment with carbon dioxide *(12)*, acids *(13)*, or salts *(14)*, and in some cases it is necessary to grind or mill the PCC to obtain the required particle size *(15)*. Commercial interest in this process ebbs and flows as the market price of NaOH cycles through highs and lows. A number of patents have appeared recently with respect to this process and use of the PCC in paper applications.

In the third process, milk of lime reacts with ammonium chloride to yield calcium chloride and ammonia gas. Following purification, the calcium chloride solution is reacted with a sodium carbonate solution to produce calcium carbonate:

$$Na_2CO_3 + CaCl_2 = CaCO_3 + 2NaCl$$

Factors that can be controlled to affect the resulting PCC product are addition times, concentrations, pH, reaction temperatures, and rate and method of agitation. This process is the simplest of the three but requires low-cost sources of calcium chloride and sodium carbonate in order to be cost effective. Production of PCC in the United States by this process ended in 1975 with the shutdown of the synthetic sodium carbonate plants that provided the raw materials.

All of these processes require the proper raw materials to ensure the quality and consistency of the final PCC product. Even though the processes seem to be very simple, stringent control is necessary at every step so the customer receives a product that meets all expectations.

## Shipping/Handling/Storage

Most, if not all, PCC pigments used in coated paper are shipped in slurry form. The ease of unloading truck or rail shipments plus the elimination of the dispersion step (less chance for variability) are seen as advantages by the paper mill. Suppliers treat the PCC slurries with proper dispersants, biocides to prevent bacterial growth, and stability packages, if necessary, to prevent settling. With the on-site "satellite concept", shipping from a distance is eliminated; it is only necessary for the paper mill to call the satellite and request a transfer from the satellite storage tank to the mill storage tank. Inventory control is simplified and on-time delivery is guaranteed. With respect to handling properties, pumping and storage tank agitation requirements may be obtained from the PCC pigment suppliers. In general, no extraordinary equipment is necessary to handle PCC slurries.

PCC shipped in dry form can be in bags, supersacks, or bulk (truck or railcar). Many of the fine particle size PCC products do not flow readily and show a tendency to bridge or clog in hopper cars and storage bins. Vibrators, air slides, air lances, and ultrasonic devices are used to assist with the unloading and handling. Each supplier is familiar with the problems associated with its products and can provide the necessary assistance.

## Dispersion

When PCC is shipped in dry form, it is critical that the dispersion be done properly so the PCC can yield optimum performance *(16-19)*. High solids, high shear mixing and using the optimum amount of the proper dispersant are all necessary for thorough wetting, deagglomeration, and achievement of the intrinsic particle size. Without proper dispersion, optical and physical properties of the coated sheet (opacity, gloss, and roughness) and coater runnability will be compromised to some extent. Almost without exception, polyacrylate dispersants are recommended for the dispersion of PCC. It is rare that polyphosphate dispersants are used in the dispersion of PCC pigments. The use of polyacrylate dispersants has eliminated the time/temperature sensitivity of PCC slurries that was common when polyphosphates were used as the primary dispersant. With respect to dispersion equipment, either high speed, open-impeller agitators or rotor-stator-type devices can be used to disperse PCC. For specific product dispersion information, the best route is to contact the PCC supplier.

## Reasons for Use

A calcitic precipitated calcium carbonate (PCC-S) was developed for use in coated freesheet grades of paper where brightness and sheet gloss are the most important specifications *(20)*. Even though it was possible to obtain higher brightness values by increasing the amount of coating grade UFGL in the formulation, the sheet gloss values tended to decrease dramatically. The PCC-S overcame this deficiency in sheet gloss and provided a number of additional benefits. The pros and cons of PCC-S versus the UFGL are summarized in **Table 6-1**, which characterizes the overall performance of PCC-S in a coated freesheet grade.

*Table 6-1 PCC-S versus UFGL*

| Property | Versus UFGL |
|---|---|
| Brightness | Better |
| Opacity | Better |
| Sheet Gloss | Much Better |
| Print Gloss | Equal or Better |
| Porosity | Increased |
| Roughness | Better |
| Picking Strength | Equal or Slightly Poorer |
| Rheology/Runnability | Poorer/Equal (Solids Dependent) |

The coating structure obtained with PCC-S produced major increases in opacity versus the UFGL. It was possible to use the gains in opacity to improve the quality of the coated sheet or reduce the amount of opacifying pigment in the formulation, leading to cost savings. The higher sheet gloss values obtained with PCC-S allowed for either a quality improvement in the sheet or a productivity increase at the calender stack. The PCC-S gave a more open and more ink receptive coated sheet. The openness could provide some or all of the following: more rapid fountain solution acceptance or dissipation, lessening the chance of ink refusal, better ink trapping, quicker ink setting, and a reduced tendency for blistering during the drying stage of the offset printing process. Even with the higher coated sheet porosity, the print gloss was not negatively affected.

The lessening of the sheet roughness, or improved smoothness, although not a major concern in the offset printing process, must still be considered a positive attribute. The smoother surface produced by the PCC-S could result in better ink lay, giving the printed signature a more glasslike appearance. The picking strength of the coated sheets containing PCC-S was not as good as those containing the UFGL. Additional work done on either pilot coaters or commercial coaters has shown that picking strength is not an issue with PCC-S. The initial results were thought to be a result of the drying equipment present on a cylindrical laboratory coater.

Any problems encountered with the use of PCC-S in current coating colors could be overcome through reformulation of the pigment, binder, and additives. The lower slurry solids of the PCC-S will limit the coating color solids to a level below that which can be attained with currently available UFGL slurries. The use of spray-dried clay in place of slurry clay is a possible solution if high solids coating is a major concern. Most PCC-S suppliers have programs under study to address the issue of higher pigment slurry solids.

To date, pilot scale and commercial coating trials have confirmed all of the data produced in the laboratory. The PCC-S product currently is being used as a coating pigment in several paper mills.

The PCC-S gives the papermaker the opportunity to make a better high gloss, high brightness coated sheet. By way of the satellite plant concept, the PCC-S can be custom produced at the paper mill site to give papermakers exactly what they want. In general, the papermaker should begin by replacing the UFGL with an equal quantity of the PCC-S pigment. Additional changes will be dictated by the composition of the coating formulation and the needs of each individual papermaker.

PCC-S was originally developed to meet the needs outlined by producers of coated freesheet grades. With "acid-tolerant" technology *(21, 22)*, it is now feasible to utilize significant quantities of calcium carbonate in the coating and wet end of groundwood-containing grades *(23)*. The pros and cons of PCC-S versus either clay or UFGL are summarized in **Table 6-2**, which characterizes the overall performance of PCC-S in a coated groundwood LWC (lightweight coated) grade.

*Table 6-2 PCC-S versus Clay and UFGL*

| Property | Versus Clay | Versus UFGL |
|---|---|---|
| Brightness | Much Better | Better |
| Opacity | Better | Better |
| Sheet Gloss | Equal | Better |
| Print Gloss | Equal | Better |
| Porosity | Increased | Slightly Increased |
| Roughness | Equal | Better |
| Picking Strength | Equal of Better | Slightly Poorer |
| Rheology/Runnability | Poorer/Equal | Poorer/Equal |

The structuring of the coating produced by the PCC-S leads to significant increases in brightness and opacity compared to either clay or UFGL. It is possible to utilize these gains in several ways. First, there is the option of improving sheet quality and possibly upgrading from a No. 5 LWC to a No. 4 coated groundwood grade. It is also possible to reduce basis weight and respond to the requests of magazine publishers who are facing higher costs due to increased postal rates. Finally, there may be a decrease in the use of calcined clay and titanium dioxide, which represents a potential cost reduction and a lessening of abrasion on converting equipment.

The glossing characteristics of the PCC-S are such that there would be no need to change the calendering conditions. The same statement cannot be made with respect to UFGL. The increased porosity of the PCC-S versus clay and to a lesser extent UFGL could translate into better blister resistance during the offset printing process. The openness of the coated surface also should aid with fountain solution acceptance. The increased porosity and ink receptivity of the PCC-S could prove beneficial in rotogravure printing processes. This point will be the focus of future coating studies.

The reduced roughness or improved smoothness provided by the PCC-S can be considered a positive factor even though it is not a prime concern in offset printing, The reduction in roughness means that the fiber coverage has been improved. This could be a very important consideration in mills using wood species that are susceptible to "fiber puffing". The improved picking strength of the PCC-S versus clay could lead to a reduction in binder content, which should translate into an improvement in optical properties along with a cost reduction.

With respect to rheology, even though the Hercules viscosity measurements show that there is a significant difference between the PCC-S and UFGL, trials on a cylindrical laboratory coater at 3500 ft/min have demonstrated that coater runnability is the same. During a pilot coater trial done in conjunction

*Figure 6-9 High Shear Rheograms for PCC and GCC Pigments*

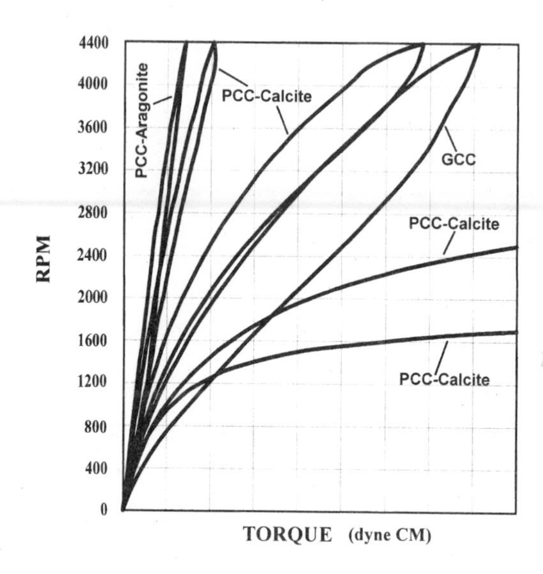


with a paper company, there were no runnability issues. At least one paper mill is currently using the PCC-S pigment to produce a No. 5 LWC grade of paper.

The use of PCC-S in coating, combined with the "acid tolerant" wet-end technology, gives the papermaker the opportunity to make a brighter and more opaque sheet along with the possibility of decreasing coat weight and reducing the use of opacifying pigments. Through the satellite PCC concept, PCC-S can be customized at the paper mill to provide the papermaker exactly what he or she needs to satisfy the requirements of his or her grade structure. The papermaker should begin by replacing 30% of the clay in his current formulation with PCC-S. Additional modifications will be dictated by the composition of the coating formulation and the requirements of the various paper mills.

A coarse PCC, designated spherical calcium carbonate (SCC), has been developed and patented *(24)* for use in low gloss coated papers *(25)*. The SCC possesses a number of desirable properties such as high brightness, blue-white color, good dry handling, low binder demand, and ease of dispersion. A study on this pigment demonstrated that the optimum usage level of the 3.0-micrometer SCC was in the 40% to 50% range. Coatings containing the SCC at this percentage of total pigment had low sheet gloss while displaying high print gloss, yielding an excellent ink snap value. Another study compared SCC to a variety of dulling pigments, including FGL, a gypsum product, and two coarse clays. The SCC produced coated sheets with the best overall balance of optical, physical, and printing properties. Of particular note was the lack of print mottle on the SCC coated sheet. Finally, the SCC and a FGL were compared in a commercial dull formulation on a pilot coater. There were no problems in running the SCC at commercial speeds, and all trends observed in the laboratory were confirmed at the pilot scale.

The SCC pigment represents a new tool available to the papermaker for producing high quality, low gloss coated papers. The SCC can be used to replace several components in current formulations since its unique structure makes SCC a multifunctional pigment. The benefits of using the SCC in a low-gloss coating formulation are:

- Better brightness and color than clays
- Lower uncalendered sheet gloss
- Lower supercalendered sheet gloss
- No need for etched or sandblasted calender rolls
- Ability to calender using normal operating conditions
- Good ink snap
- Reduced print mottle
- Fewer pigments in the formulation
- Good coater runnability
- Lower abrasion than coarse ground calcium carbonates.

The papermaker should start his or her trial work with the SCC in the 40% to 50% range and adjust the amount accordingly to accomodate the needs of his or her particular formulation. There are also indications that the SCC pigment could be used as a gloss control agent for coated papers that have a stringent smoothness requirement but must stay below an upper sheet gloss limit. There are also other coarse particle size PCC pigments which can be used in the production of low gloss coated papers.

## Analytical Procedures

The following TAPPI Useful Methods and Test Methods provide information related to the analysis or physical properties of calcium carbonate: UM 470, UM 664, T 266, T 421, T 554, and T 646. In addition, the following TAPPI Technical Information Sheets give valuable information regarding physical properties and sources of calcium carbonate: TI 0106-01, TI 0106-05, TI 0106-08 and TI 0607-05.

Historically, transmission and scanning electron micrographs have been used to determine the particle size of PCC pigments. Presently, there are a variety of instruments that use sedimentation or laser light-scattering techniques to determine particle size distributions.

*Figure 6-10 Processes used for manufacturing PCC Filler and Coating Pigments.*

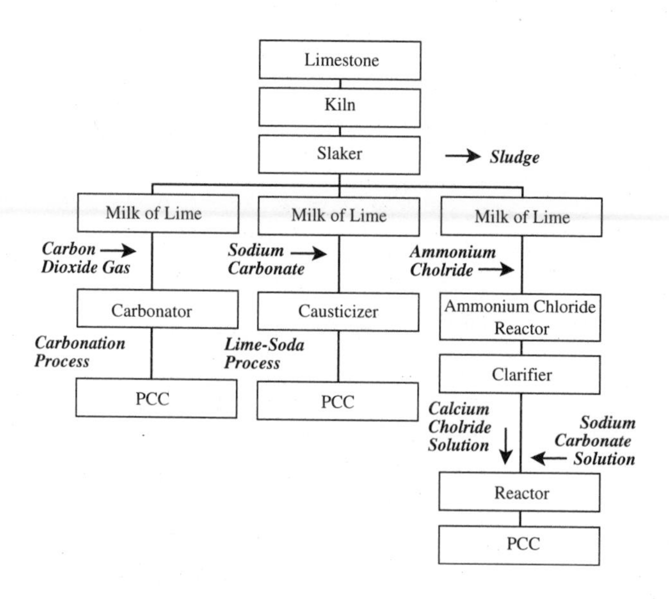


Chemical methods are of little or no value when trying to determine the ratio of calcite to aragonite in a PCC sample. This ratio can be determined accurately (less than 1% of either type of crystal in the presence of the other) by means of x-ray diffraction techniques since the two crystal classes give unique x-ray diffraction patterns.

Individual suppliers of PCC pigments also have specific tests for the characterization of their products. A partial list of tests would include dispersion time, dispersant demand, low and high shear viscosity, total residue, acid-insoluble residue, hard particle counts, qualitative identification of residues, surface area by various techniques, Hegman readings, pH, abrasion values, color values (L,a,b), oil absorption, slurry density, and other proprietary tests.

## Economic and Market Factors

PCC has been used in the paper industry to some extent for many years, but its real growth began in 1985 with the construction of the first on-site "satellite plant". Over the next 10 years, approximately 40 satellite plants were constructed in North America and Europe. Most of these plants supplied only filler pigments, but several were designed to produce PCC for coating applications. One supplier of PCC operates only a merchant plant (single location), which produces both filler and coating grades that are shipped to customers by truck or railcar.

The "push" for mills in North America to convert to alkaline papermaking coincided with the advent of PCC satellite plants. In Europe, the changeover to the alkaline process happened much earlier due to the presence of inexpensive and readily available GCC. The PCC products displaced not only the traditional clay fillers but also reduced or eliminated the use of premium pigments such as titanium dioxide. The switch to PCC also reduced the cost through the elimination of transportation costs for clay and GCC.

Most coated and uncoated wood-free grades in both Europe and North America are alkaline. Over 50% of the minerals used by European papermakers, both in filler and coating, is calcium carbonate (predominantly GCC). In North America, 50% of filler consumption is calcium carbonate (predominantly PCC), but only 10-15% of coating pigment usage is calcium carbonate (2% PCC).

PCC has been used as a coating pigment for more than 20 years by a leading producer of wood-free coated papers, but most other producers of these grades have found it difficult to use PCC. Pigment solids at 67% was too low, and the high-shear rheology was thought to be excessively high. Therefore, the market for coating grade PCC did not develop. Recent improvements in PCC technology have improved the solids (71%) and rheology issues while maintaining PCC's good qualities. New PCC pigments have been discovered which are capable of developing higher sheet gloss than traditional GCC pigments. A mill can take advantage of this attribute in at least three ways:

1. More productivity on the supercalender through higher speeds
2. Reduction in plastic pigment usage for cost savings
3. Increased sheet gloss values.

In addition, some of these PCC pigments provide opacity improvements which can lead to a reduction or elimination of higher cost pigments such as calcined clay and titanium dioxide.

In both Europe and North America, there has been significant movement in the neutral conversion of wood-containing grades using both GCC and PCC. Included in this movement are newsprint, uncoated groundwood specialties, supercalendered papers, and lightweight coated papers that are printed by the offset process. Paper grades printed by the rotogravure process have not converted to neutral because of concern for print quality when GCC is used as a filler or coating pigment. Early work with various PCC pigments has shown that the inherent smoothness of PCC coatings, coupled with coating structure, may lead to a more compressible coating with a flat surface, characteristics which may result in improved rotogravure printing (fewer missing dots). Developments in this area could open up a currently untapped market for PCC *(26)*.

## Future Outlook

Until the turn of the century, consumption of printing and writing papers is predicted to grow at 3-5% per year, depending on the particular grade. Over the same time period, growth in the consumption of minerals will continue to exceed that of paper due to higher filler levels, increased coated paper consumption and further advances with alkaline/neutral conversion *(27)*.

All mills, including groundwood operations, will have to accelerate the shift to neutral/alkaline chemistry to accommodate calcium carbonate (PCC and GCC) coming from recycled fiber sources. The unique potential of PCC will continue to impact paper quality, grade changes, new paper products, and market dynamics for the remainder of the century.

Satellite plants are especially suited to dealing with this change. They offer a genuine opportunity for partnership, resource sharing, and the continual evolution of crystal engineering technology directed at high-performance PCC products and reduced papermaking costs.

## Literature Cited

1. Hagemeyer, R. W., *TAPPI* 43(3): 277(1960).
2. Hagemeyer, R. W., *TAPPI* 47(2): 74(1964).
3. Hagemeyer, R. W., *TAPPI* 47(10): 595(1964).
4. Palache, C., Berman, H., and Frondal, C., *Dana's System of Mineralogy*, Vol. ll, 7th Edn., John Wiley and Sons, New York, 1951, pp. 141-161, 181-193.
5. Ota, Y., Goto, N., Motoyama, I., Iwashita, T., and Nomura, K., Japanese pat. 63-50316 (March 3, 1988).
6. Waldeck, W. F., U.S. pat. 3,320,026 (May 16, 1967).
7. Passaretti, J. D. and Kunesh, C. J., U.S. pat. 5,215,734 (June 1, 1993).
8. *Handbook of Chemistry and Physics* (R. C. Weast, ed.), 55th Edn., CRC Press, Cleveland, 1974, p. B-77.
9. SMI internal document, unpublished data.
10. Boynton, R. S., *Chemistry and Technology of Lime and Limestone*, John Wiley and Sons, New York, 1966.
11. Church, J. W. and Elledge, H. G., U.S. pat. 1,862,176 (June 7, 1932).
12. Pennock, J. D., U.S. pat. 802,657 (Oct. 24, 1905).
13. Lauderman, V. A., U.S. pat. 1,863,633 (June 2, 1932).
14. Church, J. W. and Elledge, H. G., U.S. pat. 1,862,176 (June 7, 1932).
15. Rafton, H. R., U.S. pat. 1,260,488 (March 26, 1918).
16. Millman, N. J. and Whitley, J. B., in *Pigmented Coating Processes for Paper and Board*, Monograph No. 28, TAPPI PRESS, Atlanta, 1964, pp. 123-144.
17. Wolfe, D. L., in *Pigmented Coating Processes for Paper and Board*, Monograph No. 28, TAPPI PRESS, Atlanta, 1964, pp. 162-165.
18. Wheeler, R. W., *Pigmented Coating Processes for Paper and Board*, Monograph No. 28, TAPPI PRESS, Atlanta, 1964, pp. 166-168.
19. Mahoney, L. H., in *Pigmented Coating Processes for Paper and Board*, Monograph No. 28, TAPPI PRESS, Atlanta, 1964, pp. 169-193.

20. Ishley, J. N. and Osterhuber, E. J., *TAPPI 1990 Coating Conference Proceedings*, TAPPI PRESS, Atlanta, pp. 237-250.
21. Evans, D. B., Drummond, D. K., and Koppelman, M. H., *TAPPI 1991 Papermakers Conference Proceedings*, TAPPI PRESS, Atlanta, p. 321.
22. Mathur, V. K. and Lasmarias, V., *TAPPI 1991 Papermakers Conference Proceedings*, TAPPI PRESS, Atlanta, p. 331.
23. Ishley, J. N., Roman, N., and Osterhuber, E. J., *TAPPI 1992 Coating Conference Proceedings*, TAPPI PRESS, Atlanta, pp. 335-348.
24. Vanderheiden, D. B., U.S. pat. 4,714,603 (Dec. 22, 1987).
25. Ishley, J. N., *TAPPI 1989 Coating Conference Proceedings*, TAPPI PRESS, Atlanta, pp. 155-167.
26. Duncan, P. A., *Pulp Paper Intl.* (5): 29(1995).
27. Patrick, K. L., *Pulp & Paper* (5): 141(1995).

# Precipitated $CaCO_3$ Fillers for Papermaking

*R. A. Gill*

The incorporation of calcium carbonate, predominately precipitated calcium carbonate (PCC), fillers in paper has been common practice for many years. Though the term "filler" is somewhat uncomplimentary, this group of inorganic materials has become a very essential component of most fine printing and writing grades of paper. The original purpose of adding filler to the paper matrix was to lower furnish costs with the amount of filler limited only by strength considerations. Today the principal need for fillers is to impart specific quality improvements to the sheet. Depending on the performance characteristics of the PCC fillers and the amount added to the paper, these products can improve the optical, physical, and esthetic properties of the finished sheet. The practice of utilizing PCC fillers is based on choosing materials that will provide both cost and quality improvements. The conversion to alkaline papermaking in North America, where PCC fillers designed to add value to the paper are routinely used, has emphasized this approach. This trend has been confirmed by the rapid growth in the tonnage of value-added specialty PCC fillers purchased by paper mills.

## Functions of PCC Fillers

PCC fillers are added to paper in various percentages, typically between 10% and 30%, to perform many different functions. The choice of which PCC filler or blend of PCC fillers to use depends upon the specific properties desired. While PCC fillers are used in many different grades of paper they find their greatest utility in printing and writing grade papers. PCC fillers can contribute the following properties to paper:

- Increase opacity and brightness
- Improve sheet formation by filling in the void areas around fiber crossings
- Provide a smoother surface
- Provide enhanced printability due to reasons such as a smoother, more uniform surface, less show through caused by increased opacity, and better ink receptivity, reducing ink penetration, wicking, and strike-through
- Improve dimensional stability (PCC fillers are not hydroscopic like fibers)
- Provide cost savings by replacing higher-cost fiber with lower-cost PCC fillers
- Provide a more environmentally friendly system (less machine corrosion and more environmentally acceptable effluent).

The properties exhibited by PCC filler in paper are dependent on two main factors: the characteristics of the filler and the way in which it is used. PCC filler characteristics of importance are refractive index, particle morphology, particle size and distribution of size, specific surface area, brightness and whiteness, particle charge (zeta potential), and abrasiveness. The manner in which PCC fillers are incorporated into paper vary considerably from machine to machine. The pulp species, type and amount of refining, wet-end furnish components such as starch, retention aids, and sizing agents, and addition point of the fillers can cause them to behave quite differently depending on furnish conditions. Certainly the amount of PCC filler incorporated into the sheet will have a dramatic impact on sheet properties. More detailed information on the important characteristics of PCC fillers will be presented next, followed by the specific properties of various PCC filler materials and some comparative data showing their performance in paper.

## Characteristics of PCC Fillers

As mentioned earlier, refractive index, particle morphology, particle size and distribution of size, specific surface area, brightness and whiteness, particle charge, and abrasiveness are some of the more important characteristics of PCC fillers which greatly impact the optical and physical behavior of the paper.

## Refractive Index

Refractive index is a fundamental property of a filler which is governed by its chemical composition and molecular structure. Atomic structure has a direct influence upon light scattering (opacity) because light entering the filler particle is bent or refracted from its normal path many times over within the particle rather than transmitted through it. The greater the refractive index of a filler the greater the amount of reflected light, which increases the opacity of the paper.

The fillers with the highest refractive indexes are anatase and rutile titanium dioxide at 2.55 and 2.76, respectively. All other commonly used fillers, including PCC, have refractive indexes much lower than titanium dioxide. Calcium carbonate fillers have a refractive index ranging from 1.58 to 1.63, depending on the form. Typically, PCC fillers of the calcite form have an average refractive index of 1.58. PCC of the aragonite form has an average refractive index of 1.63. As a reference, the refractive index of cellulose is 1.55, starch is approximately 1.49, and air is 1.00.

## Particle Morphology

Particle morphology or shape has been shown to be a significant characteristic of fillers. The shape of the particles will influence the way light is scattered. This in turn will affect the optical performance of the filler in paper. An example of this is illustrated in **Fig. 6-11**. It has been proven in studies by Gill, Passaretti, and Fairchild *(1-3)* that different morphologies of precipitated calcium carbonate (PCC) fillers cause different behavior in their ability to scatter light. The prismatic and rhombohedral crystalline habits of PCC form barrel and cubic-shaped solid particles, respectively, and tend to follow the Mie Theory for light scattering. The scalenohedral crystalline habit of PCC forms rosette-shaped particles with many microvoids. It is the size of the air microvoids that optimize light scattering and not the size of the particles directly, hence a different optimum for light scattering based on particle size among the different morphologies.

*Fig. 6-11 Sheet Opacity Performance of Precipitated Calcium Carbonates of Different Morphologies*

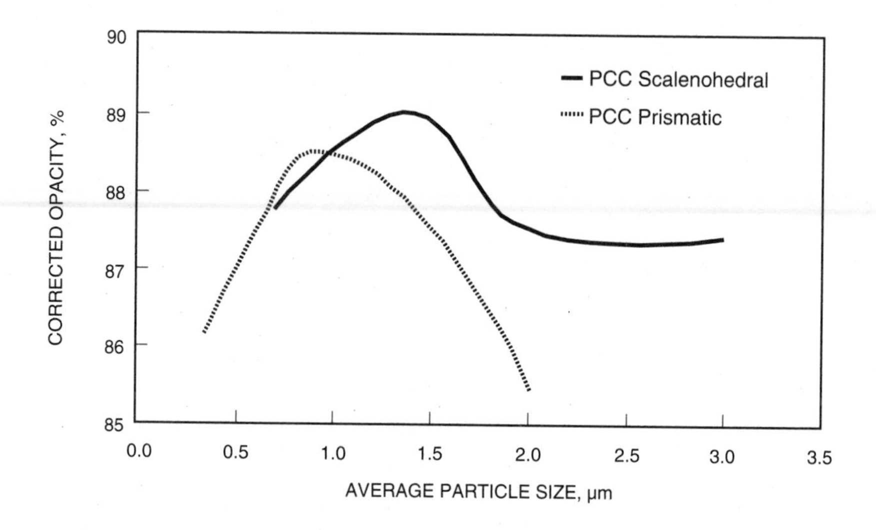


The Mie Theory predicts that the maximum scattering of light is obtained by spherical particles one-half the wave length of light or between 0.20 µm and 0.30 µm in diameter *(4)*. Particles outside of this size range scatter light with less efficiency. However, this theory only holds true for spherical particles such as plastic pigment, titanium dioxide, and certain types of "spherical" calcium carbonates. Fillers of a nonspherical nature such as kaolin, talc, and the "nonspherical" forms of precipitated calcium carbonate do not behave in a way predicted by the classic Mie Theory as was shown in Fig. 6-11.

Particle shape also dictates the packing nature of the filler particles and greatly affects the fiber structure of the sheet, influencing sheet bulk and porosity as illustrated in **Fig. 6-12**.

*Figure 6-12 Sheet Bulk and Porosity as Influenced by Filler Morphology*

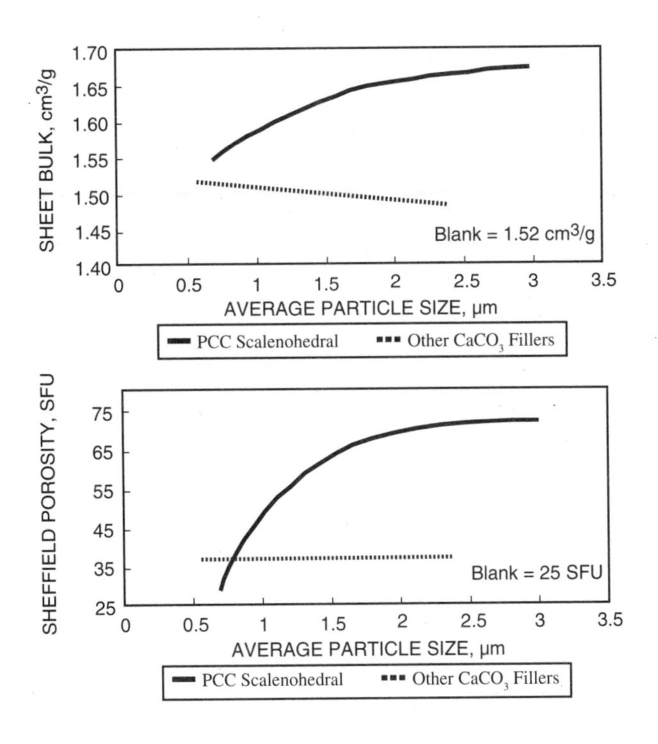


There are common shapes associated with the different types of fillers. Titanium dioxide, silicas, and plastic pigments tend to form spherical particles. The particle shape of precipitated calcium carbonate is controlled by the manufacturing process, producing four basic crystalline forms: acicular rods or needle-shaped aragonite crystals, rhombohedral or cubic-shaped calcite crystals, scalenohedral or rosette-shaped calcite crystals, and prismatic or barrel-shaped calcite crystals. Scanning electron micrographs illustrating the various shapes of PCC fillers are presented in **Fig. 6-13**. Ground calcium carbonates tend to be irregular in shape, which is caused by intensive milling of limestone rock; kaolins, along with talcs, form platy shapes due to their crystalline structures.

*Figure 6-13 Scanning Electron Micrographs of Various Forms of PCC Fillers (10,000X)*

a.) scalemohedral-calcite b.) prismatic-calcite

c.) rhombohedral-calcite d.) orthorhombic-aragonite

## Particle Size and Size Distribution

The optical properties of all fillers are strongly influenced by the particle size, size distribution, and the degree of agglomeration of the filler particles. Studies have shown that a narrow particle-size distribution promotes better light-scattering efficiency, especially when the filler is uniformly distributed throughout the sheet *(7)*. As mentioned previously, the Mie Theory predicts that the maximum scattering of light is obtained by spherical particles one-half the wavelength of light or approximately 0.20-0.30 μm in diameter. This only holds true for spherical particles, and few fillers are spherical.

Independent studies by Zeller *(7)* and Gill *(1)* showed that maximum opacity was obtained when the particle size for prismatic-precipitated calcium carbonate was between 0.40 μm and 0.50 μm equivalent spherical diameter and between 0.90 μm and 1.5 μm equivalent spherical diameter for scalenohedral-precipitated calcium carbonate. Also, the more narrow the particle-size distribution around the optimum particle size for these fillers the greater will be their contribution to paper opacity. PCC fillers are noted for their narrow particle-size distribution.

In paper mill situations retention aids help to retain fillers within the sheet, however, they also cause the fillers to agglomerate. The negative effect of PCC filler agglomeration on opacity is shown in **Fig. 6-14**. Filler agglomeration can be controlled by proper use of all wet-end chemicals, especially retention aids and starches, and optimizing the method and order of addition of the filler with the rest of the papermaking furnish.

*Figure 6-14 The Effect of Filler Agglomeration on Sheet Opacity Caused By Increasing Use of anionic-PAM Retention Aid*

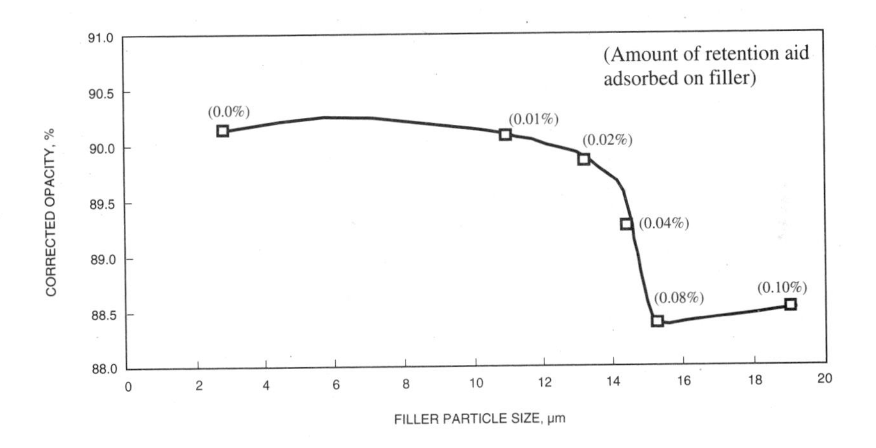


## Specific Surface Area

The particle size, size distribution, and shape of the filler have a direct impact on its specific surface area. The filler's surface area affects light scattering and also influences the strength and printing characteristics of the paper. In general, higher-surface-area fillers provide enhanced printability but at the expense of strength and ease of sizing. The principle cause for this weakening effect is related to the filler interfering with fiber-to-fiber bonding within the matrix of the sheet.

The most common measure of surface area for fillers is the Brunauer, Emmett, and Teller (BET) nitrogen-adsorption method *(8)*. The surface area of PCC fillers can be controlled by changing the morphology and size of the particles. Rhombohedral PCC fillers typically will exhibit a surface area ranging from 2 $m^2/g$ to 10 $m^2/g$. Scalenohedral PCC fillers range from 5$m^2/g$ to 25 $m^2/g$, prismatic PCC fillers range from 3 $m^2/g$ to 15 $m^2/g$, and orthorhombic PCC fillers range from 9 $m^2/g$ to 13 $m^2/g$.

## Brightness/Whiteness/Light Reflectance

The light reflectance behavior of a filler is important to its functionality in paper. Measurements of reflected light using a recording spectrophotometer can reveal differences in the way fillers reflect light throughout the visible spectrum. It is easier for the papermaker to meet paper specifications for brightness, opacity, and shade when the reflectance curve of a filler is flat (between 380 nm and 700 nm). The specific wavelength of 380 nm is important to reveal ultraviolet light absorption. PCC fillers yield a very flat reflectance curve. Also, these fillers are very compatible with optical brightening agents, which are commonly used in printing and writing grade papers to enhance whiteness. This tends to be a problem for anatase and rutile forms of titanium dioxide. Anatase titanium dioxide absorbs approximately 50% of the light at 380 nm wavelength, while the rutile form absorbs close to 85%. This strong absorption of UV light by titanium dioxide inhibits the effectiveness of optical brightening agents. Other fillers that have a tendency to absorb ultraviolet light are kaolin, talc, and ground calcium carbonates. Typical reflectance curves for PCC and rutile $TiO_2$ are shown in **Fig. 6-15**.

*Figure 6-15 GE Recording Spectrophotometer Plot of Reflectance (std. MgO)*

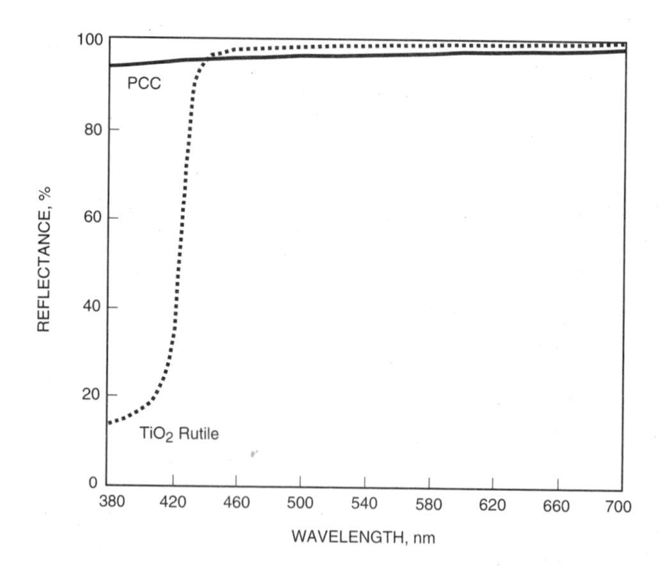


Whiteness and "brightness" are measurements used to characterize fillers. Measurement of TAPPI brightness is performed at a specific wavelength of 457

nm (blue-green). Hunter color utilizes the concept of color-space information to describe lightness/darkness (l), red/green(a), and yellow/blue (b) over the visible spectrum from 400 nm to 700 nm *(9)*.

Aluminum trihydrates show the highest brightness and reflectance spectrum, with a near flat curve throughout the light spectrum where values are typically greater than 99%. Other fillers with high brightness and whiteness values are plastic pigments, precipitated calcium carbonates, precipitated silicas, and sodium silico aluminates.

## Particle Charge

The electrostatic charge that surrounds a filler particle plays an important role both in maintaining proper dispersion of the filler as it is fed to the paper machine and in retaining the filler within the paper. The nonhydrodynamic forces that affect the behavior of filler particles are of three basic types: van der Waals (always attractive), electrostatic (requires unbalanced electrostatic charge; may be attractive or repulsive), and steric (between adsorbed molecules or polymers; usually repulsive if the molecules or polymers are water soluble). The balance between these forces (which vary with interparticle distance) determines whether the particles will remain dispersed or flocculated. Zeta potential is a convenient measure of the electrostatic charge on a colloidal particle which arises from the interaction of the particle's surface with its solution environment. It is important to point out that the chemical nature of a particle's surface is not given by knowledge of its bulk composition, nor is it necessarily consistent from one sample of a given material to the next. It is equally important to take into account the contribution of the solution environment around the particle to the zeta potential. Both specific ion concentrations and total ionic strength effect zeta potential (and thereby the electrostatic contribution to colloidal behavior) as illustrated by **Figs. 6-16 and 6-17.** Note that hydrogen ion (pH) is not the only zeta potential-determining ion for filler particles. The concentration of the potential-determining ion at which the particle has a zeta potential of zero is known as the isoelectric point.

*Figure 6-16 The Variation of the Zeta Potential of 0.05-g/L Colloidal $TiO_2$ as a Function of pH in Aqueous Solutions of $KNO_3$ at 25°C* (10)

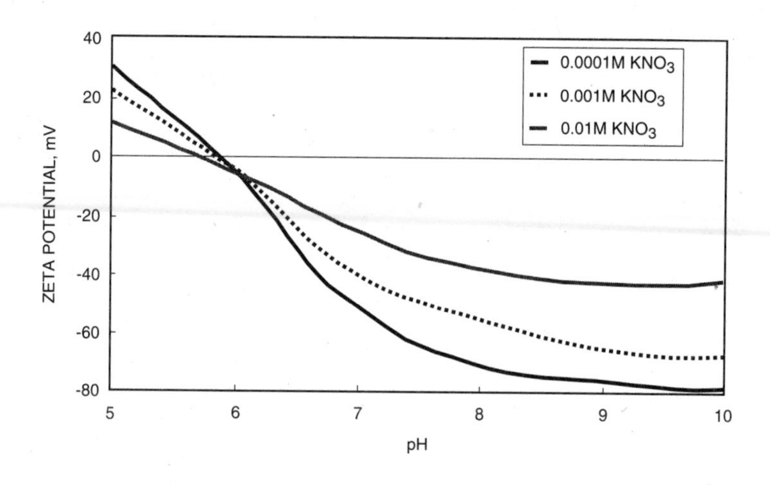


*Figure 6-17 Zeta Potential of Precipitated Calcium Carbonate vs. Calcium Ion Concentration in 0.01M KCL at pH 8.0* (11)

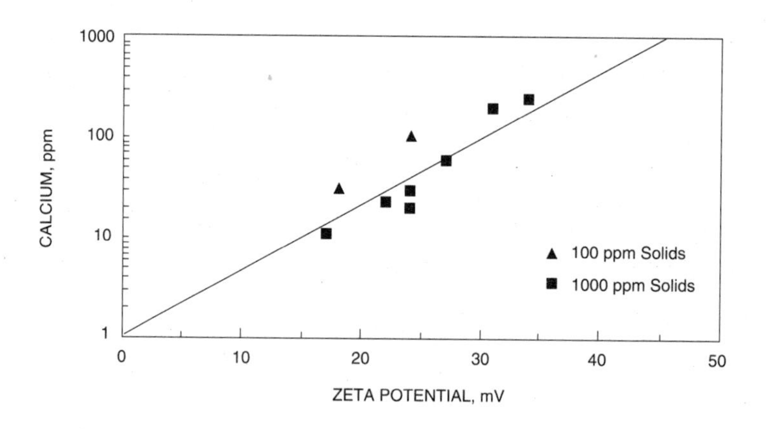


The presence of other inorganic or organic surface-active agents either as additives to the filler (slurry or dry) or to the papermaking system will affect the colloidal behavior of the particles if they are adsorbed on the particle surface. Such agents may modify zeta potential or may contribute steric repulsive forces. Low-molecular-weight polyelectrolytes (polyphosphases, polyacrylates, polydadmac) act as strong dispersants by both strong electrostatic and steric repulsion. Moderate- to high-molecular-weight polymeric papermaking additives (starches, polyacrylamides) may act as dispersants or flocculants depending on the exact method of their use.

Most PCC fillers are supplied to the papermakers as a 20% solids slurry without the need for dispersants, thereby providing a cationic filler that makes retention easier and provides improved wet-end control. **Figure 6-18** shows the retention characteristics of a PCC filler compared to the same filler dispersed with a common anionic polyacrylate.

*Figure 6-18 Effect of Particle Charge on Filler Retention (vacuum draining jar at 750 rpm, furnish at 0.5% consistency, 75% bleached hardwood/25% bleached softwood kraft at 16% filler level)*

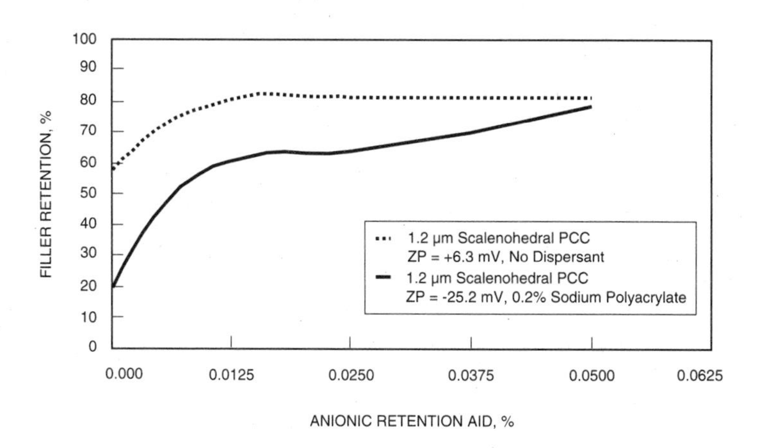


## Abrasion

Abrasion is an important characteristic of all filler pigments. Highly abrasive pigments cause excessive wear to paper machine wires and printing plates. Cutter and trimmer knives in the converting area of the mills are also susceptible to excess wear. The abrasiveness of a filler is principally caused by two factors: the crystalline nature or hardness of the filler (strength of the atomic bonds, spatial arrangement, impurities, etc.) and a filler's physical characteristics (size, particle-size distribution, shape, surface area, etc.). Small quantities of impurities such as silica and quartz can cause severe abrasion problems, and larger particles tend to be more abrasive than smaller particles of the same crystalline form. The hardness of PCC fillers is relatively low, ranging from 2.5 to 4.0 (e.g., calcite:2.5-3.0, aragonite:3.5-4.0). Both wire wear and internal sheet abrasion have been shown to be quite low for PCC fillers *(1)*.

# PCC Filler Types

The most commonly used fillers are clay, calcium carbonate, kaolin clays, titanium dioxide, and talc. In addition, smaller quantities of amorphous silica and silicates, aluminum trihydrate, diatomaceous silica, barium sulfate, and calcium sulfate are used for special applications. Calcium carbonate filler (in particular PCC filler) dominates as the filler of choice for papermaking today.

Worldwide consumption of calcium carbonate has been steadily growing since the successful commercialization of on-site precipitated calcium carbonate in the mid 1980s. For many years, traditional acid papermaking systems, in most instances, precluded the use of calcium carbonate as a paper filler. Aside from cigarette paper, where levels of precipitated calcium carbonate as high as 40% served to control paper porosity and burning rate, other uses for calcium carbonate in paper were quite limited. In the early 1950s, growing pressure from the major libraries for long-life book papers, coupled with the introduction of alkaline sizing agents, fostered an interest in alkaline papermaking systems. For an industry long accustomed to acid papermaking, such a change represented a revolutionary development. Alkaline papermaking provides a number of economic advantages including the opportunity to use relatively low cost, high-brightness calcium carbonate fillers. North American demand for calcium carbonate fillers has grown from an insignificant quantity in 1950 to an estimated 1.8 million tons in 1996, and worldwide consumption exceeds 3.0 million tons. As environmental and economic quality incentives prompt additional conversions to neutral or alkaline papermaking systems, further growth in the demand for calcium carbonate fillers is expected.

## Source

Calcium carbonate in its most common form, limestone, is found throughout the world. The dominant source is fossiliferous, from shells and skeletons of animals being transported by runoff and gradually depositing in warm shallow ocean lagoons. Most limestones were formed in the Paleozoic Era, 220-500 million years ago. The initial purity of the deposit was dependent upon the conditions under which it was accumulated. Localized geologic events caused various alterations varying from numerous cycles of solution and reprecipitation to thermal modification by high temperature and intense pressure causing some melting and recrystallization to form marble. In regions where pressures were not great enough to form marble, the material is known as chalk, and the presence of shells and skeletal remains is evident. The greatest quantity of this material can be found in Europe along coastal regions.

There are two basic chemical types of limestone designated as calcite (95+% calcium carbonate) and dolomite (70% calcium carbonate and 30% magnesium carbonate). Dolomite is of little or no significance in the manufacture of filler grades for papermaking. A similar limitation applies to many of the calcite deposits which, despite excellent chemical purity, are significantly off-white in color. Most limestones can be used to manufacture precipitated calcium carbonate fillers.

## Physical and Performance Properties

Calcium carbonates fall into two general classifications: the natural products made directly by physically grinding limestone and the precipitated products manufactured by chemically reacting various raw materials. Within the two major groups, there are several categories based on differences in particle size, shape, size distribution, and crystalline form. Normally, natural products have a lower brightness and a broader particle size distribution than the precipitated materials.

The manufacture of precipitated calcium carbonate (PCC) filler was explained in detail earlier in this chapter. Therefore we know that many complex reaction parameters, including reaction temperature, solution concentration, and speed of agitation, are controlled to alter the dimensions (size and shape) and performance characteristics of the final product. By controlling the precipitation conditions, either prismatic-calcite, rhombohedral-calcite, scalenohedral-calcite, orthorhombic-aragonite or mixtures can be obtained.

*Table 6-3 Typical Physical Properties of Calcium Carbonate Fillers*

| | **Rhombohedral Calcite PCC** | **Scalenohedral Calcite PCC** | **Prismatic Calcite PCC** | **Orthorhombic Aragonite PCC** | **Fine GCC** | **Ultrafine GCC** |
|---|---|---|---|---|---|---|
| Refractive Index | 1.58 | 1.58 | 1.58 | 1.63 | 1.58 | 1.58 |
| Specific Gravity, g/cm$^3$ | 2.71 | 2.71 | 2.71 | 2.92 | 2.71 | 2.71 |
| TAPPI Brightness, % | 99 | 99 | 99 | 99 | 95 | 95 |
| Particle Size (Sedigraph Mean), μm | 0.2-0.4 | 0.7-3.0 | 0.5-2.0 | 0.5-2.0 | 1.5-2.0 | 0.7-1.1 |
| Surface Area, m$^2$/g | 7-12 | 5-25 | 3-15 | 7-13 | 5-7 | 10-12 |
| Einlehner Abrasion,* mg | 2-4 | 3-5 | 3-6 | 4-8 | 6-10 | 3-5 |

*174,000 rev.

*Table 6-4 Paper Properties of $CaCO_3$ Fillers (60 g/m² sheet with 20% filler)*

| | Blank | 1.2 µm PCC-S | 3.0 µm PCC-S | 0.7 µm PCC-P | 0.7 µm PCC-A | 2.0 µm GCC | 0.8 µm GCC | 2.2 µm Chalk |
|---|---|---|---|---|---|---|---|---|
| Pigment Scattering Coefficient,[a] cm²/g | ... | 3063 | 2372 | 2781 | 2658 | 1766 | 1871 | 1712 |
| Corrected TAPPI Opacity, % | 73.6 | 89 | 87.4 | 88.6 | 87.8 | 85.3 | 85.1 | 85.9 |
| TAPPI Brightness, % | 85.3 | 90.7 | 90.7 | 91.9 | 90.8 | 89.5 | 90.2 | 84 |
| Breaking Length, km | 11.08 | 4.74 | 5.79 | 5.52 | 5.96 | 6.34 | 6.72 | 6.82 |
| Taber Stiffness, 100 mN·m²/g | 5.84 | 4.12 | 4.59 | 4.08 | 4.12 | 4.2 | 4.32 | 4.37 |
| Sheffield Porosity, SFU | 25 | 60.6 | 71.5 | 37.2 | 40.2 | 38 | 31.8 | 35.3 |
| Bulk, cm³/g | 1.52 | 1.62 | 1.66 | 1.61 | 1.52 | 1.52 | 1.5 | 1.47 |
| HST, s | 420 | 38 | 128 | 98 | 29 | 132 | 73 | 162 |
| Internal Sheet Abrasion,[b] µg loss | 10 | 30 | 180 | 240 | 610 | 400 | 290 | 300 |

PCC-S = scalenohedral habit, calcite; PCC-P = prismatic habit, calcite; PCC-A = acicular habit, aragonite; GCC = ground calcium carbonate.
[a]Measured at 8% filler level.
[b]Needle abrasion test at 10,000 penetrations.

Since this is a chemical process needing only minimal space and few raw materials a new method of providing these types of fillers to a paper mill has been developed called the "on-site" plant concept. This operation has worked quite effectively for the manufacture and supply of PCC filler to a host paper mill. The concept itself is simple. A small plant is built within the confines of a paper mill site to manufacture PCC. Certain raw material such as water and $CO_2$ are supplied by the host mill. The product(s) are then sent via pipeline directly to the paper mill, typically at 15-25% solids. Due to the short run and the low-solids viscosity of the PCC slurry, no dispersant is necessary. Therefore, the system has proven to be advantageous for better wet-end control. Another benefit of this system is that, since each on-site plant is associated with a particular mill, customized fillers and even coating-grade products can be made for a particular paper mill's needs.

PCC fillers are manufactured with high chemical purity, which provides a consistently "clean" particle surface. This surface characteristic along with uniform particle size and unique morphologies are felt to be the predominate reasons for the substantial differences observed in the paper filling performance of PCC when compared to GCC fillers.

Typical physical properties of precipitated calcium carbonate for use as paper fillers compared to ground calcium carbonate are listed in **Table 6-3**. Paper properties for the different types of PCC fillers compared to other forms of calcium carbonate are shown in **Table 6-4**. Depending on which PCC filler you choose, dramatic differences in sheet properties will be observed. Proper care should be taken to determine which sheet properties must be improved to select the right PCC filler or blend of fillers.

## Handling or Dispersion of PCC Fillers

Prior to the 1960s, the common method for adding filler was by feeding it as a dry powder to the pulp in the beater. The relatively coarse materials and low levels of addition did not warrant dispersing the filler separately. Actually, upon request, most PCC producers would supply their fillers in beater-dispersible bags to facilitate this operation by eliminating the need to open and empty bags. With the advancing displacement of the beater and the growing use of finer-particle-size fillers and specialty fillers to achieve specific improvements in paper quality, newer systems have been developed for handling, dispersing, and adding fillers to the fiber furnish. While these systems and fillers permit a significant quality improvement over the coarse-particle and beater addition practice, they have created other problems, some of which are only partially resolved.

To begin with, fine-particle-size materials are inherently more difficult to disperse. While the use of high-shear mixing equipment provides a partial offset, in most cases this must be augmented by adding some quantity of chemical dispersant. Without the dispersant (or the use of predispersed materials), the mixing solids cannot be raised to the level needed for developing adequate shearing action to wet-out very fine particles and break down particle aggregates. Unfortunately, the presence of the dispersant on the filler and in the system inhibits retention. The situation is even worse for fillers that are purchased in slurry form where the material is already in an optimized state of dispersion due to the incorporation of dispersant. A highly-dispersed, fine filler particle will be neither chemically adsorbed nor physically entrapped by the fiber web. **Figure 6-19** shows how filler retention can be significantly altered when a dispersant is added to a filler, in this case to a PCC filler.

*Figure 6-19 Effect of Dispersant on Filler Retention (vacuum draining jar at 750 rpm, furnish at 0.5% consistency, 75% bleached hardwood/25% bleached softwood kraft, 16% filler level, no retention aid)*

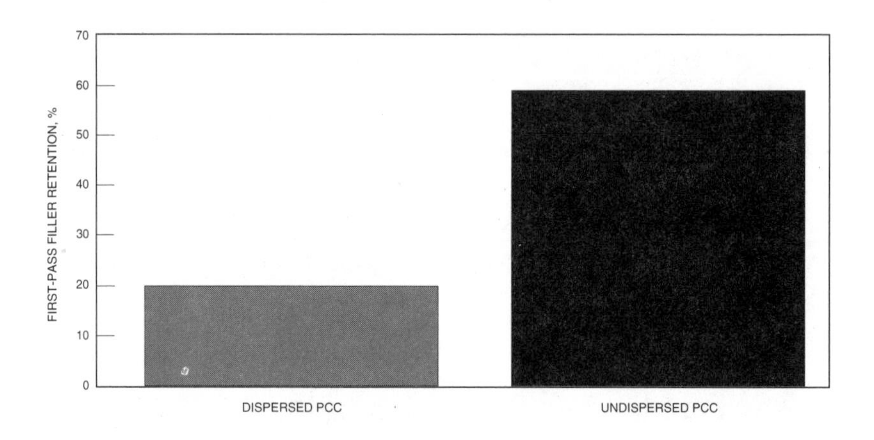


The usual method for coping with this problem is to add a polymeric retention aid such as a polyacrylamide, either alone or in conjunction with an auxiliary material. Unfortunately, wet-end systems are very sensitive to the relative concentration of these additives and, as a result, normal operating fluctuations can cause electrochemical imbalances leading to poor formation, overflocculation of the filler, and low filler retention *(12)*. An example of overflocculation from excessive use of polymeric retention aid is illustrated in **Fig. 6-20**, which shows that as filler floc size increases the optical performance decreases. Some people believe minimizing or eliminating the use of a dispersant would be desirable. While this may have conceptual merit, wet processing and handling of fillers without dispersant would be highly impractical if not impossible. Discovery of a fully neutralizable or short-life dispersing agent would provide a viable alternative. One such approach has been the "on-site" precipitated calcium carbonate plant concept, which provides PCC filler to the host paper mill at 15-25% solids without dispersant.

*Figure 6-20 Effect of Filler Agglomeration Size on Filler Optical Performance (PCC filler agglomerated by adding high-molecular-weight polymer directly to it before sheetmaking process.)*

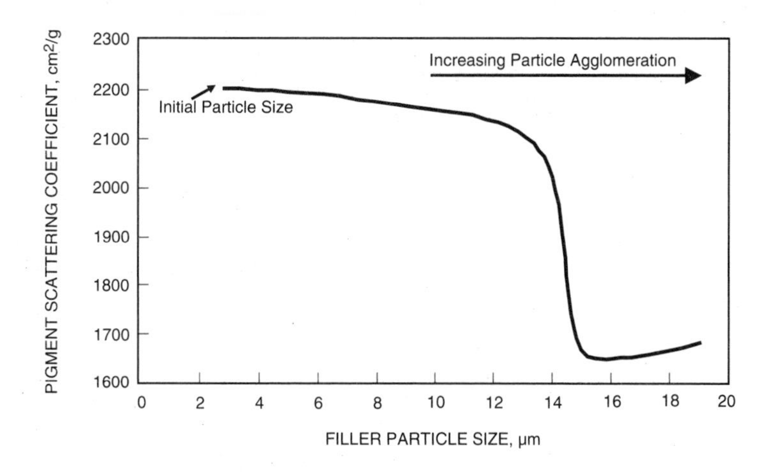


## Selecting PCC Fillers

The choice of filler to be used is dependent upon several factors, the foremost of which is the basic performance objective. If the filler is being added strictly to provide fiber extension, then a large-particle-size scalenohedral or prismatic product would be the filler of choice. Of course, there are upper limits on particle size dictated by the need to keep the particles in suspension and to minimize abrasion.

The dominant purpose for adding fillers has become far more sophisticated and is now directed at improving the quality of the filled sheet. Since there are a number of properties to be considered, there is a rapidly growing trend toward the use of filler combinations or blends somewhat paralleling the practice in coating formulations. This provides a number of alternatives for achieving the desired sheet properties. For this reason, broad generalizations on filler selection are of limited value. One should always consider the cost of the filler so the performance-to-cost ratio is always maximized. **Table 6-5** should provide some guidelines on PCC fillers to be considered for specific performance properties.

*Table 6-5 Enhancing Paper Properties with PCC Fillers*

| Property | PCC Fillers to be Considered |
|---|---|
| Brightness | All PCC fillers |
| Opacity | 1.1-1.5 µm scalenohedral PCC<br>0.5-0.9 µm prismatic PCC<br>0.2-0.4 µm rhombohedral PCC |
| Bulk | All scalenohedral PCC fillers larger than 1.0 µm average particle size. The larger the size the better. |
| Strength | All low-surface-area PCC fillers, expecially prismatic morphology. |
| Porosity | Small-particle-size PCC fillers work best at closing up the sheet.<br>0.6 µm prismatic PCC filler is the best choice, followed by 0.8 µm scalenohedral PCC. |
| Sizing | All low-surface-area PCC fillers.<br>Hydrophobic surface-modified PCC fillers. |

With the exception of refractive index, most filler properties that provide enhanced optical performance and bulking ability can be detrimental to strength properties. But, when one filler is not suitable to provide all of the necessary benefits then blends of two or more PCC fillers can usually meet the quality needs of most paper grades.

## Future Outlook

With the growing interest and demand for PCC fillers, manufacturers can be expected to focus more attention on the development of products designed for specific filler applications. Moves to increase filler levels will continue as better fillers are developed and paper machine technology advances. This would parallel the developments that took place in the paper coating area in years past. And, just as improved quality and more cost-efficient coating pigments contributed to the growth of coated paper, so, too, improved PCC fillers can be expected to expand the demand for highly filled papers. Chemically surface-modified PCC fillers is a development that will aid in the growth of specialty paper products such as multipurpose ink jet papers, specialty groundwood papers, and new recycled grades to name a few.

## Acknowledgements

The authors wish to acknowledge the special contributions made to this chapter by Nigel D. Sanders, David L. Peters, and Patrick C. Kelly.

# Literature Cited


1. Gill, R. A., *Nordic Pulp Paper Res. J.* 4(2): 120(1989).
2. Passaretti, J. D. and Gill, R.A., *TAPPI 1991 Papermakers Conference Proceedings*, TAPPI PRESS, Atlanta, pp. 293-298.
3. Fairchild, G. H., *TAPPI J.* 75(8): 85(1992).
4. Maron, S. H. and Lando, J. B., *Fundamentals of Physical Chemistry*, Chap. 19, Macmillan Publishing Co., New York, 1974, pp. 775-799.
5. Hagemeyer, R. W., *TAPPI* 43(3): 277-288(1960).
6. Gill, R. A., *TAPPI 1991 International Paper Physics Conference Proceedings*, TAPPI PRESS, Atlanta, pp. 211-218.
7. Zeller, R. C., *TAPPI 1980 Coating Conference Proceedings*, TAPPI PRESS, Atlanta, pp. 103-109.
8. Bovin, A. and Carno, B., *Svensk Paperstidn.* 15: 483-486(1977).
9. Judd, D. B. and Kelly, K. L., *Color—Universal Language and Dictionary of Names*, National Bureau of Standards Special Publication 440, U.S. Dept. of Commerce, Washington, DC, 1977.
10. Wiese, G. R. and Healy, T. W., *J. Colloid Interface Sci.* 51: 427(1975).
11. Gill, R. A. and Hagemeyer, R. W., *Pulp and Paper Manufacture* (M. J. Kocurek, ed.), 3rd Edn., Vol. 6, Chapter. 2, 1992.
12. Gill, R. A., *Nordic Pulp Paper Res. J.* 8(1): 167(1993).

# 7.

# Natural Ground Calcium Carbonate as Coating Pigment and Filler

*Ludwig Huggenberger and Hans B. Neubold*

Natural ground calcium carbonate (GCC) is an important coating and filler pigment for technological and economic reasons. In the early 1960s European paper mills started to use natural ground calcium carbonate as a filler. A few years later, it was also used as a coating pigment *(1)*. Towards the end of the 1970s, North America started down the same path.

## Product Description

Natural calcium carbonate ($CaCO_3$) occurs mainly as the mineral calcite in various rock forms: chalk, limestone, and marble *(2-4)*. These three rock formations consist of individual rhombohedral calcite crystals. Calcite is one of the most abundant minerals in the earth's crust.

### Classification

The three rock formations are classified as follows:

- Chalk: Loosely layered sedimentary rock, biogenic origin (scalenohedrons and skeletons of nannofossils, e.g., coccoliths and foraminiferes). **Figure 7.1.**
  Age: about 80-110 million years.

- Limestone: Stronger layered sedimentary rock, biogenic origin (snails and shells). The crystal size is between chalk and marble.
  Age: about 110-150 million years.

- Marble: Metamorphic carbonate rock formed through tectonic changes (recrystallization) of limestone.
  Age: about 300-500 million years.

*Fig. 7-1 Chalk Consisting of Coccoliths*

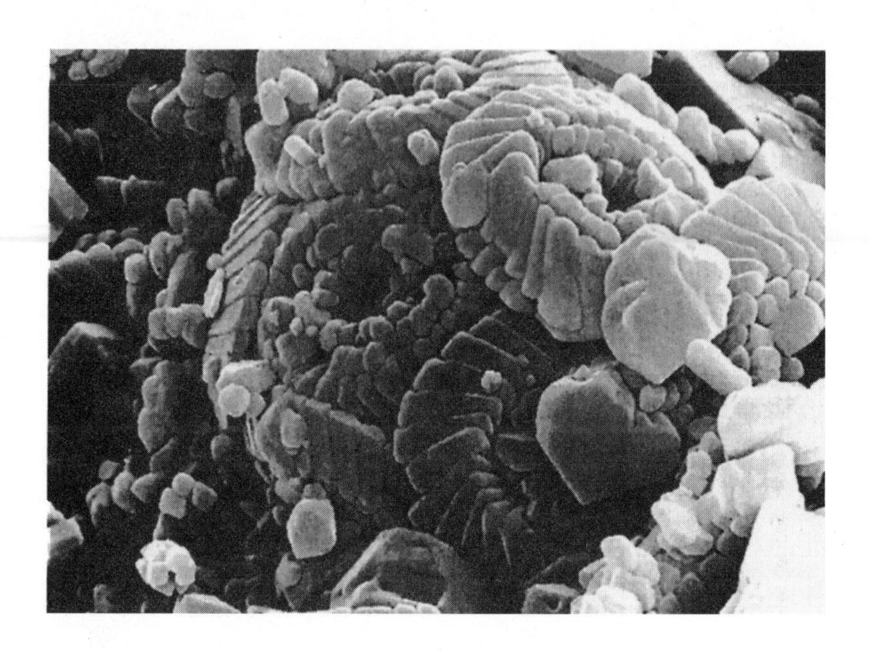

## Chemical, Physical, and Mineralogical Properties

**Table 7-1** lists some of the attributes of natural calcium carbonate (chalk, limestone, marble).

*Table 7-1 Attributes of Natural Calcium Carbonate*

| | |
|---|---|
| Chemical Formula | $CaCO_3$ |
| Crystallography | Trigonal |
| Crystal Structure | Rhombohedral<br>(sometimes scalenohedral or prismatic) |
| Refractive Index | 1.48/1.66 |
| Mohs' Hardness | 3 |
| Density, g/cm$^3$ | 2.6-2.8 |
| pH of a 10% Suspension | About 9 |
| Solubility | Calcium carbonate dissolves under acid conditions. |

*Fig. 7-2 Solubility of $CaCO_3$ — pH and Temperature*

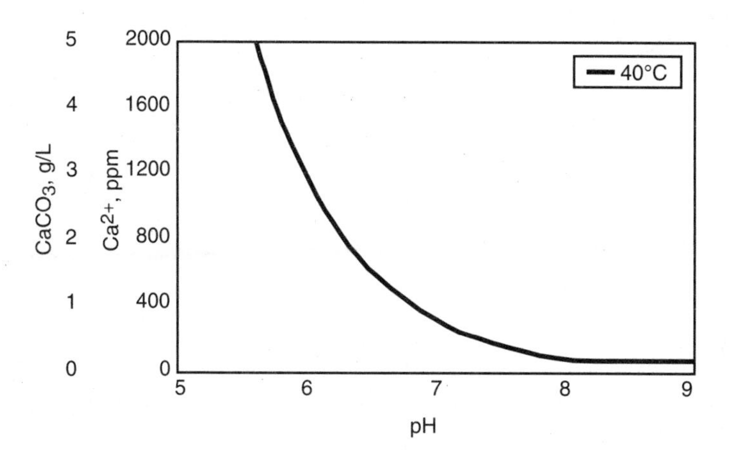


The speed of solubility and decomposition of calcium carbonate depends mainly on acidity, particle size, amount of dissolved $CO_2$, and temperature.

## Methods of Manufacture

The grinding of natural calcium carbonate is done in wet or dry processing *(5)*. In most cases the crude in the deposits consists of more than 96% $CaCO_3$. The portion of impurities to be removed is in the range of four percent maximum.

*Fig. 7-3 GCC Production Process for Dry and Wet Grinding*

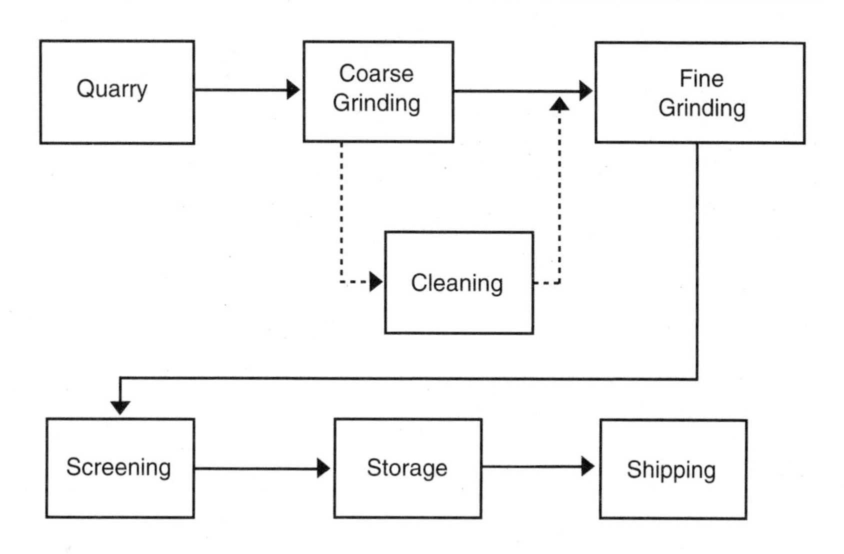

Today, more than 80% of all natural $CaCO_3$ used in the paper industry is delivered in slurry form because of several advantages: energy savings, free of dust, can be pumped, small storage volume, less environmental stress, direct application ("ready made form" for the papermaker). Dispersing agents are often anionic in nature and are primarily based on sodium polyacrylate or sodium polyphosphate. The amount of dispersant is dependent on the fineness and the percent solids of the slurry. In practice this means that the amount of dispersants varies between 0.1% and 1.0%.

Also, cationically wet-ground and stabilized $CaCO_3$ slurries are produced and are in use.

## Product Characteristics, Availability, and Handling *(6)*

Natural ground $CaCO_3$ is produced in a particle-size range of 40% to 98% (<2 µm) and a brightness between 80% and 96% (TAPPI Test Method T-452). The solids contents of the slurry can be up to 78%, with a Brookfield viscosity of about 500 mPa·s (100 rpm).

*Fig. 7-4 Qualities of Natural GCC for the Paper Industry*

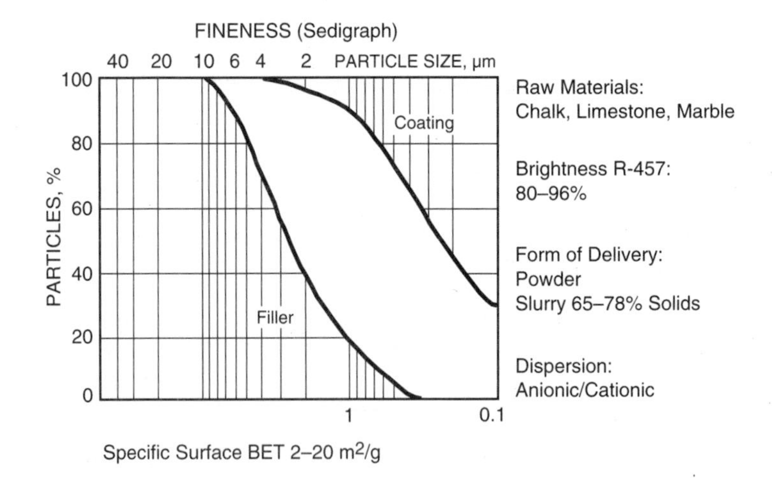


There are about 60 GCC production sites around the world, with the highest concentration (more than 30) found in Europe. Additional tank farms make this infrastructure even more complete. For instance, most paper mills in Europe can be served with GCC within a 250-km delivery radius.

In North America there are identical plants capable of supplying slurry products to the paper industry. They are primarily located on the East and West Coasts, in the South, and one plant is located in the upper Midwest.

*Fig. 7-5 Availability and Logistics*

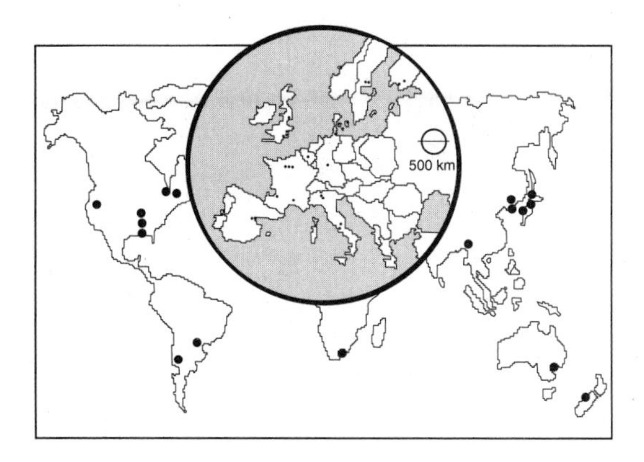


The delivery of $CaCO_3$ in slurry form has constantly increased in recent years. One advantage to using slurry is that less warehouse space is needed (**Table 7-2**).

*Table 7-2 Slurry Requires Less Warehouse Space*

| $CaCO_3$ (slurry), % | Density | Metric tons $CaCO_3$ (dry) per $m^3$ slurry | Slurry ($m^3$) per metric ton $CaCO_3$ (dry) |
|---|---|---|---|
| 65 | 1.69 | 1.10 | 0.90 |
| 70 | 1.79 | 1.25 | 0.80 |
| 75 | 1.89 | 1.42 | 0.70 |
| 78 | 1.96 | 1.53 | 0.65 |
| 80 | 2.01 | 1.61 | 0.62 |

As a comparison, let's look at the storage requirements for powder:

- "Coarse" $CaCO_3$ (30% <2µm): 1.0 ton $CaCO_3/m^3$
- "Fine" $CaCO_3$ (98% <2µm): 0.5 ton $CaCO_3/m^3$

Various forms of packaging, shipping, and warehousing are available:

- Packaging: paper bags and big bags for dry $CaCO_3$
- Type of shipping:
  By rail or truck: silo or tank cars
  By ship: bulk carriers and tankers
- Storage: warehouse, silos, and tanks.

# Reasons for Use

## In Paper Coating

The upswing usage of natural ground $CaCO_3$ began in Europe in the 1970s *(7-10)*. Today, the percentage of carbonate used in coating in Europe is about 50% *(11,12)* of total pigment consumption.

**Percent Carbonate Used in Various Coating Color Formulations. Figure 7-6** gives a general overview (mainly European) of the present situation. Some lightweight coated (LWC) mills already use 20% carbonate in their rotogravure formulations to improve the rheological behavior, to increase the brightness of the paper, and to reduce costs.

*Fig. 7-6 Natural GCC in Coating Formulations* (13, 14)

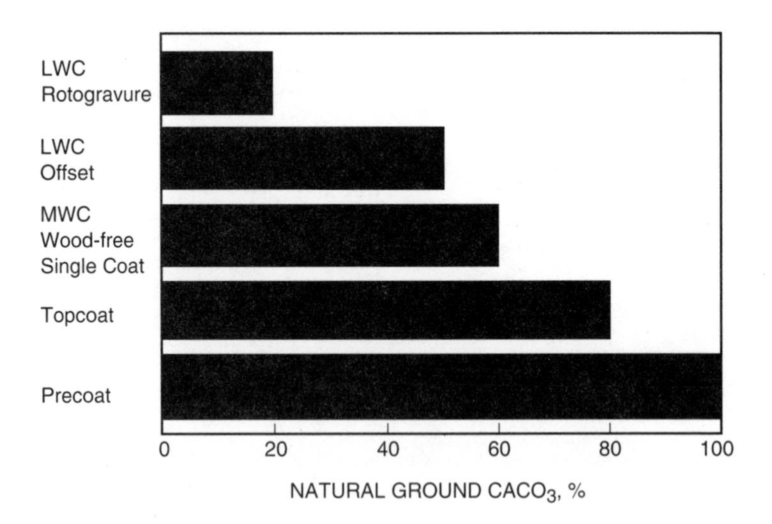


LWC and MWC offset papers as well as wood-free, single coated offset papers contain approximately 50-60% natural carbonate in their formulations *(15)*. Even these levels of carbonate in a formulation make it possible to run higher coating color solids. Many paper and board mills *(16)* use up to 80% $CaCO_3$ in their glossy top-coat formulations (90-98% <2 μm) and 100% in their precoat (60-75% <2μm). Similar concepts are applied in matte coatings *(17, 18)*. In that case, the fineness of the grades for pre- and top coat is between 60% and 90% less than 2 μm. It is not uncommon to find precoats containing 100% carbonate with 65-72% coating solids. The main advantages are no blade scratches and an increase in brightness.

**Rheological Behavior.** Natural ground calcium carbonate shows such excellent rheological behavior mainly because of its rhombohedral structure. The addition of $CaCO_3$ shows a noticeable viscosity reduction (**Fig. 7-7**). This allows the paper mill to make-down coating colors at high solids and still run at high speeds without any problems.

*Fig. 7-7 Rheology of Different Pigment Slurries*

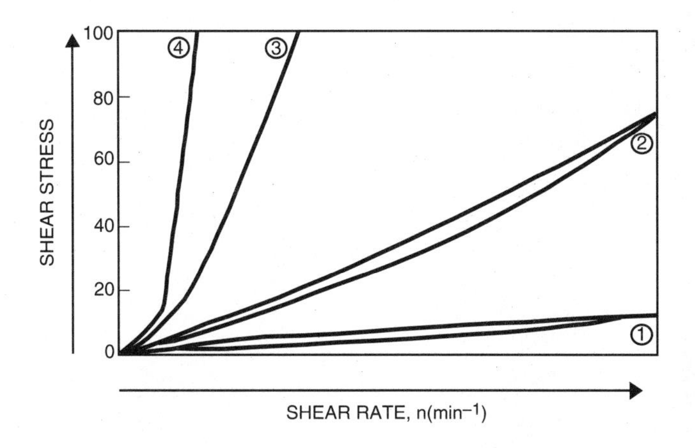


Solids content is 73%, and Brookfield viscosity is measured at 100 rpm. Slurry 1 represents 100% natural ground $CaCO_3$ (90% <2 μm, 90 mPa·s); No. 2 shows 65% natural ground $CaCO_3$ (90% <2 μm, 170 mPa·s) and 35% U.S. No. 2 clay. Slurry 3 is composed of 35% natural ground $CaCO_3$ (90% <2 μm, 380 mPa·s) and 65% U.S. No. 2 clay; No. 4 is 100% U.S. No. 2 clay (600 mPa·s).

**Gloss Development. Figure 7-8** shows the gloss development of different pigments or pigment combinations at solids of 56% and 67-70%, respectively (high-solids coating). The particle size of the carbonate and the coating color solids play an important role in gloss development.

*Fig. 7-8 Gloss Development of Various Pigment Combinations*

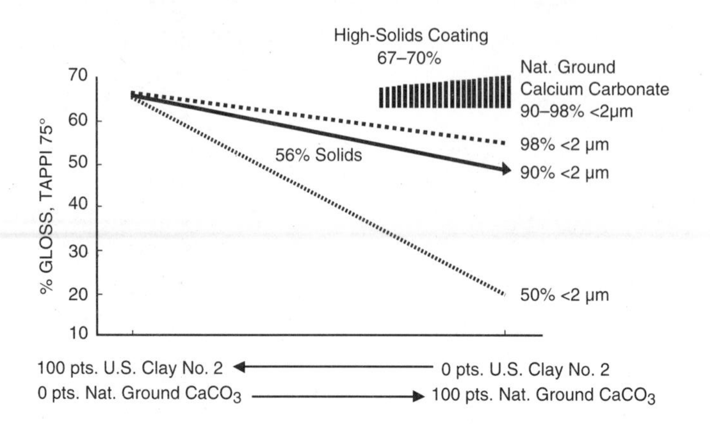


The coatings were formulated with 100 parts pigment, 12 parts latex, and 0.5 parts CMC. The paper was single coated (12 g/m²/side) on a 1200-m/min blade coater. The 38-g/m² base paper was wood-containing and was calendered at 150 kp/cm.

Compared to kaolin, carbonates with a particle-size distribution between 90% and 98% less than 2 µm show the least loss of gloss. A noticeable increase in gloss is achieved through higher coating-color solids. When these solids are run, the portion of kaolin is limited to about 30% (because of rheological problems which could result in streaking and piling). When double coating, 100% carbonate can be used in the precoat as well as in the topcoat and still reach gloss values higher than 80% (high-solids coating).

**Brightness and Opacity.** The raw material used to make natural GCC will markedly influence the brightness and opacity of the coating: chalk yields the lowest brightness, limestone and marble the highest. In addition, particle size and the percentage of carbonate in the coating will play an important role. The pigment brightness spectrum already discussed (Fig. 7-4) is mainly in the range of 86% to 96% (R-457). This shows that high-brightness carbonate used in coating formulations at a high percentage can improve the brightness of coating colors. Newly developed, very fine carbonates improve coverage in board coating, thereby reducing the use of expensive extenders.

**Binder Demand.** The coatings were formulated with 5.5, 9.5, or 13.5 parts latex, and 0.5 parts CMC. The 80-g/m² wood-free base paper was blade coated with 12 g/m²/side and then calendered at 150 kp/cm.

To determine the binder demand, the wet pick test of a lab print tester was used in addition to very extensive commercial print trials (MAN Roland Offset

Printing Press). Of particular interest was the tendency towards picking and piling for various levels of binder.

**Figure 7-9** clearly shows the differences in binder demands. Because of the dense packing, the binder level is lower, even for the extremely fine calcium carbonates, when compared to commonly used coating clays. Commercial trials have shown that two to three parts of synthetic binder can be saved over that required with a 100% kaolin formulation.

*Figure 7-9 Comparison of Binder Demands of Coating Colors for Offset Printing*

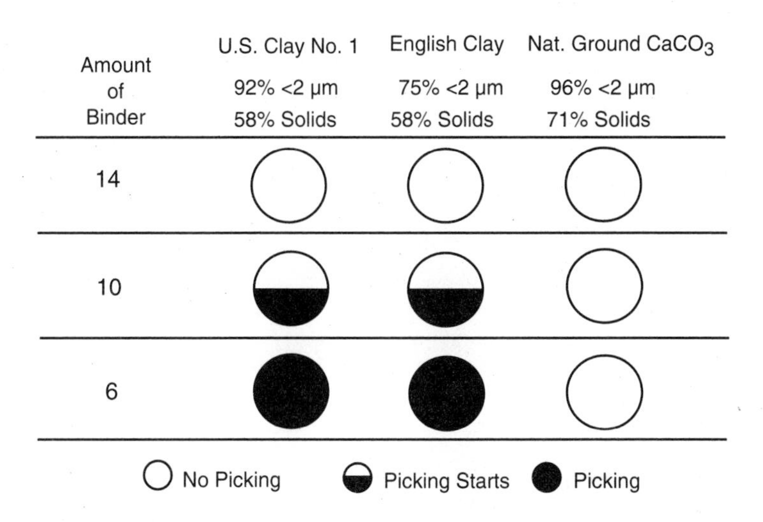


**Cationically Dispersed $CaCO_3$ Slurries** ***(19).*** Cationic coating colors containing 70% calcium carbonate show better fiber coverage, especially for the coat weights less than 7 g/m$^2$/side, when compared to anionic systems. The same holds true for opacity, brightness, gloss, and print gloss. In addition, there is less anionic trash originating from recycled coated broke.

**Performance.** The important reasons for using natural ground $CaCO_3$ as a coating pigment can be summarized as follows:

- Favorable rheological properties
- High coating solids
- Better runnability (coater)
- Energy savings (coater)
- Lower binder demand
- High brightness

- Better optical brightener efficiency
- Good print qualities and high print gloss.

## In Paper Filling

Modern alkaline papermaking began in Europe in the early 1960s. The driving forces behind that shift were the technological and economic advantages of using natural ground $CaCO_3$.

**Use of Natural Ground $CaCO_3$ and Filler Levels in Woodfree Papers.** The four main areas where natural GCC and fillers are used in woodfree papers are:

| | |
|---|---|
| Printing and Writing Papers | 10-30% |
| Continuous Forms and Copy Papers | 10-28% |
| Laser Printing Papers and NCR Base Papers | 10-15% |
| Coated Base Paper | 3-8% primary filler (12-20% total pigment) |

Compared to the rest of the world, Europe uses the highest filler levels. In the United States the filler levels are about three to five percent lower. While the European papermaker mainly uses a particle-size distribution (PSD) of 40-60% <2 μm for filler applications, his or her North American counterpart sometimes works with much finer fillers (up to 90% <2 μm). In special cases (for instance, to obtain higher opacity), modified products are used up to 95% <2 μm.

How does natural ground $CaCO_3$ influence properties such as opacity, brightness, tensile strength, and wire abrasion?

**Opacity vs. Brightness. Table 7-3** and **Fig. 7-10** show that there is a substantial increase in paper brightness when using marble as a filler instead of chalk. However, at about the same particle size, there is a certain decrease in opacity when going from either chalk or limestone to marble. This lost opacity can be regained by using a specially designed product with a particle size of 93% <2 μm.

*Table 7-3 Opacity vs. Brightness*

| Filler | Percent (<2 μm) | Brightness, % (R-457) |
|---|---|---|
| Chalk | 60 | 83 |
| Limestone | 60 | 88 |
| Marble | 60, 90, 93 | 95 |
| Pulp | — | 86 |

*Figure 7-10 Opacity vs. Brightness (Handsheets, 75 g/m²)*

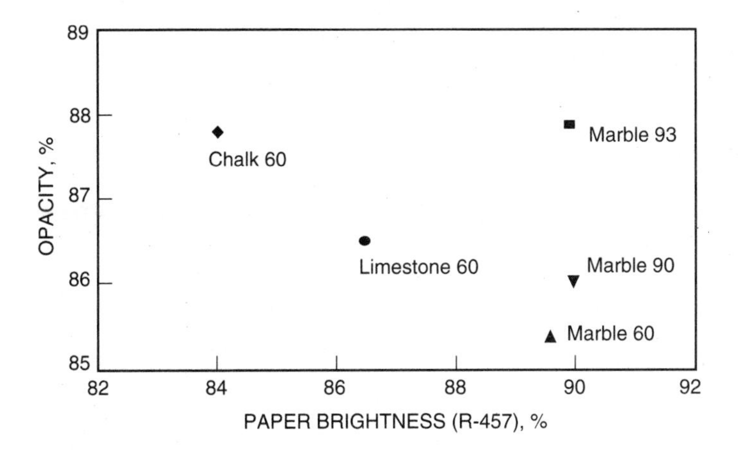


**Brightness/Opacity vs. Filler Level. Figure 7-11** shows clearly that higher filler levels also increase brightness and opacity. The absolute values will depend on, among other things, filler brightness, degree of fineness of the filler, and type of chemical pulp.

These results were obtained using marble filler with 60% less than 2 µm and a brightness of 95% and pulp with a brightness of 86% after refining.

*Fig. 7-11 Filler Loading vs. Brightness and Opacity (Handsheets, 75 g/m²)*

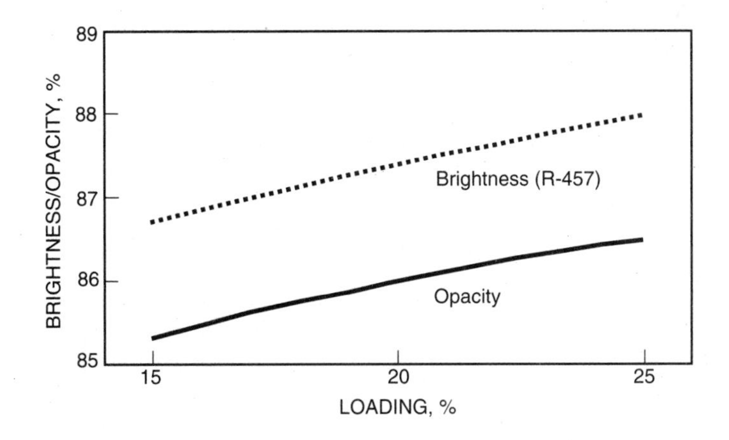

**Tensile Strength vs. Filler Level.** In general, as filler levels increase paper strength decreases (**Fig. 7-12**). The whole concept of strength is also slightly influenced by the degree of fineness of the filler. In this case the filler was marble with 60% less than 2 μm.

*Figure 7-12 Filler Loading vs. Paper Tensile Strength (Handsheets, 75 g/m²)*

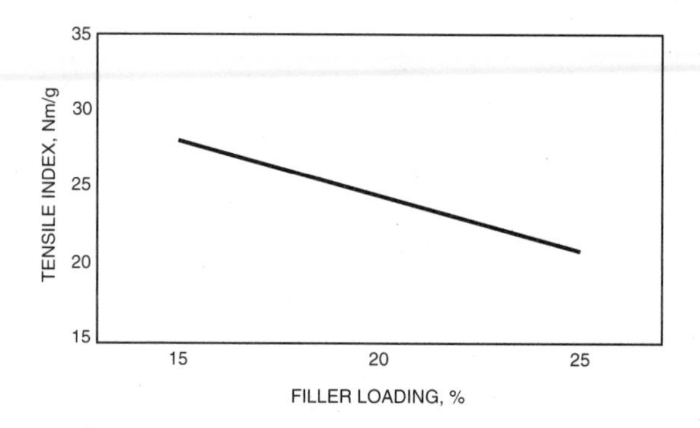


**Synthetic Wire Wear vs. $CaCO_3$ Fineness** ***(20).*** Abrasion is markedly reduced with increased fineness of the filler. Mill studies as well as tests on the pilot scale Schoedel machine have confirmed this (**Fig. 7-13**). Machine technical conditions and factors such as filler retention are affecting wire abrasion behavior noticably.

*Figure 7-13 Synthetic Wire Wear (Schoedel) vs. $CaCO_3$ Fineness*

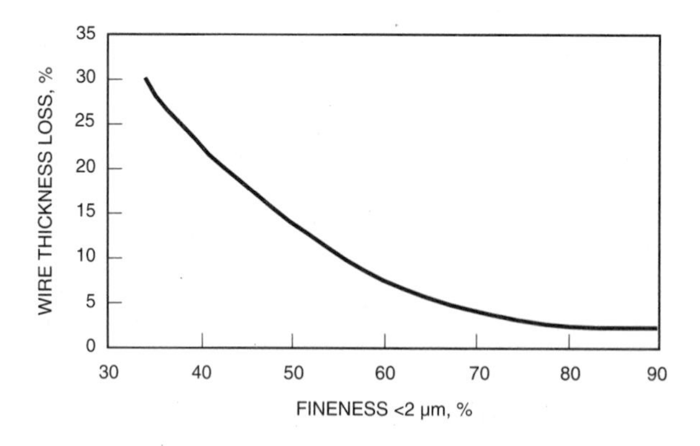


**Wood-Containing Papers** ***(21, 22).*** To use increased amounts of natural ground $CaCO_3$, many heavy- and lightweight coating mills in Europe produce base paper at a neutral pH. The uncoated base sheet will then be loaded with the secondary pigment from the coated broke plus about 2-3% $CaCO_3$ as the primary filler. The fineness of the primary filler equals 60% less than 2 µm. In the recent past, natural ground $CaCO_3$ was being used in supercalendered papers as well. First field results have shown that substitution with up to 30% kaolin with $CaCO_3$ is possible without a negative influence on the final quality.

**Cationic, Wet Ground Slurries** *(23)*. Most GCC shipments today are delivered as anionically stabilized, wet ground $CaCO_3$ slurry. Some paper mills, however, use cationically dispersed slurries with the following advantages:

- Easier retention for fast running paper machines and single-polymer retention systems
- Use in wood-containing systems (adsorption of disturbing substances).

**Performance.** Alkaline papermaking using natural ground $CaCO_3$ in wood-free paper shows several major advantages when compared to acid papermaking using kaolin as a filler *(24)*. Paper improvements involve strength, brightness, and durability. Process improvements include refining, dewatering and drying, and pH stability.

*Strength.* In the absence of aluminum salts and a lower overall salt concentration, the papermaker is able to increase filler levels by 1-5% without jeopardizing paper strength.

*Brightness.* The application of high-brightness natural ground $CaCO_3$ can save up to 80% of optical brighteners.

*Durability and Permanence.* The permanence of the paper is greatly increased because of the absence of alum and the acid pH values. $CaCO_3$, with its buffering ability against acidic influences, provides a more durable, longer lasting paper.

*Refining.* Slightly alkaline pH values and a low salt load require up to 30% less refining energy.

*Dewatering and Drying.* Due to its rhombohedral structure, natural ground $CaCO_3$ creates a more open surface (microporosity). Natural ground calcium carbonate is more hydrophobic than kaolin and has no inner space; therefore, it releases water faster.

*pH Stability.* $CaCO_3$ contributes to the system's stable pH values at levels between 7.2 and 8.4 because of its strong buffering ability.

# Analytical Procedures

## Critical Properties and Specifications

The following criteria are important for natural $CaCO_3$:

- Chemical purity: The percentage of $CaCO_3$ should be as high as possible and the percent of HCl insolubles as low as possible.
- Physical properties: degree of fineness, brightness, pH value, percent solids of the slurry, viscosity, and charge.

## Measuring Techniques

Chemical analysis can be carried out in many different ways; it's lab specific. Today, these methods are used to measure physical properties:

- Particle-size distribution: sedimentation analysis using the sedigraph 5100 (Micromeritics)
- Brightness (R-457):
  United States: Technadyne, et al.
  Europe: Elrepho 2000 (Datacolor)
- pH Value: Regular pH meter
- Percent Solids: Determination by drying
- Viscosity: Brookfield 100-rpm and high-shear methods.

# Economic and Market Factors

The producers of natural ground $CaCO_3$ have always tried to offer the paper industry a low-cost pigment. Today large production and logistical facilities are available world-wide to ensure a steady supply of product. There are also well equipped sales and technical service facilities in place to serve the customer. The complexity of this system leads automatically to different price structures in different countries and paper mills. Of all the pigments used, natural ground calcium carbonate has one of the most favorable price:performance ratios. Some of the reasons for this positive performance include: good dewatering and drying behavior for the ever-faster paper machines, excellent sizing ability (less sizing agent needed), good rheological behavior, low binder demand, and good optical and print qualities. When you look at total system cost, natural $CaCO_3$ is an attractive option.

In 1993, natural ground $CaCO_3$ had a market share of 23% (**Fig. 7-14**); it was less than one percent 25 years ago *(25)*. Commanding more than 40% of the business in Europe, $CaCO_3$ has the highest market share in that part of the world.

*Figure 7-14 Filler and Coating Pigment Consumption 1993—world-wide*

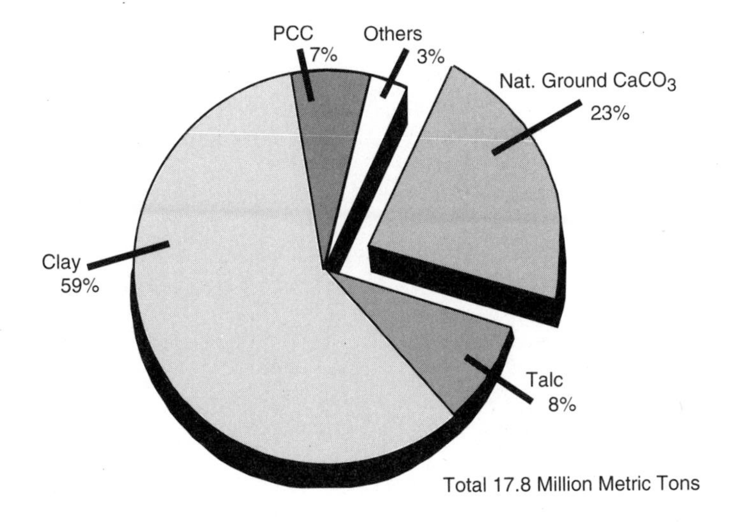


## Future Outlook

In the future, the paper and board industry will increasingly choose pigments according to the following criteria: availability, environmental considerations, applicability, economy, and quality. The environmental considerations will play a very important role. Natural ground calcium carbonate causes no problems physiologically and is available in vast amounts for a long time to come. The yields are high, and calcium carbonate has a naturally high brightness.

When a paper mill uses $CaCO_3$, it must change to neutral or slightly alkaline papermaking. Most wood-free paper mills in Europe (nearly 100%)— coated and uncoated — are running alkaline. In North America there are about 70% in that category.

This trend — to run neutral or slightly alkaline — will continue world-wide, especially as recycled paper, which contains carbonate more often than not, is used more.

It is expected that by the year 2005 the amount of natural ground carbonate consumed around the world will double to nearly eight million tons. That growth will include the different natural ground carbonates available today and newly developed GCC products designed to accommodate the specific and changing needs of the paper industry *(26)*.

# Literature Cited

1. Davidson, R.R., "The Future of Whiting in Paper Coatings", *Paper Tech.* 9(3):T60-T65(1968).
2. Delfosse, P., "Nature et Peinture-Origine, Differences et Proprietes des Differentes Carbonates de Calcium", Extrait de "Double Liaison" 152:24(April 1968).
3. Bosshard, A.W., "Die Entstehung der OMYA Füllstoffe", *OMYA Publication* 1976.
4. Geyssant, J., "Geologische Geschichte des Calciumcarbonats", Plüss-Staufer AG, 1993.
5. Strutz, M.D. and Sweeney, C.T.,"Natural Ground Calcium Carbonate", *TAPPI 1990 Neutral/Alkaline Papermaking Short Course Notes,* TAPPI PRESS, Atlanta, pp. 99-105.
6. Wener, C., "The Handling and Storage of OMYA Calcium Carbonate Slurries", *OMYA Publication,* 1989.
7. Huggenberger, L., "Calciumcarbonate-Einsatzmöglichkeiten und Grenzen (Calcium Carbonates-Scope of Application and Limitations)", Wochenbl. Fur Papierfabr. 102(10):pp. 353-362(1974).
8. Dennison, S.R.,"The Development of a Fine Natural Calcium Carbonate for Paper Coating", *TAPPI 1978 Coating Conference Proceedings,* TAPPI PRESS, Atlanta, pp. 95-103.
9. Price, C.R. and Hagemeyer, R.W., "Ultrafine Ground Calcium Carbonate for Use in Paper Coatings", *TAPPI 1978 Coating Conference Proceedings,* TAPPI PRESS, Atlanta, pp. 85-94.
10. Huggenberger, L., Kogler, W., and Arnold M., "The Future Role of Ground Calcium Carbonate in Paper Coating", *Tappi J.* 62(5):pp. 37-41(1979).
11. Huggenberger, L. and Arnold, M., "Pigments for paper Quality", *22nd PRIMA Annual Confernce Proceedings,* Internal PRIMA Report "Paper Europe", pp. 40-44(July 1991).
12. Bown, R., Drage, P.G., Golley, C.R.L., and Skuse, D.R.,"Neuerungen beim Einstaz von Calciumcarbonat im Strich (Calcium Carbonate Developmetns for Paper Coating)", *Proceedings of the 16th PTS-Caoting-Symposium,* Munich (1993), Deutscher Fachverlag GmbH, D-603236 Frankfurt am main, Germany, p. 7.
13. Huggenberger, L., Arnold, M., Laufmann, M., and Kogler, W., "Natural Ground Calcium Carbonate-An Essential Pigment for the Paper Industry", *Internal STFI-Report No. D 347,* Stockholm, Sweden, pp. 16-35.
14. McAuley, D., "Die mardtalge bei Streichpigmenten und Gestrichenen papieren (The Market Situation for Coating Pigments and Coated papers)", *Wochenbl. fur papierfabr.* 121(17):pp. 695-699(1993).
15. Huggenberger., L., Arnold, M., Kogler, W., and Laufmann, M., "Natural Ground Calcium Carbonate in LWC Papers", *TAPPI 1983 Coating Confernce Proceedings,* TAPPI PRESS, Atlanta, pp. 189-199.
16. Wintgen, M., "Board Coating with Natural Ground Clacium Carbonate in Europe:Technology Today", *Tappi J.* 70(5):pp.79-83(1987).
17. Huggenberger, L., and Niessner, G., "Mattgestrichene papiere (Matte Coated Papers)", *Wochenbl. fur papierfabr.* 100(23/24):pp. 878-888(1972).
18. Huggenberger, L., Arnold, M., and Kogler, W., "Gestrichene mattpapiere-Gegenwartiger Stand und Zukunft (Coated matte papers-State of the Art and Future), *Wochenbl. fur papierfabr.* 106 (11/12): pp. 453-458(1978).

19. Kogler, W., Spielmann, D., Huggenberger, L., "Kationische Streichgarben-Derzeitiger Stand und Ausblick", *Proceedings fo the 15th PTS-Coating-Symposium,* Munich (1991), Deutscher Fachverlag GmbH, D-60326 Frankfurt am main, Germany, pp. 61-66 and "Cationic Coating Colors-Present State and Outlook", *TAPPI 1992 Coating Conference Proceedings,* TAPPI PRESS, Atlanta, pp. 313-324.
20. Laufmann, M., and Rapp, H., "Pegmente und Kunststoffsieb-Arbrasion (Pigments and Synthetic Wire Abaraion)", *Wochenbl. fur papierfabr.,* 114(16):pp. 615-622(1986).
21. Laufmann, M., "Neutrale Holzhaltige Paperierherstellung 1896 (Neutral Wood-ContainingPapermaking 1986)", *Proceedings of the 7th PTS-Sysposium,* Munich (1986), on "Chemisch-Technologische Probleme der Papierherstellung", *Buntter-Staib Berlag, D-88400 Biberach,* Germany, pp. 15-23.
22. Laugmann, M., and Hummel, W., "Neutrale Holzhaltige papierherstellung 1990-Ubersicht, Störstoffewältigung, Umstellung (Neutral Groundwood-Containing Papermaking 1990-Overview, Mastering Anionic Trash, Conversion)", *Proceedings of the 9th PTS-Symposium,* Munich (1990), on "Chemische Technologie der paierherstellung", *Deutscher Fachverlag Gmbh, D-60326 Fankfurt am main,* Germany, pp. 111-126.
23. Goodwin, L., "Benefits of Cationic Ground Calcium Carbonate", *Tappi J.* 72(8):pp. 109-112(1989).
24. Laufmann, M., "Woodfree Alkaline Papermaking 1991", *1991 TECNICELPA Confernce Proceedings,* Vol. 1, pp. 147-173, TECNICELPA, Tomar, Portugal, 1991.
25. Strutz, M.D., "Sizing and Natural Ground Calcium Carbonate", *TAPPI 1992 Sizing Short Course Notes,* TAPPI PRESS, Atlanta, pp. 81-85.
26. Laufmann, M., Rapp, H., Huggenberger, L., and Naydowski, C., Hohe Opazitat und andere Wichtige Eigenschaften mit Natüralichem $CaCO_3$ (High Opacity and other Important Attrributes with Natural Ground $CaCO_3$)", *Proceedings of the 10th PTS-Symposium,* Munich (1992), on "Chemische Technologie der papierherstellung", *Deutscher Fachverlag GmbH, D-60326 Frankfurt am main,* Germany, pp. 59-67.

# 8.

# Titanium Dioxide

*Robert A. Kwoka*

## Product Description

### Principle Classes

Titanium dioxide pigments are finely divided, chemically inert white powders which possess a higher refractive index than any other commercially available pigment. These properties enable $TiO_2$ to provide brightness and opacity to paper, plastics, and paints at relatively low concentrations.

Commercial titanium dioxide pigments are available in two distinct crystal forms: anatase and rutile. The American Society for Testing and Materials (ASTM) has published specifications covering both anatase and rutile pigments *(1)*. Type I applies to anatase and specifies a minimum 95% titanium dioxide content. Types II, III, and IV apply to rutile. Type II specifies 92% minimum titanium dioxide content, while 80% minimum $TiO_2$ content is specified for types III and IV. The high $TiO_2$ content of Type I anatase and Type II rutile make them the most efficient pigments for most paper applications. The lower titanium dioxide contents of Type III and Type IV pigments result from oxide surface treatments applied to the pigment to enhance properties like durability and chalking resistance. These properties are usually not important to paper applications and therefore are not warranted for paper grades of $TiO_2$.

### Chemical and Physical Properties

As already mentioned, commercial titanium dioxide pigments are available in two distinct crystal forms, anatase and rutile, which are represented in **Fig. 8-1A**. High-resolution, scanning electron microscopy images of rutile and anatase pigments in **Fig. 8-1B** also show differences in particle shape. As one may expect from their differing crystal structures and particle shapes, anatase and rutile $TiO_2$ differ in properties that affect their performance in paper. The next several sections examine the differences between rutile, anatase, and other commonly used coating pigments and how these differences affect paper qualities.

*Figure 8-1A Molecular Model of $TiO_2$ Crystal Structures*

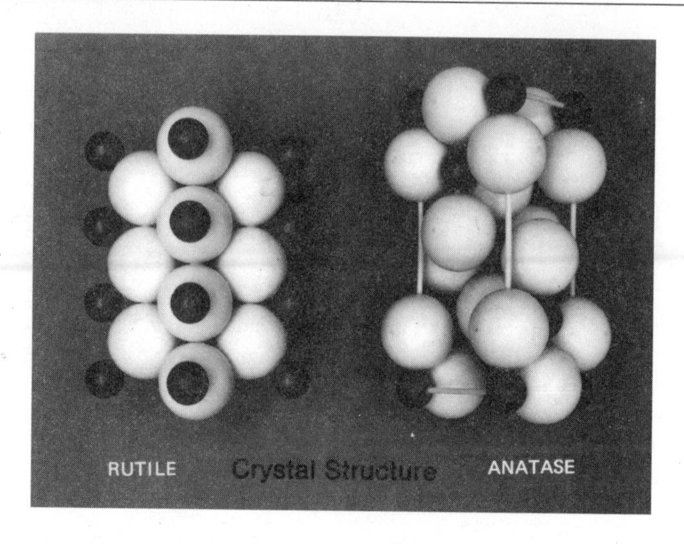


*Figure 8-1B Scanning Electron Microscope Image of $TiO_2$ Particles (250,000X)*

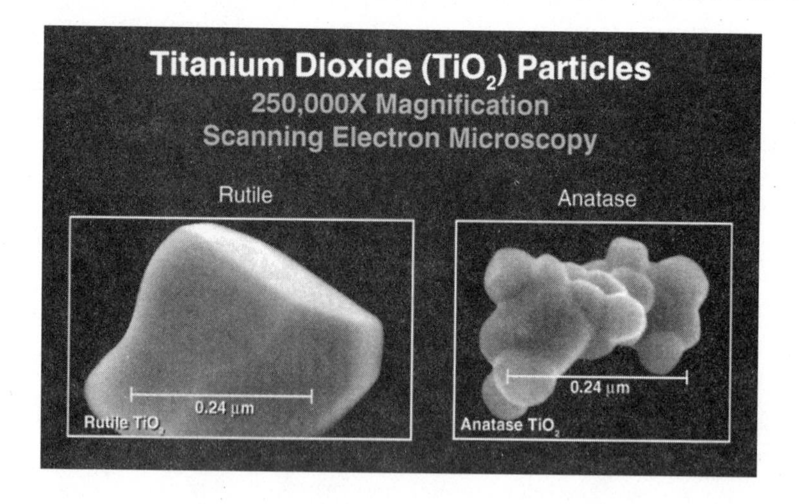


**Refractive Index.** The opacity and brightness of a sheet of paper are determined by its ability to scatter and absorb light. One mechanism of light scattering is refraction, the bending of light that occurs when light passes from a medium such as air to a particle such as pulp, clay, or $TiO_2$. The magnitude of light bending by refraction is proportional to the square of the difference in refractive indices of the medium and the particle. As the difference in refractive indices increases, more light is scattered by refraction, and higher opacity and brightness are achieved.

Titanium dioxide's high refractive index is what makes it so effective for scattering light, thereby imparting opacity and brightness to paper coatings. As shown in **Table 8-1** *(2, 3)*, rutile's 2.72 refractive index and anatase's 2.55 refractive index are well above those of other common paper coating pigments.

*Table 8-1 Paper Pigment Properties*

| Pigment | Refractive Index | Density, g/cc | Mohs Hardness | Surface Area, $m^2/g$ |
|---|---|---|---|---|
| Titanium Dioxide | | | | |
| Rutile | 2.72 | 3.8-4.2 | 6.0-6.5 | 7-30 |
| Anatase | 2.55 | 3.7-3.9 | 5.5-6.0 | 10-14 |
| Kaolin Clays | | | | |
| Coating | 1.57 | 2.6 | 1.5-2.0 | 8-16 |
| Delaminated | 1.57 | 2.6 | 1.5-2.0 | 11-15 |
| Calcium Carbonate | | | | |
| Natural Ground | 1.56 | 2.7 | 3.0 | 3-11 |
| PCC-Calcite | 1.66 | 2.9 | 3.0 | 5-25 |
| Extenders | | | | |
| Calcined Clay | 1.57 | 2.6 | ... | 18-19 |
| Alumina Trihydrate | 1.57 | 2.4 | 2.5-3.5 | 6-14 |
| Precipitated Amorphous Silica | 1.45 | 2.2 | ... | 60-300 |

**Particle Size.** Another mechanism of light scattering is diffraction: the bending of light that occurs as it passes by very small particles. Particle size and distribution are both important. If the particles are too large, there are fewer particles per unit weight and their influence on the light photon is slight. If the particles are too small, the light waves pass by the particles without being bent significantly, as would occur in a colloidal suspension or solution. For the most effective scattering of visible light, the particle diameters should be roughly 40% of the wavelength of the light to be scattered—or 0.16-0.28 μm *(4)*. Pigmentary titanium dioxide is manufactured to yield a median particle size in this range.

Titanium dioxide light-scattering efficiency is maximized by generating a narrow particle-size distribution near the optimum diameter *(5)*. The width of

$TiO_2$ particle-size distributions can be characterized by geometric standard deviation (GSD). GSD is calculated by:

$$GSD = (d84/d16)^{0.5}$$

where

d84 = diameter for 84% finer
d16 = diameter for 16% finer.

The minimum GSD of 1.0 is achieved only when all particles are the same size. **Figure 8-2** shows the correlation between rutile light-scattering efficiency in a typical paper coating formulation and particle-size GSD. Particle-size measurements were made using laser light-scattering technology. Light scattering coefficients were determined by applying paper coatings to Mylar® base at precise coat weights and measuring reflectance and transmittance. The data clearly show the benefits for commercial pigments with a narrow size distribution (low GSD).

*Figure 8-2 $TiO_2$ Particle-Size Distribution Effect on Light Scattering*

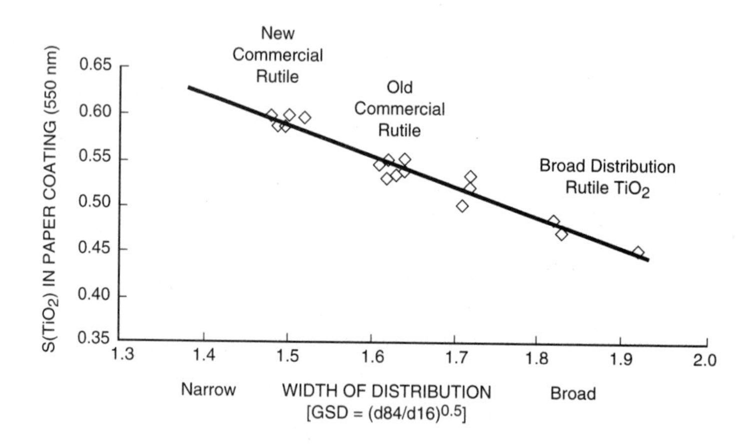


**Reflectance.** The reflectance characteristics of a coating pigment are important in that they dictate the brightness and color of the pigment. **Figures 8-3A-C** *(6)* show the reflectance curves of $TiO_2$ and other coating pigments. Figure 8-3A shows the very high reflectance of $TiO_2$ in the visible region, which characterizes its very high pigment brightness.

*Figure 8-3A $TiO_2$ Reflectance Curves*

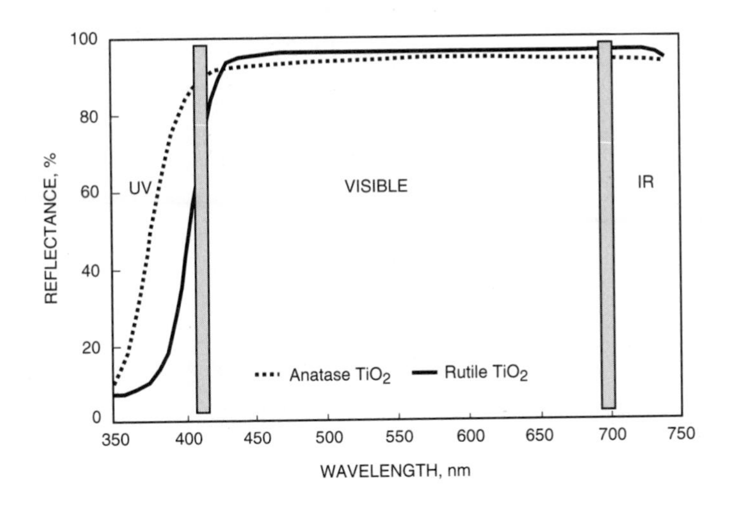


*Figure 8-3B Kaolin Clay and $CaCO_3$ Reflectance Curves*

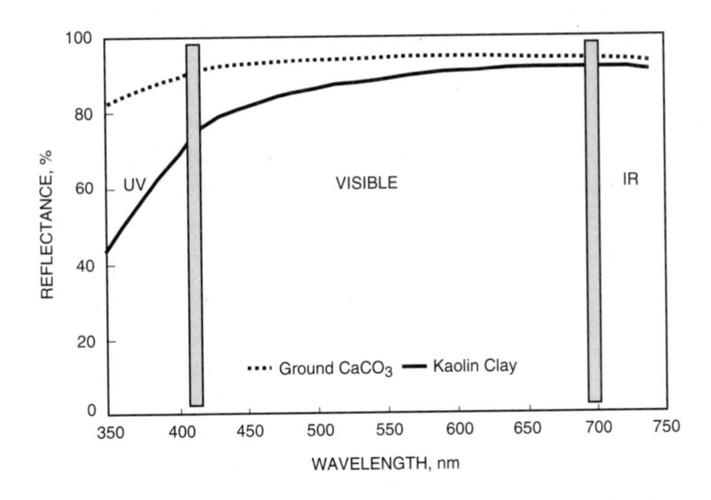

*Figure 8-3C Extender Pigment Reflectance Curves*

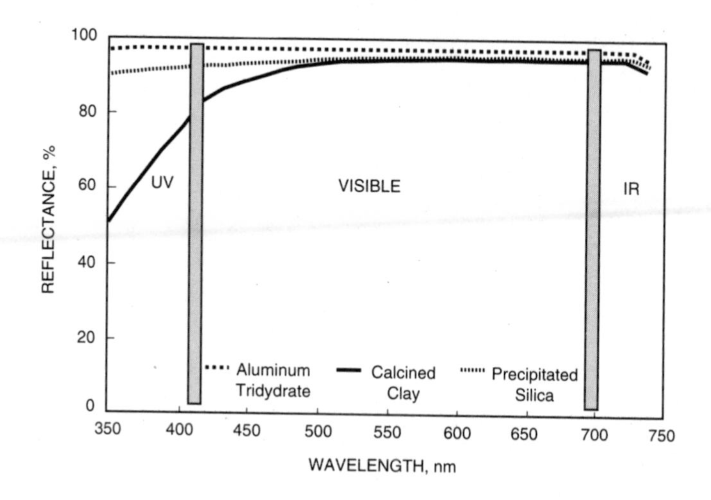


**Other Physical Properties.** Though few direct correlations have been shown, it is reasonable to expect that pigment properties like particle density, surface area, and hardness will affect a pigment's performance in the papermaking and coating process, as well as the final paper properties. For example, particle density and size will affect hydrodynamic tendencies, which may impact retention. Surface area will affect the number of light-scattering sites, thereby impacting optical performance. Surface area will likely impact sizing demand in the wet end and binder demand in the coating. Particle size, shape, hardness, and concentration will also affect a pigment's abrasion tendencies.

Table 8-1 compares particle density, hardness, and surface area of rutile, anatase, and other common papermaking pigments. As expected from the dense packing array of rutile represented in Fig. 8-1A, its particle density and hardness are higher than that of anatase. The wide range of $TiO_2$ surface areas results from differences in particle-size distributions and oxide surface treatments.

## Method of Manufacture

The primary raw material for producing pigmentary titanium dioxide is a titanium-bearing ore. The commonly used ores are rutile, a 90% $TiO_2$ composition contaminated with small amounts of iron and other metal oxides, and ilmenite, a 40-60% $TiO_2$ composition. Titanium ore sources are located worldwide, with mineral rutile usually found in beach sand deposits and ilmenite occurring in either beach sand or rock deposits.

For practical purposes, anatase and rutile produced for the paper industry are manufactured by different chemical processes. Anatase is the dominant product of the older sulfate process, but rutile is also produced by this route. Only rutile is currently produced by the newer chloride process.

**Sulfate Process.** The sulfate process is outlined in **Fig. 8-4**. In this process, finely ground ore concentrate is reacted with sulfuric acid to obtain a reaction mass consisting of soluble iron and titanium sulfates. After unreacted ore and insolubles are removed by clarification and filtration, the solution is concentrated by evaporation and cooled to crystallize the iron and other metals as sulfates, which are separated and discarded.

The remaining solution is heated and seeded to hydrolyze the titanium and precipitate it as amorphous hydrous titanium dioxide. If rutile is the desired end product, the solution prior to hydrolysis must be nucleated with rutile crystallites to obtain a hydrolysis product suitable for conversion to rutile crystals. The slurry is then filtered and washed to recover and purify the hydrous titanium dioxide.

The hydrous titanium dioxide is then calcined in rotary kilns under conditions to crystallize and grow the pigmentary titanium dioxide crystals to the desired 0.25-μm particle size. The particle-size distribution achieved by the sulfate process is typically wider than that of the chloride process *(3)*.

*Figure 8-4 Sulfate $TiO_2$ Manufacturing Process*

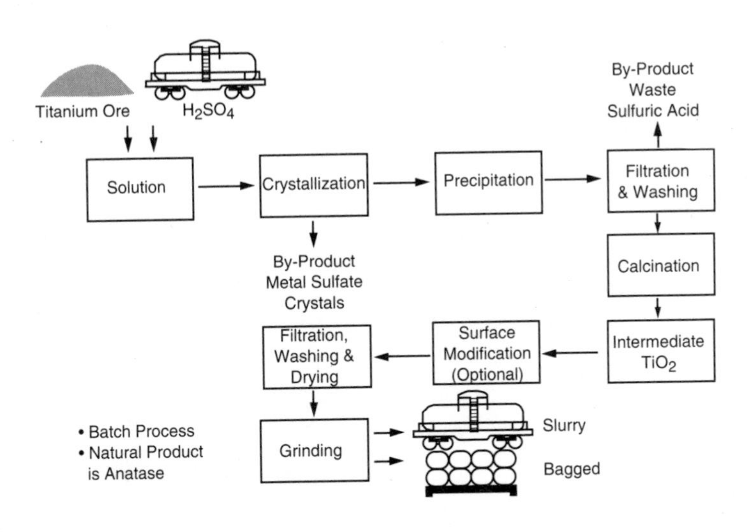


**Chloride Process.** In the chloride process shown in **Fig. 8-5**, titanium ore concentrate is reacted with gaseous chlorine at high temperature in the presence of carbon to produce anhydrous titanium tetrachloride, iron chlorides, and chlorides of other metals in the ore. The gaseous products are then cooled to effect the primary separation of titanium tetrachloride from the high-boiling iron chlorides. The crude liquid titanium tetrachloride is then fractionally distilled to remove low and close boiling components.

*Figure 8-5 Chloride $TiO_2$ Manufacturing Process*

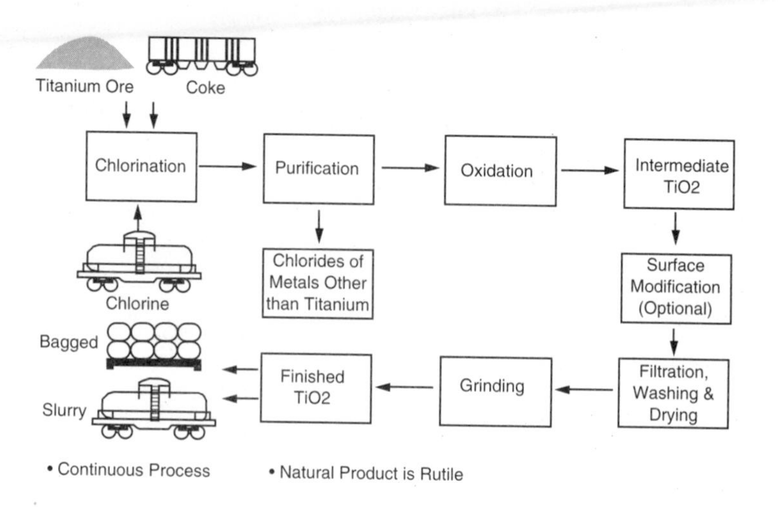


The purified titanium tetrachloride is vaporized and reacted with preheated air or oxygen to form titanium dioxide crystals and chlorine. After the product stream is cooled, the solid titanium dioxide is separated from the gaseous chlorine, which is recycled to the chlorination step.

**Surface Treatment and Finishing.** After production of the crude titanium dioxide product by either the sulfate or chloride processes, the pigment can be surface treated to enhance properties that may be important to a particular application. The variety of surface treatments available, combined with some particle-size variation, account for the wide range of $TiO_2$ grades available in the market.

The surface treatments consist of an inorganic coating, typically alumina or silica, which is deposited from a solution. The hydrated oxides are precipitated onto the $TiO_2$ pigment surface by varying the pH. This pigment coating process is carried out under carefully controlled conditions to achieve just the right amount and type of coating to obtain the desired pigment performance *(7)*.

Some Type II rutile pigments have a small amount of alumina surface treatment to enhance water dispersibility. Type III and IV pigments are surface treated with substantial amounts of alumina and silica. These surface treatments are applied to achieve properties like durability, chalking resistance, and photostability in paints. These properties have little or no value in paper applications, so the added cost of these highly surface treated pigments is usually not justified.

After surface treatment, the pigments are filtered, washed, and dried. The final steps in $TiO_2$ processing, whether surface treated or not, involve some form of mechanical grinding to break up agglomerated particles. The ground $TiO_2$ can be packed for delivery as a dry pigment or dispersed in water and delivered as a slurry.

## Handling, Transporting, Storing, Mixing, and Dispersing

By far, most of the $TiO_2$ used in paper mills today is delivered as a high-solids (70+%) slurry. Substantial improvements in slurry technology over the past 15 years have made $TiO_2$ slurry delivery extremely reliable and economical. Slurry delivery eases transloading, allows controllable feed to the paper machine or coater, and improves housekeeping by eliminating dust. In addition, the $TiO_2$ efficiency is usually enhanced because proper dispersion, required for good $TiO_2$ efficiency, is provided by the supplier.

Most commercial $TiO_2$ slurries used in the paper industry today have low-shear Brookfield viscosities less than 1000 cP (at 100 rpm). While high-solids $TiO_2$ slurries can be dilatant (shear thickening) at higher shear rates, they are Newtonian at shear rates typically realized in pumps and agitated storage tanks. Therefore, today's $TiO_2$ slurries are very easy to unload, store, and distribute around the mill. In addition, at levels typically used in coating colors, $TiO_2$ slurries do not negatively affect coating high-shear rheology.

$TiO_2$ slurries are delivered by tank truck or rail car depending on the paper mill's consumption rate and storage capabilities. Tank trucks and rail cars can be unloaded by pumping or, if the storage tank is not too much higher than the unloading spot, by carefully pressurizing the car or tanker with air and "blow casing" the slurry into the storage tank.

Proper storage tank design and operation is key to maintaining good slurry properties. The agitator must be designed so that the whole tank is agitated and there are no "dead zones" in the tank where the slurry can stagnate. A properly designed agitator need only run a few minutes every few hours to maintain dispersion and prevent settling. It is also recommended that a humidification system such as a fog nozzle be installed in the storage tank. Keeping the tank air space humidified will minimize the amount of $TiO_2$ that dries on the storage tank walls. This wall scale can flake off, resulting in undesired grit. However, the humidification system should only be operated a few minutes every hour to minimize the amount of water added to the storage tank to prevent significant slurry dilution. Finally, periodically emptying and cleaning the storage tank will prevent microbial buildup in the tank, which left unchecked could begin to degrade slurry properties.

With the continued growth of alkaline papermaking and increased use of calcium carbonate, it is appropriate to discuss the compatibility of $TiO_2$ and $CaCO_3$ slurries. Some $TiO_2$ slurries may have an interaction with $CaCO_3$ slurries, which cause particle flocculation and slurry thickening. The most notable consequences of this interaction have occured when $CaCO_3$ slurry has been mistakenly added to concentrated (>70% solids) $TiO_2$ slurries, resulting in severe slurry thickening. It is suspected that the Ca++ ions present in a $CaCO_3$ slurry may impair dispersant on the surface of $TiO_2$, which causes $TiO_2$ flocculation.

Dry $TiO_2$ is typically delivered to paper mills in 50-lb or 25-kg bags. If these bags are repulpable, they can be thrown whole into a repulper or blend chest. However, for coating applications and improved efficiency in the wet end, the $TiO_2$ should be dispersed in water to wet out and deagglomerate the $TiO_2$ particles to obtain maximum optical performance. $TiO_2$ can either be dispersed alone or co-dispersed with another non-calcium containing pigment.

One consideration in preparing $TiO_2$ aqueous dispersions is the dispersant demand of the particular pigment grade. $TiO_2$ suppliers provide information which will guide the papermaker in selecting the most suitable dispersants to accommodate the end use. **Figure 8-6** *(3)* shows the differences in dispersant demand of different $TiO_2$ grades designated by their ASTM classifications. These curves were developed using distilled water; some increase in dispersant level would be required with water having higher hardness, but the curves would look very similar.

*Figure 8-6 $TiO_2$ Dispersant Demand Curves*

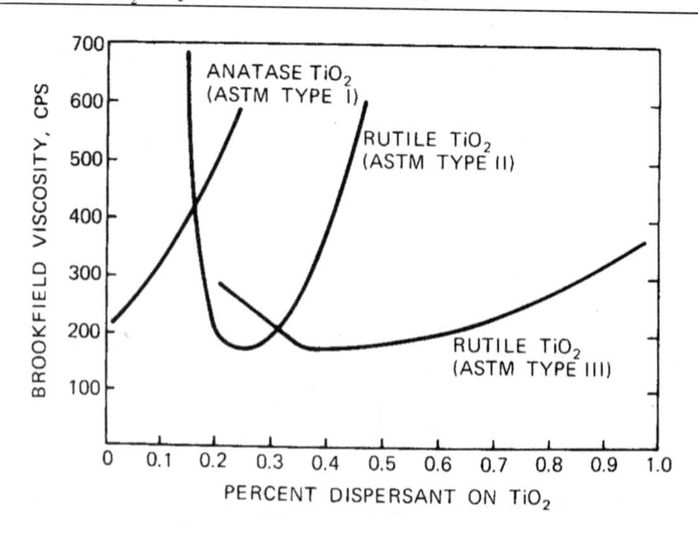

All known types of dispersion equipment are used successfully to prepare $TiO_2$ dispersions. The optimum deagglomeration of $TiO_2$ pigments results when the pigment dispersant demand is satisfied and the dispersion is prepared at a high solids level. Generally, dispersion solids levels of 60% to 70% yield slurries with the lowest level of undispersed agglomerates.

# Reasons for Use

## Paper Coatings

**Typical Formulations.** Titanium dioxide is used in paper coatings to increase coated sheet opacity while maintaining or even increasing brightness. The amount of $TiO_2$ used in the coating depends on the opacity development required. In higher basis-weight coated papers, where the thicker basestock and higher coat weight provide sufficient opacity, no $TiO_2$ is used. In light- to medium-weight coated papers, four to eight parts $TiO_2$ in the coating are typical. In ultra-lightweight coated papers, the coating may contain up to 15 parts $TiO_2$ to achieve the desired opacity in the very thin sheet.

In paperboard coatings, $TiO_2$ is used to opacify the coating so that the coating hides a lower-brightness basestock. The amount of $TiO_2$ used in the coating depends on the brightness of the basestock to be hidden, the coat weight applied, and the degree of hiding desired. Paperboard-coating $TiO_2$ concentrations can range from 15 parts to 40 parts of the total coating pigment. It is usually more economical to increase coating $TiO_2$ concentration for increased hiding rather than increase coat weight *(4)*.

It was previously mentioned that Type I and Type II are usually most effective in paper applications because they have the highest $TiO_2$ content. An exception could be a paperboard coating that contains a high concentration of $TiO_2$, say, greater than 25 parts. In some cases, a Type III rutile grade designed for flat paints, which contains a fluffy silica coating around the $TiO_2$ particle, may provide superior optical performance versus an untreated paper grade. At high $TiO_2$ concentrations, where $TiO_2$ normally loses some light-scattering efficiency because the particles are not adequately spaced, the fluffy silica coating acts as a particle spacer to maintain high $TiO_2$ efficiency *(8)*. The trade-off is that the silica treatment comprises about 15% by weight of the product. Unless the spacing enhances the $TiO_2$ light scattering by more than 15%, the silica treatment does not balance the weight loss of molecular $TiO_2$. The conditions under which the silica-treated grade outperforms an untreated grade are very dependent on the coating system and very hard to predict.

**Optical Properties.** *Opacity.* Earlier, the high refractive index of $TiO_2$ was described as a key property for imparting opacity to a coated paper. The importance of pigment refractive index on the opacifying ability of a pigment is demonstrated in **Figs. 8-7 and 8-8**. Figure 8-7 *(9)* shows the opacity development of a coated one-side (C1S), lightweight coated (LWC) sheet as concentrations of $TiO_2$, calcined clay, alumina trihydrate (ATH), and precipitated amorphous silica (PAS) in the coating are increased. Even though the calcined clay, ATH, and PAS vary in particle size and shape, they all have a refractive index of 1.5-1.6. They therefore do not increase coated sheet opacity to the same extent as rutile $TiO_2$, which has a 2.72 refractive index.

*Figure 8-7 Coating Pigment Effect on Coated Paper Opacity*

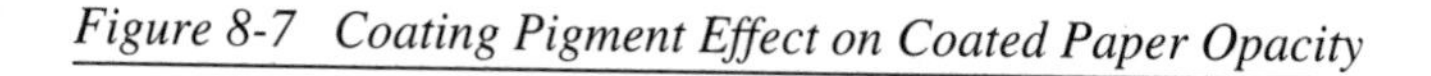

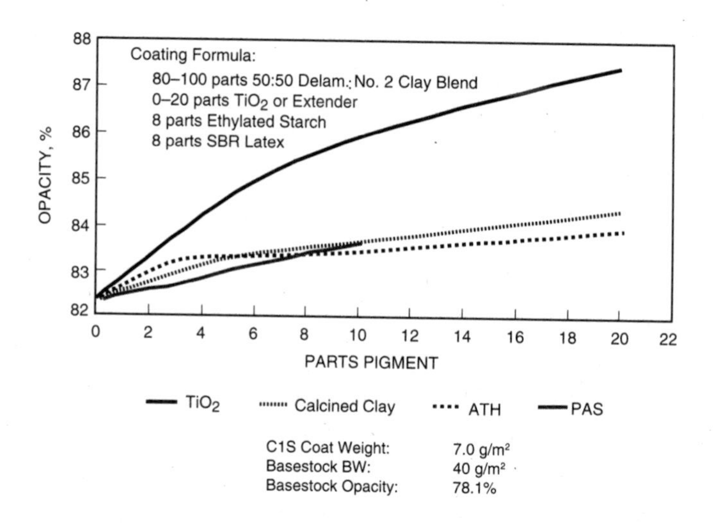


Even the difference between the refractive index of rutile (2.72) and anatase (2.55) has a significant impact on the opacifying ability of the pigment, as shown in Fig. 8-8. Figure 8-8 *(9)* shows the opacity development of a C1S freesheet with increasing concentrations of rutile and anatase in the coating. Clearly, rutile has an opacifying advantage, which typically results in 10-15% less rutile required to achieve equal opacity.

*Figure 8-8 Rutile vs. Anatase $TiO_2$ Coated Paper Opacity*

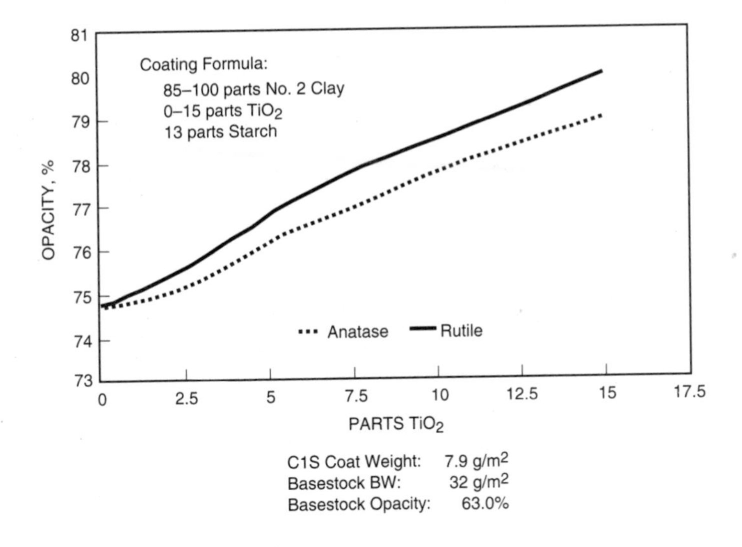


*Brightness.* High pigment brightness and reflectance are necessary but not sufficient to increase coated sheet brightness. **Figure 8-9** *(9)* shows the brightness development of a C1S LWC sheet with increasing $TiO_2$, calcined clay, ATH, and PAS concentrations in the coating. Figure 8-8 shows that the pigment reflectances of ATH and PAS are at least as high as that of $TiO_2$. However, $TiO_2$ still has a paper brightening advantage due to its higher refractive index.

*Figure 8-9 Coating Pigment Effect on Coated Paper Brightness*

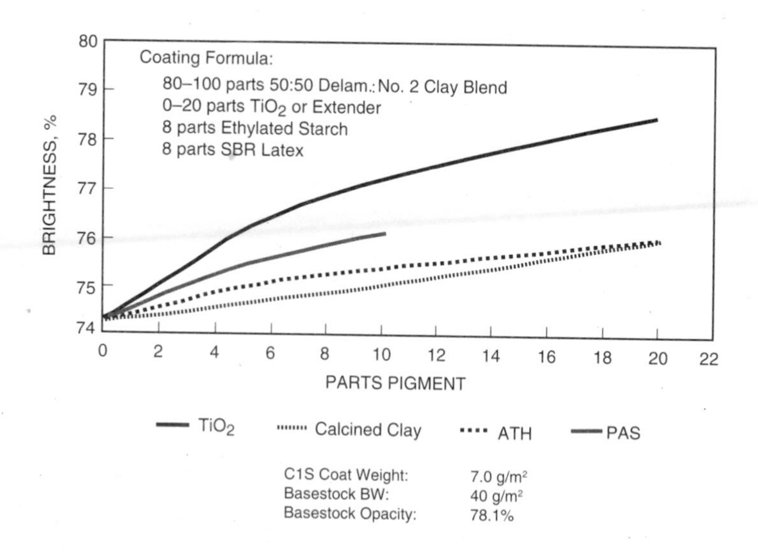


To ensure good $TiO_2$ optical efficiency in coatings, the $TiO_2$ must be properly dispersed into the coating. When $TiO_2$ particles are in close proximity, as would occur in an undispersed aggregate or agglomerate, the $TiO_2$ optical efficiency is diminished. If $TiO_2$ slurry from the supplier is used, the supplier has already imparted sufficient dispersion energy to deagglomerate the particles and has added dispersants to stabilize the dispersion. In this case, simply mixing the $TiO_2$ slurry into the paper coating is usually adequate to ensure good $TiO_2$ efficiency. However, if dry $TiO_2$ is used, it must first be dispersed alone or in combination with other coating pigments at high solids in a high-energy disperser.

**FWA Interaction.** Figure 8-1A shows a significant decrease in reflectance, or increase in absorbance, for titanium dioxide, especially rutile, in the near ultra-violet (UV) region. This may pose problems when fluorescent whitening agents (FWAs) or "optical brighteners" are used to enhance sheet brightness. FWAs function by absorbing near UV light energy at 350-400 nm and re-emitting that light energy in the visible blue region. This enhances the apparent brightness and whiteness of the sheet. When titanium dioxide, particularly rutile, is present, it absorbs some of the incident UV radiation, thereby lowering FWA efficiency.

**Table 8-2** shows the impact on coated freesheet fluorescence (FWA brightness contribution) and shade when 10 parts of rutile and 10 parts anatase $TiO_2$ are incorporated into coating containing a relatively high loading of three parts FWA. The drop in fluorescence and the shift to less red (lower a*) and more yellow (higher b*) shade are consistent with $TiO_2$'s FWA "quenching" effect.

*Table 8-2 Coating $TiO_2$-FWA Interaction*

| Coating | Fluorescence | a* | b* |
|---|---|---|---|
| No $TiO_2$ | 4.1 | 0.63 | 1.78 |
| 10 parts Anatase | 3.3 | 0.52 | 1.81 |
| 10 parts Rutile | 2.0 | 0.19 | 2.65 |

* Data regressed to 24 g/m² C2S coat weight.

*Coating Formula:*

- 60 parts No. 1 Hi-Brite Clay
- 30 parts Fine Ground $CaCO_3$
- 10 parts $TiO_2$
- 10 parts SBR Latex
- 3 parts Ethylated Starch
- 1 part Polyvinyl Alcohol
- 3 parts (wet basis) FWA.

*Basestock:*

- 74.3 g/m² Basis Weight
- 4.6% $CaCO_3$
- No $TiO_2$, No FWA.

To minimize this quenching effect, segregating the $TiO_2$ and FWA, e.g., concentrating the FWA in the coating while concentrating the $TiO_2$ in the basesheet, is recommended. If high levels of $TiO_2$ and FWA are needed in the coating, anatase should be used to minimize the FWA quenching as shown in Table 8-2. Rutile could still be used in the basesheet to take advantage of its superior light scattering and opacifying ability.

**Print Properties.** Titanium dioxide has a high particle density (3.7-4.2 g/cc), which means that when it is incorporated into the coating at moderate levels, its volume is relatively much smaller than the other components. For example, in a typical paper coating containing 10 parts $TiO_2$, the $TiO_2$ only accounts for about 5% of the total pigment and binder volume. When the dried coating voids are considered, the volume impact of $TiO_2$ is smaller still. This low volume of $TiO_2$ combined with its relatively small particle size suggests that, at normal paper coating loadings, $TiO_2$ will have very little impact on the surface, strength, and print properties of the coating.

**Figure 8-10** shows the impact of increasing LWC coating $TiO_2$ concentration on sheet gloss and print gloss. This graph shows that increasing $TiO_2$ content has no significant effect on either sheet gloss or print gloss.

*Figure 8-10 $TiO_2$ Effect on LWC Paper and Print Gloss*

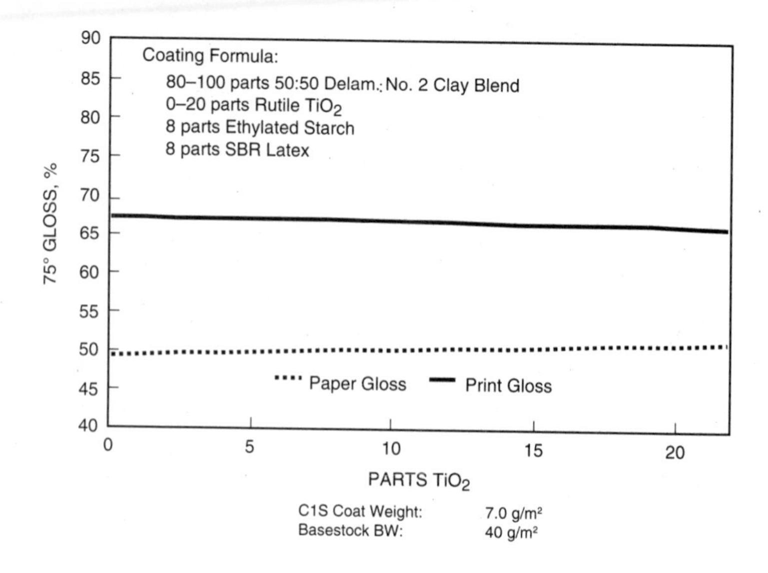


**Coating Rheology and Runnability.** The spherical shape, relatively small particle size, and low specific volume of $TiO_2$ minimizes its impact on paper coating rheology. **Figure 8-11** *(9)* shows that increasing rutile $TiO_2$ content in a LWC coating has very little effect on its high-shear viscosity. The result is that titanium dioxide has relatively little impact on coater runnability.

*Figure 8-11 $TiO_2$ Effect on Paper Coating Rheology*

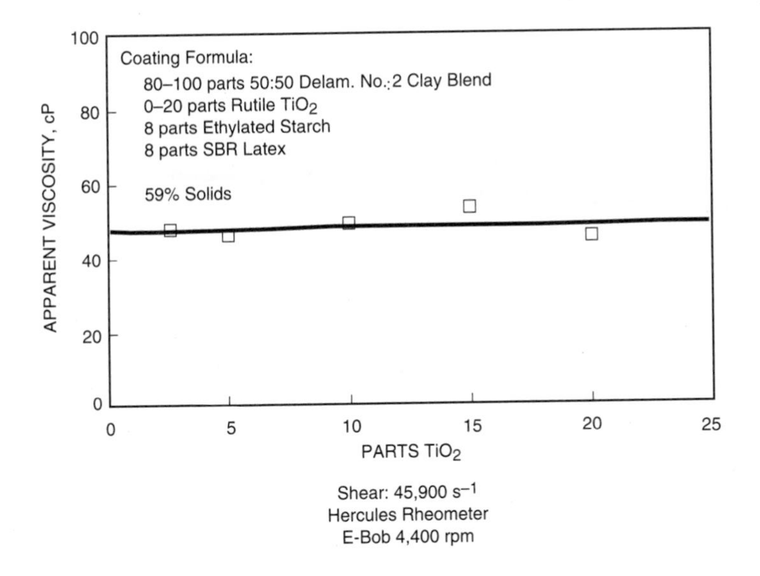


**$TiO_2$ Extenders.** Pigments like calcined clay, alumina trihydrate, and precipitated amorphous silica are sometimes referred to as "$TiO_2$ extenders" because they effectively increase sheet brightness and opacity, thereby reducing the amount of $TiO_2$ required to achieve optical targets. However, these extender pigments do not enhance $TiO_2$ performance, and there is no synergy between extenders and $TiO_2$ *(9)*.

While extenders are effective, they are not "one-for-one" $TiO_2$ substitutes, and multiple parts of an extender are required to replace one part of $TiO_2$. Extenders are usually bulky pigments which enhance opacity and brightness by introducing pigment-air interfaces into the coating. This results in a more porous and somewhat weaker coating structure. The amount of extender that can be incorporated (and the amount of $TiO_2$ replaced) is typically limited by coating rheology or dried coating strength and printability concerns.

## Paper Filling

**Furnish Formulations.** Most commodity papers do not require any titanium dioxide to be added as a filler pigment because the desired opacity and brightness are achieved with the pulp and other less expensive fillers like calcium carbonate and clay. However, high-opacity premium papers like lightweight opaque offsets, envelope stock, and bible papers usually require some $TiO_2$ addition to achieve optical targets. Opaque offsets and envelope grades may contain up to about 8% $TiO_2$ in combination with other pigments, and lightweight bible papers may contain up to 15% $TiO_2$ as the sole pigment added to the furnish. At these higher $TiO_2$ loadings, abrasion is more of a concern and should be considered when selecting a $TiO_2$ grade. Anatase grades are generally less abrasive than rutile grades.

**Optical Properties.** Again, the value of $TiO_2$ in these applications is its ability to substantially increase sheet opacity at relatively low concentrations due to its high refractive index. The importance of refractive index on opacifying ability is demonstrated in **Fig. 8-12** *(6)*. The unfilled sheet opacity is due to the difference in refractive indices of air (R.I. = 1.0) and pulp fibers (R.I. = 1.53). Adding filler clay (R.I. = 1.57) does little to change the difference in refractive indices; therefore its affect on light scattering and opacity is slight. Adding anatase titanium dioxide (R.I. = 2.55) significantly increases the refractive index differences within the sheet causing substantial opacity increases.

*Figure 8-12 $TiO_2$ vs. Clay Uncoated Paper Opacity*

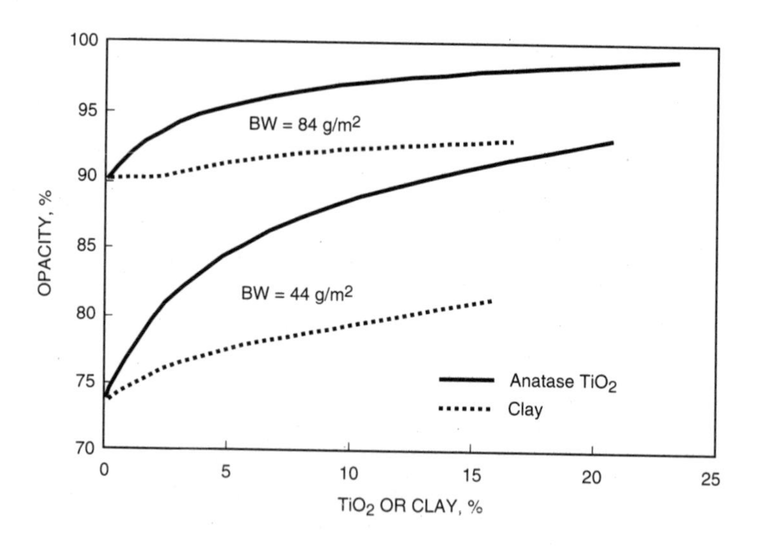


**Figure 8-13** *(5)* shows the effect of the difference of refractive index between rutile and anatase on their opacifying power. Because of its higher refractive index, rutile provides higher light-scattering ability and therefore better opacity development than anatase. Though these differences appear slight, the difference in the amount of $TiO_2$ required to achieve a given opacity is represented by the horizontal separation of the lines. Typically, a given opacity can be achieved with 10-15% less rutile $TiO_2$ than with anatase.

*Figure 8-13 Rutile vs. Anatase $TiO_2$ Uncoated Paper Opacity*

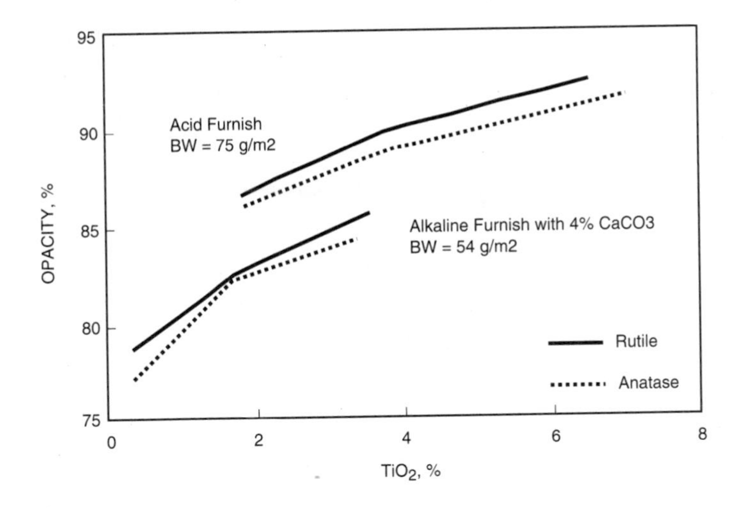


**Retention.** To achieve optimum efficiency from titanium dioxide added as a filler, it must be retained in the sheet, and the individual $TiO_2$ particles should be well dispersed. Maximum $TiO_2$ optical efficiency is achieved with individual, well spaced $TiO_2$ particles. Unfortunately, the goals of maximum retention and maximum particle dispersion are somewhat mutually exclusive. Because the $TiO_2$ particles are so small, they will not be retained by any filtration mechanism. Also, anionically dispersed $TiO_2$ particles will not self-adhere to the anionic pulp fibers. Therefore, $TiO_2$ must be retained by some retention aid-induced flocculation mechanism, which can be detrimental to pigment dispersion and optical efficiency *(11, 12)*.

This indicates that there will be some optimum level of first-pass retention, as indicated by the generalized behavior in **Fig. 8-14** *(3)*. As retention-aid dosage increases, first-pass $TiO_2$ retention increases quickly at first and then at a much slower rate. However, sheet opacity, which initially increases rapidly due to increased retention, levels off or may even decrease slightly due to over-flocculation and hence lower $TiO_2$ efficiency.

*Figure 8-14 Retention Aid Effect on $TiO_2$ Performance*

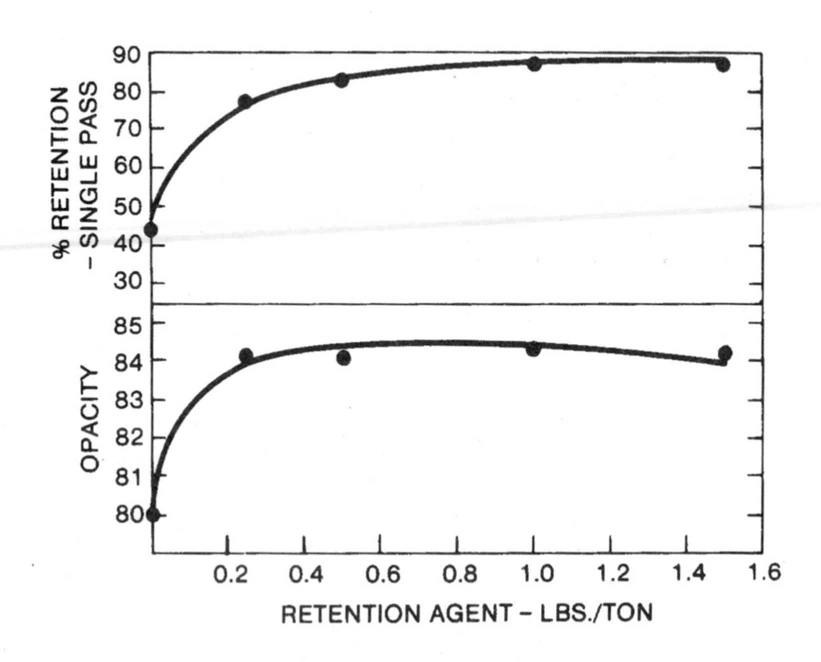


Using a predispersed $TiO_2$ slurry will ensure that the $TiO_2$ is at least initially well dispersed and will provide higher $TiO_2$ optical efficiency than adding dry $TiO_2$ to a pulp furnish. This was demonstrated in a lab handsheet study which compared the optical performance of dry $TiO_2$ and slurry $TiO_2$ addition to the furnish. **Figures 8-15 and 8-16** *(13)* show better opacity and brightness development using $TiO_2$ predispersed at 70% solids to deagglomerate the particles versus adding dry $TiO_2$ directly to the furnish.

*Figure 8-15 Slurry vs. Dry $TiO_2$ Handsheet Opacity*

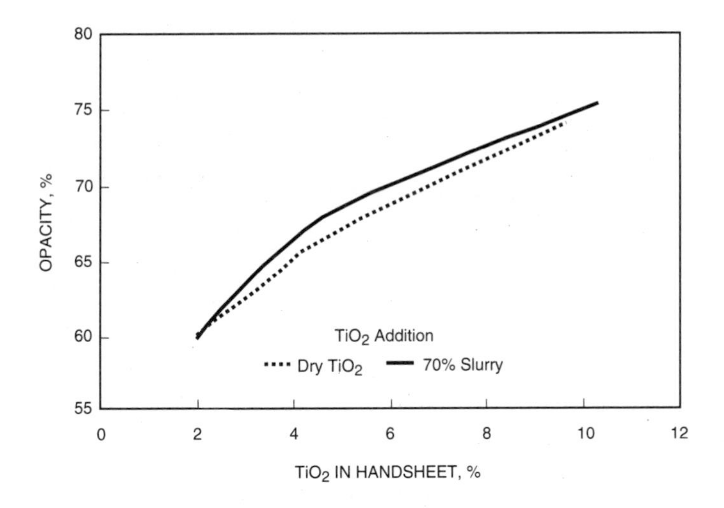


*Figure 8-16 Slurry vs. Dry $TiO_2$ Handsheet Brightness*

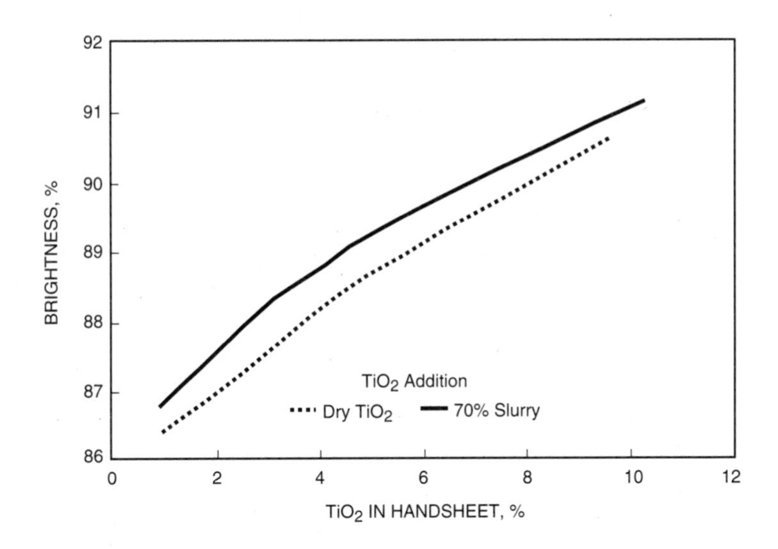


**Strength Properties.** It is obvious that fillers reduce paper strength. If fibrous material having definite fiber strength and cohesive properties is replaced with an equal weight of mineral particles having no inherent strength, the sheet strength will decrease. The strength loss is generally proportional to filler content *(11, 14)*. At equal mineral content, $TiO_2$ causes about the same degree of strength loss as other filler pigments. However, since lower concentrations of $TiO_2$ are required to achieve desired levels of opacity and brightness, the effect of $TiO_2$ on strength is less than that of other filler pigments at equal opacity.

Handsheet studies showed that $TiO_2$ concentrations less than three percent caused no appreciable loss in burst, tear, and tensile strengths *(15)*. Higher concentrations resulted in the expected strength loss. The same conclusions were reached based on testing of semicommercial paper *(16)*.

**Printability.** Titanium dioxide not only increases sheet opacity, it very effectively reduces show-through, as shown by the data in **Table 8-3** *(3)*. Two 55-lb papers, one containing 5% $TiO_2$ and the other containing 15% kaolin clay, were printed on one side with black ink using a Vandercook proof press. The degree of show-through is indicated by taking the ratio of reverse-side reflectivity of the printed sample to the reflectivity of the unprinted sample. If there were absolutely no show-through, this ratio would be 1.0. Table 8-3 shows that the sheet containing 5% $TiO_2$ has higher opacity and a higher show-through ratio than the sheet containing 15% clay. The improvement in show-through ratio is greater than the improvement in opacity.

*Table 8-3 Impact of $TiO_2$ on Print Show-Through*

| | 15% Clay | 5% $TiO_2$ |
|---|---|---|
| Opacity | 91.4 | 93.9 |
| Reflectivity: Reverse side of black print | 66.6 | 72.0 |
| Reflectivity: Unprinted paper | 78.8 | 81.6 |
| Show-through Ratio | 0.845 | 0.882 |

## $TiO_2$ Distribution Between Coated Paper Base Sheet and Coating

A key to using $TiO_2$ effectively in coated paper is to optimize its distribution between the base sheet and coating. The results of a pilot paper machine and laboratory coater study simulating coated wood-free paper production showed that, overall, $TiO_2$ use can be reduced by splitting $TiO_2$ addition between the base sheet and coating *(17)*. Basesheet $TiO_2$ develops coated sheet opacity more effectively than coating $TiO_2$ when the base-sheet $TiO_2$ concentration is low or the coating $TiO_2$ is high. Brightness, whiteness, and shade are affected more by changes in coating $TiO_2$ content than by base-sheet $TiO_2$ concentration.

The benefits of splitting $TiO_2$ between the base sheet and coating versus concentrating it all in the coating were also demonstrated on a coated groundwood paper machine where $TiO_2$ use was reduced 23% by implementing $TiO_2$ addition with on-line opacity control *(17)*.

## Other Uses in Papermaking

**$TiO_2$ as a UV-Light Barrier to Control Photo-Yellowing.** Fine papers traditionally have been produced using fully bleached chemical pulps. It is now possible to produce papers containing high-brightness, high-yield pulps that blur the conventional distinction between wood-free and groundwood grades. Pulps such as hardwood chemithermomechanical pulp (CTMP) are equivalent to hardwood kraft pulps in most properties, but their application in fine papers has been limited by susceptibility to photo-yellowing (loss of brightness when exposed to ultraviolet light).

Figure 8-1A shows that $TiO_2$, particularly the rutile crystal form, is a strong absorber in the near-UV wavelengths (300-400 nm) that cause photo-yellowing. Therefore, use of rutile $TiO_2$ in surface treatments or in coatings can improve brightness stability by shielding the base sheet from the yellowing effects of UV light. Examples are shown in **Fig. 8-17** *(18)*.

*Figure 8-17 $TiO_2$ to Control Photo-Yellowing*

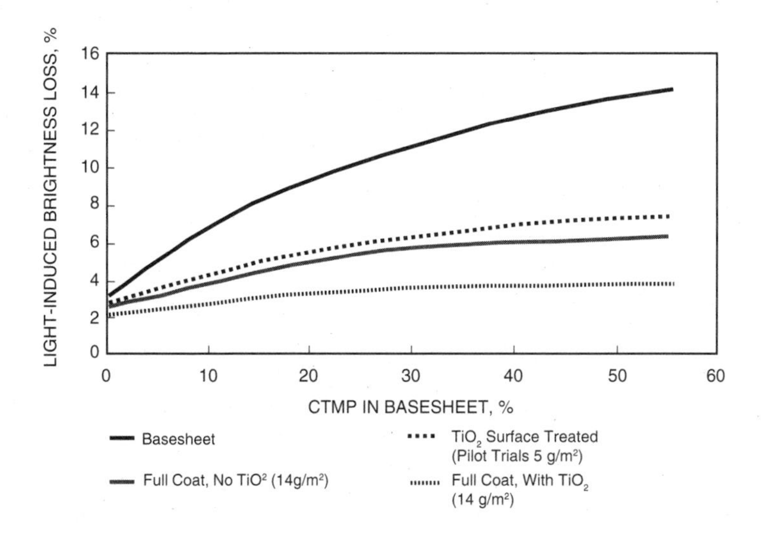


For uncoated grades, brightness reversion can be reduced by more than 50% by applying a thin surface treatment containing $TiO_2$. Cost efficiency peaked with a blend of 10% $TiO_2$ and 90% clay or $CaCO_3$. Suitable application devices demonstrated in pilot trials were a hydrophilic-transfer-roll coater, a Billblade/metering roll combination, and a gate-roll size press. Surface treatment to improve brightness stability further supports the developing trend toward pigmented surface treatments to improve smoothness, opacity, porosity, pick resistance, and printability *(19)*.

For coated grades, incorporation of $TiO_2$ enhances the UV barrier properties of clay or $CaCO_3$ coatings. With 50% CTMP in the base sheet, brightness stability equivalent to wood-free papers can be achieved when $TiO_2$ is used in the coating.

**$TiO_2$ for Decorative Laminating Papers.** The primary role of $TiO_2$ decorative laminating papers is to provide opacity. Since the purpose of decorative laminates is to provide aesthetically pleasing functional surfaces, it is desirable that the brown kraft, wood, or particle board substrates be covered. During the process of lamination, a composite of resin, pulp, and filler is formed which is void of most air. The refractive index of the pulp and cured resin are similar, so there is very little hiding from the pulp. White and light laminates require a filler with a high refractive index; thus rutile $TiO_2$ is used. Some simulated wood laminates and dark colored laminates get opacity through absorption of the colorants, so they require very little $TiO_2$. In some white laminates, the $TiO_2$ loadings approach 50% by weight.

When $TiO_2$ is put in an oxygen-free environment and exposed to sunlight, it will darken. This phenomena is known as photo-graying. The reduction mechanism for photo graying can be described by the following *(20)*:

$$Ti(+4) + hv(-) \rightarrow Ti(+3)$$

The reaction proceeds in an oxygen-free environment, and oxygen leaves the crystal lattice. The discoloration is due to Ti(+3) centers, but the reaction is reversible. When the light source is removed, the $TiO_2$ will revert to its original color as long as oxygen can return to the lattice. However, a laminate system is void of most oxygen, and the $TiO_2$ is incorporated in the system as opposed to being on the surface. Therefore, the absence of photo-graying or light stability is an important attribute required of a laminate-grade $TiO_2$. The required photostability can be achieved by thermal treatment *(21)* or by binding ceric ion to the pigment *(22)*. The amount of resin involved with the laminate has an impact on light stability. The more resin used, the less oxygen in the system and the more graying occurs.

Laminates come in a variety of colors and shades. In addition to solid colors, some papers will be printed. Since $TiO_2$ can be a large percentage of the final paper, the color of the $TiO_2$ is a critical property. When paper producers talk about color they talk about absolute level and consistency. The absolute color level determines the colors they can achieve; consistency deals with being able to reproduce the color time and time again. Many times a papermaker will be asked to produce an exact color match on paper produced many years prior.

# Analytical Procedures

## Critical Properties

Probably the most important properties of titanium dioxide that must be specified are the $TiO_2$ content and whether it is the rutile or anatase crystal form. This information will define the pigment's refractive index and therefore its optical efficiency. Titanium dioxide suppliers will designate the minimum titanium dioxide content and crystal type for all of their various grades of $TiO_2$. $TiO_2$ concentration typically is determined by quantitative X-ray fluorescence analysis and the crystal type can be determined by X-ray diffraction.

As discussed previously, particle size and distribution are critical to $TiO_2$ optical performance. Numerous techniques are used to measure $TiO_2$ particle size and distribution, but two used routinely in industry are sedigraph and laser scattering particle-size analyzers. The sedigraph determines particle size (equivalent spherical diameter) based on measured particle settling velocity. The laser scattering analyzer determines equivalent spherical diameter by measuring the light-scattering pattern and calculating particle size based on Mie light-scattering theory. For $TiO_2$, the laser scattering particle-size analyzer has the advantage of being able to measure particles down to 0.04 μm *(5)*. The sedigraph can only effectively measure particle size down to about 0.2 μm. The laser scattering analyzer generally reports particle sizes larger than those reported by the sedigraph. The particle-size distribution reported by the laser scattering analyzer is usually broader than that reported by the sedigraph.

Low-shear and high-shear viscosity measurements can help define the state of pigment dispersion in either a predispersed slurry from the supplier or a dry pigment made down into a slurry at the mill. For the same pigment grade, lower viscosity at equal solids concentration indicates better pigment dispersion. Viscosities that are much higher than normal sometimes can mean loss of dispersion stability due to contamination of the slurry or microbiological degradation of the dispersant. Titanium dioxide slurry viscosities can be measured using TAPPI Test Method T 648 om-88.

Pigment brightness is not as important to titanium dioxide as it is to clay products because all titanium dioxide grades have very high pigment brightness. Slight differences in $TiO_2$ pigment brightness will have no affect on opacifying efficiency and very little affect on its paper brightening capability. However, subtle differences in $TiO_2$ pigment brightness can sometimes be related to contamination by colored mineral impurities such as iron. Titanium dioxide pigment brightness can be measured using TAPPI Test Method T 646 om-86.

Like all mineral products, titanium dioxide will contain some level of undispersed grit particles, usually defined as the residue left on a 325-mesh (44-μm opening) screen. The amount of grit or residue must be minimized, especially in coating applications where these oversized particles could potentially cause blade scratches or other surface imperfections. Most titanium dioxide grades have a maximum 325-mesh grit specification of 0.02% by weight or less. Titanium dioxide grit levels can be determined by TAPPI Test Method T 681 cm-83.

### Measurement Methods and Techniques

Instruments have been developed to analyze directly the concentrations of titanium dioxide and calcium carbonate in paper *(23)*. These instruments, available from a number of manufacturers, are based on X-ray fluorescence spectroscopy. The titanium and calcium atoms in the sheet are excited by a low-level radiation source (a radioactive Fe-55) housed within the instrument. When the electrons from the titanium and calcium atoms return to their ground state, characteristic X-rays are emitted which are detected and counted by the instrument. The instruments are calibrated to convert these "counts" to $TiO_2$ and $CaCO_3$ weight concentrations. This testing method is quick, accurate, and nondestructive, and can replace time-consuming wet chemical procedures such as TAPPI Test Method T 627 om-85.

## Economic and Market Factors

### Performance Economic Values

Titanium dioxide is more expensive than most other pigments used in coatings or as wet-end fillers. However, to judge the true value of $TiO_2$ as an opacifying pigment, both price and optical performance must be compared against other pigments. The optical efficiency of a pigment can be characterized by a light-scattering coefficient, which characterizes its ability to scatter light and therefore contribute to opacity and brightness *(24, 25)*. The relative value-in-use of titanium dioxide and other pigments can be demonstrated by showing each pigment's relative position on a scattering coefficient versus price matrix, as shown in **Fig. 8-18**. Pigments having the highest opacifying value will gravitate to the upper left corner of this figure (higher scattering coefficient at lower price). Pigments having lower opacifying value will congregate at the lower right corner (lower scattering at higher price).

*Figure 8-18 Value-in-Use of Pigments*

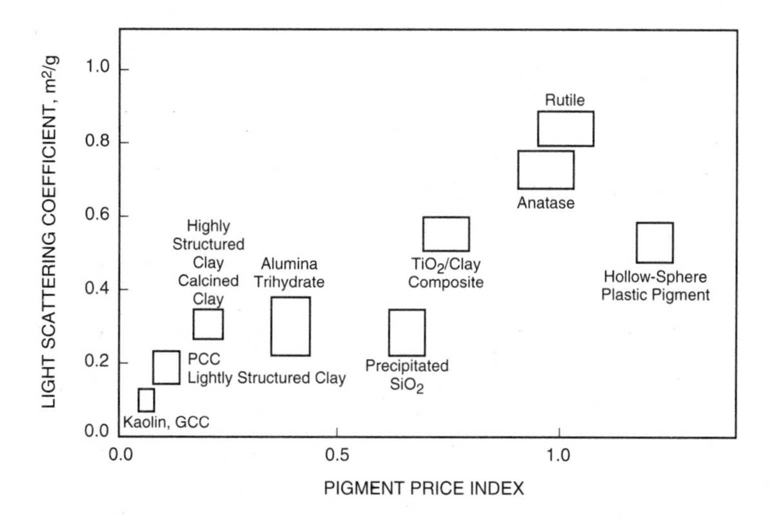


Most of the pigments shown in Fig. 8-18 fall very closely along a diagonal line going from the bottom left to the top right, indicating that, for the most part, they are priced appropriately based on their optical performance. However, this figure only considers optical performance. It does not take into account other positive attributes like the easy glossing characteristics of hollow-sphere plastic pigments or negative attributes like calcined clay's relatively poor rheology.

## Differences in World Usage

Approximately two-thirds of the titanium dioxide used in worldwide paper production is consumed in North America. In North America, about half of the $TiO_2$ is used in the production of coated paper and nearly a quarter in uncoated printing and writing paper. Other $TiO_2$ consuming segments — in order of $TiO_2$ usage — are coated paperboard, decorative laminates, and specialty papers.

Europe accounts for about a quarter of the world $TiO_2$ demand for paper. Titanium dioxide use in Europe is largely restricted to decorative laminates, coated and uncoated board, and special lightweight opaque papers. Titanium dioxide use in coated and uncoated printing and writing papers is not as common as in the United States. However, European coated papers are generally less opaque than comparable U.S. papers. The more liberal use of titanium dioxide in the production of U.S. coated and uncoated papers is reflected in higher opacity at any given basis weight *(26)*.

# Future Outlook

## Market Trends

A growing shortage of landfill space and concerns around deforestation will drive increased use of recycled fiber. Recycled fibers will likely be less bright, less opaque, and weaker than virgin fibers. To maintain paper optical and strength properties, pigments will need to contribute more optical performance at lower concentrations in the sheet. This is likely to cause increased $TiO_2$ usage because of its superior opacifying and brightening capabilities.

Increasing postal rates and source reduction goals will continue driving coated-paper basis weights down. Increased $TiO_2$ use will be needed to maintain sheet optical properties demanded by printers and publishers.

The packaging industry continues to demand improved printing graphics to take full advantage of the growth in point-of-purchase packaging. This will likely drive coated paperboard (recycled, unbleached kraft, and bleached kraft) growth and increased use of titanium dioxide.

A major trend in papermaking is the reduction in chlorine and chlorine-based compounds in the pulp bleaching process. This trend has been driven by social and governmental concerns over chlorinated compounds such as dioxin entering the food chain. Totally chlorine free (TCF) pulps may be less opaque than those bleached with chlorine compounds. Therefore, paper made from TCF pulps may require more $TiO_2$ to maintain opacity specifications.

## Impact of Developing Technology

Conversions to alkaline papermaking and increased use of precipitated and ground calcium carbonate as fillers significantly reduced titanium dioxide consumption in the U.S. uncoated freesheet market through the late ’80s and early ’90s. This was accomplished by using higher filler loadings of calcium carbonate pigments that were brighter and developed higher opacity than the kaolin clay fillers they replaced. However, this trend appears to have reached an equilibrium and is not expected to have any further impact on uncoated or coated freesheet $TiO_2$ consumption.

Neutral or alkaline groundwood papermaking technology would allow greater use of calcium carbonate in coated groundwood papers. Calcium carbonate grades suitable for use in high-speed coating applications are brighter than coating clays but in most cases will not result in higher opacity. This might result in some reduction in titanium dioxide use in cases where it is used for brightness development. Overall, however, this trend is expected to have minimal impact on $TiO_2$ use in coated groundwood papers.

Structured kaolin pigments are being developed which enhance the inherent opacity of paper coatings by increasing coating bulk and the contribution of air-pigment interfaces to coating optical performance. To the extent that these pigments can be implemented without detrimental effects on coating runnability, coating strength, sheet printability, etc., they could result in some reduction in $TiO_2$ use in coated papers and coated paperboard.

### Volume Growth

Paper industry demand for $TiO_2$ is expected to grow about evenly with paper production growth. Potential increases in $TiO_2$ use due to market trends, such as increase recycled fiber use or lower basis weights, will tend to be offset by decreases in $TiO_2$ use from technology developments such as structured clays.

## Literature Cited


1. *ASTM $TiO_2$ Pigment Specifications*, ASTM Standards, Section 6, 06.02, D476-73, ASTM, Philadelphia, 1979.
2. Blakely, R. R. and Hall, J. E., in *Pigment Handbook* (P. A. Lewis, ed.), Wiley-Interscience, New York, 1988, pp. 1-42.
3. McGinnis, W. J., in *Pigments for Paper* (R. W. Hagemeyer, ed.), TAPPI PRESS, Atlanta, 1984, pp. 241-281.
4. Riches, W. W. and Pascal, R. H., *Chemical Engineering Progress* 63(3): 52-56(1967).
5. Johnson, R. W., Thiele, E. S., and French, R. H., *Tappi J.*, in press.
6. Kwoka, R. A., *TAPPI 1990 Dyes, Fillers and Pigments Short Course Notes*, TAPPI PRESS, Atlanta, pp. 31-37.
7. Braun, J. H., Baidins, A., and Marganski, R. E., *Progress in Organic Coatings* 20: 105-138(1992).
8. Braun, J. H., *Introduction to Pigments*, Federation of Societies for Coatings Technology, Blue Bell, PA, 1993.
9. Kwoka, R. A., *TAPPI 1992 Coating Conference Proceedings*, TAPPI PRESS, Atlanta, pp. 325-334.
10. McGinnis, W. J., *TAPPI 1989 Coating Conference Proceedings*, TAPPI PRESS, Atlanta, pp. 23-32.
11. Robinson, J. V., *TAPPI* 59(2): 77-82(1976).
12. Brill, H. C. and Hecklau, F. L., *TAPPI* 43(4): 229A-237A(1960).
13. Puffenberger, A. P., *DuPont "TI-PURE" $TiO_2$ Technical Information*, "The Competitive Advantages of $TiO_2$ Slurry Over Dry in Wet End Papermaking", DuPont Co., Wilmington, DE, 1992.
14. Alince, B., *Tappi J.* 70(10): 114-117(1987).
15. Willets, W. R., *Tech. Assoc. Papers* 19: 228-231(1936).
16. Willets, W. R., *Paper Mill and Wood Pulp News* 58(45): 15-18(1935).
17. Kwoka, R. A. and Logan, T. W., *Tappi J.* 77(10): 136-144(1994).
18. Johnson, R. W., *Tappi J.* 74(5): 209-217(1991).
19. Klass, C. P., *Tappi J.* 73(12): 69-75(1990).
20. Volz, H. G., Kampf, G., and Fitzky, H. G., *Progress in Organic Coatings* 2: 232(1973/1974).
21. Siuta, W. T., U.S. pat. 3,035,966 (May, 1962).
22. Barnard, B. and Laverick, W. T., U.S. pat. 4,239,548 (December, 1980).

23. Bauman, H. D., *Pulp & Paper* 46(5): 120-122(1972).
24. Judd, D. B. and Wyszecki, G., *Color in Business, Science and Industry*, 2nd Edn., John Wiley and Sons, New York, 1963, pp. 387-405.
25. Van den Akker, J. A., *TAPPI* 32(11): 498-501(1949).
26. McAuley, D. and Veness, J. C., *The Western European Printing and Writing Paper Industry to 1994: A View from ECC International*, "A Comparison of European and US Printing and Writing Papers", ECC International Limited, Cornwall, UK, 1990, pp. 18-24.

# 9.

# Synthetic Plastic Pigments

*James T. Brown and Femi O. Kotoye*

Inorganic pigments such as clay and calcium carbonate are used in paper coatings to provide a surface with the desired appearance and printability. Properly chosen and formulated, these pigments provide a coating with surface smoothness, brightness, opacity, and a balance of ink holdout and ink receptivity upon which to print. Organic pigments, commonly referred to as "plastic pigments", are used as partial replacements for inorganic pigments to improve the optical and print properties of coated paper and paperboard.

This chapter is a review of the synthetic polymeric latexes that are used primarily to enhance the appearance and printability of coated paper and paperboard. Heiser *(1, 2)* first described the use of polymeric latexes based on styrene as gloss additives for coated paper in 1972. These synthetic, nonfilm-forming polymers were used to replace some of the inorganic pigments. Hence the term, "plastic pigments" was coined to describe this class of pigments. Many researchers such as Alince *(3)*, Lepoutre *(4)*, Hagymassey *(5)*, Brown *(6)*, and others have reported on the use of these thermoplastic pigments, their contribution to optical properties, and their response to varied finishing conditions.

## Principal Classes

There are two general classes of plastic pigments used in the preparation of coatings for paper and paperboard: solid bead and hollow sphere. Both are available in a variety of particle sizes and compositions and, in the case of hollow spheres, in a range of void volumes. **Figure 9-1** shows an assortment of plastic pigments and demonstrates the ranges of particle size and distribution available. These SEMs do not reveal the hollow core of the hollow spheres, but these are revealed by a freeze fracturing technique.

*Figure 9-1 SEMs of a Variety of Plastic Pigments*

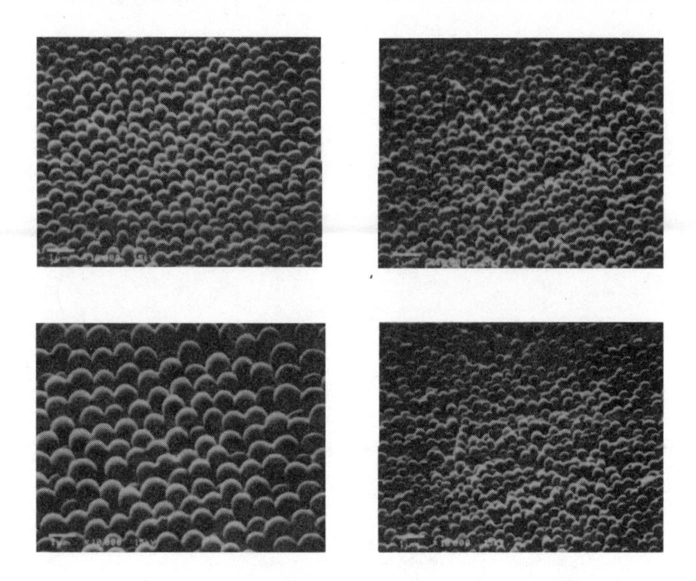

# Chemical and Physical Properties

All plastic pigments are supplied as polymeric particles dispersed in water. In the case of hollow-sphere pigments those particles are water-filled spheres. When drying occurs the water diffuses through the shell, leaving an air-filled core, hence the term "hollow sphere".

A variety of synthetic polymers can be used to make plastic pigments. The main requirement for a polymer to act as a pigment is that it be nonfilm-forming and remain as discrete particles during coating application and drying. Should a polymer particle form a film on drying, it would retard coating consolidation and interfere with the development of gloss, which is one of the primary reasons for using plastic pigments. In addition, if film formation occurred, the interstitial air voids between the mineral pigments would be partially filled with polymer, thus detracting from opacity and brightness. In the case of hollow-sphere pigments, film formation would result in the loss of the encapsulated air void, greatly diminishing opacity contribution.

Due to the aforementioned performance constraints, and for reasons of cost and availability, styrene is the building block of choice for most plastic pigments. However, any monomer or copolymer that possesses a glass transition temperature (Tg) greater than 50°C can be used as a plastic pigment. Since polystyrene and copolymers that are mostly styrene dominate the commercial scene, plastic pigment examples used throughout this chapter will be of that type (whether solid or hollow) unless otherwise specified.

**Table 9-1** lists the typical range of pigment properties for plastic pigments.

*Table 9-1 Typical Range of Properties for Plastic Pigments*

| Appearance | Milky White Liquid |
|---|---|
| Weight Solids, % | |
| Solid Bead | 48-55 |
| Hollow Sphere | 27-40 |
| Volume solids, % | 47-57 |
| pH 6-10.5 | |
| Brookfield viscosity, cps | <500 |
| Particle size, nm | |
| Solid Bead | 100-550 |
| Hollow Sphere | 300-1100 |
| Particle charge | Anionic |
| Level of carboxylation | Low |
| Tg, °C | 80-105 |
| Specific Gravity of Aqueous Dispersion | 1.03-1.06 |
| Specific Gravity of Solid | |
| Solid Bead | 1.01-1.05 |
| Hollow Sphere | 0.5-0.85 |

## Method of Manufacture

Like most emulsion polymers, plastic pigments, whether hollow or solid, are manufactured using a free-radical polymerization in water. In very general terms, a synthetic route like this is used:

*water + emulsifying agent + polymerizable monomer +*
*source of free-radicals → emulsion polymer*

In the case of most solid-bead plastic pigments, the polymer composition is fairly uniform throughout the polymerization. However, for hollow-sphere pigments, a more complicated polymerization sequence is required to produce water-filled spheres which, on drying, form encapsulated air voids. In either case, a high level of expertise is required to produce a consistent product of well-defined particle size and narrow particle-size distribution.

## Shipping, Handling, and Storage

Plastic pigments are generally nonreactive and quite versatile in the ways they can be shipped and stored. Plastic pigments can be shipped in rail cars, tank trucks, drums, or tote bins. As a class, plastic pigments are much more resistant to settling than mineral pigments, although hollow-sphere pigments can be more prone to settling than their solid-bead counterparts. In either case some settling can occur on long-term storage so, when using drums, a first-in first-out inventory system should be used. Stirred bulk storage may not be necessary when using plastic pigments; consult the manufacturer's technical literature.

Stainless steel, glass lined, or reinforced plastic tanks can be used to bulk store plastic pigments. Similar materials should be used in piping, pumping, and filtering equipment. Mild steel, black iron, copper, and brass should be avoided because polymers can form deposits on these surfaces.

Air diaphragm pumps are the preferred types of pumps to use for transferring plastic pigments. Open impeller, centrifugal, and screw-type (Moyno) pumps are usable although not ideal. Pumping problems are more likely to arise when the pumps have restricted passageways where surface-to-surface clearances are small. Polymer can build up on the surfaces in the restricted regions of the pump. This can be caused by mechanical breakdown of the emulsion polymer. It is also possible that a very small amount of "plating out" of the polymer on these surfaces could contribute to excessive shear rates being developed in pumping. For these reasons gear pumps and piston-type pumps should be avoided. Whatever the pump type, it is very important that all components be either neoprene (as in the case of air diaphragm pumps) or stainless steel.

Plastic pigments are not normally freeze-thaw stable, therefore, freezing must be avoided. Should freezing occur it is very likely that the polymer will coagulate, rendering it useless.

Incorporation of plastic pigments into a coating color is quite simple. The aqueous polymer emulsions do not require high-speed mixing or the use of additional dispersants. They are readily pumped as supplied and their low viscosities allow for easy mixing into an existing coating color. They can be added to the coating color with either high-shear or low-sheer mixing. As with almost all polymer dispersions, foam generation can be an issue. Consequently, high-shear mixing for long periods of time should be avoided to discourage air entrainment.

## Reasons For Use

### Typical Formulations

Plastic pigments can enhance the performance of pigmented coatings for paper and paperboard in a variety of ways. In most cases they are used as additives where they are substituted for mineral pigments in the range of 3% to 20% by dry weight of pigment. At these levels the pigment volume of the coating is increased somewhat. The increase in pigment volume is offset by having smooth, uniformly spherical particles which have a low per particle binder demand. The end result is that, at these substitution levels, it is not usually necessary to increase binder levels to maintain coating strength.

## Rheology

The major factors that influence the rheology of pigmented coatings are particle packing, chemical interaction, and solids per unit volume (i.e, volume solids). The rheological properties of coatings containing plastic pigment are usually similar to those of all-mineral systems. At equal weight solids, Brookfield and Hercules high-shear viscosity are sometimes slightly higher because, as plastic pigment is substituted for mineral pigment, volume solids increase due to density differences. The density of plastic pigment particles is between 0.2 and 0.4 that of clay. In other words, plastic pigment contributes between 2.5 and 5 times the volume solids as an equal weight of clay. This large difference in volume solids is somewhat offset by the fact the irregularly shaped clay particles are being replaced by smooth, spherical particles. In general, the coating formulation solids are adjusted slightly to produce equal volume solids; then there are usually no significant differences in rheological properties between all-mineral and plastic pigment-containing coatings.

## Optical Performance

Plastic pigments enhance the optical performance of coatings by increasing sheet gloss, brightness, and opacity. The degree to which these properties are enhanced is dependent upon the particle size of the plastic pigment, its void volume (if a hollow sphere), the mineral pigments used, and the type and degree of finishing. Print performance is often enhanced as a result of improved sheet gloss and smoothness, as well as an improved balance of ink receptivity and ink holdout. In offset printing this improved balance often leads to higher-quality images through increased ink density at constant ink levels, sharper dot definition, and reduced dot gain.

Because plastic pigments are finishing aids, milder calender conditions often can be used to achieve a target gloss value. These milder conditions lead to less compaction of the coated paper, thus increasing bulk and stiffness. Increased bulk leads to improved compressibility and this, in turn, leads to improved ink transfer in rotogravure printing. With fewer missing dots, the sharpness of the image is enhanced.

Less intense finishing requirements when using plastic pigments can also lead to improved production efficiencies. Supercalenders can be operated at lower temperatures and pressures to achieve the target gloss values, which translates to increased roll life. More commonly the improved finishing response is used to speed up the supercalenders, thus increasing output and allowing the supercalenders to keep up with the ever increasing speeds of modern paper machines.

## Specific Uses

Plastic pigments are used in paper coatings wherever improvements in finishing efficiency, sheet gloss, or print gloss are important. They are used extensively in coated SBS and SUS board, in premium No. 1 grades, and in LWC and ULWC. The small-particle-size solid beads are more prevalent in the coated board area to enhance finishing and print performance. Gloss calenders are commonly used in this segment of the paper industry, and plastic pigments can reduce the temperatures and pressures required to achieve the desired level of finishing. In unbleached board, coating opacity is required to cover the dark base stock; hence the light-scattering contribution of the plastic pigment can be very important. In bleached board, coating opacity is less critical. Here the contribution of plastic pigments to brightness, gloss development, and printability are their primary reasons for use.

Hollow-sphere plastic pigments are used extensively in LWC and ULWC where finishing efficiency and high bulk are very important. Their exceptionally low density, as well as their ability to reduce calender intensity, make them well suited for a market that places high value on bulk, stiffness, and runnability. Due to their contribution to coating bulk, hollow-sphere pigments can allow for reduced coating weights to achieve a desired coating thickness. This, in turn, allows for more fiber to be used in a given grade, resulting in a stronger sheet with fewer breaks and improved productivity.

# Mechanism of Performance

## Gloss

There are several factors at work that are responsible for the enhanced performance levels achieved with plastic pigments. Depending upon the formulation used and the particular grade of plastic pigment, particle packing can result in increased smoothness and gloss. However, the main contribution of plastic pigments to gloss and smoothness is the result of improved response to finishing. The plastic pigment particles are somewhat thermoplastic in nature and more readily deform on calendering than do mineral pigments. The flattening of the particles at the coating's surface produces a smoother, less porous, higher gloss surface. An additional benefit is increased ink holdout and improved printed gloss. **Figure 9-2** is a freeze fractured, supercalendered coating containing 10 parts of a 0.5-micron, solid bead plastic pigment. **Figure 9-3** is an analogous freeze fracture of a supercalendered coating containing 10 parts of a 1-micron, 50% voided hollow-sphere plastic pigment.

*Figure 9-2 Supercalendered Coating Containing a Solid-Bead Plastic Pigment*

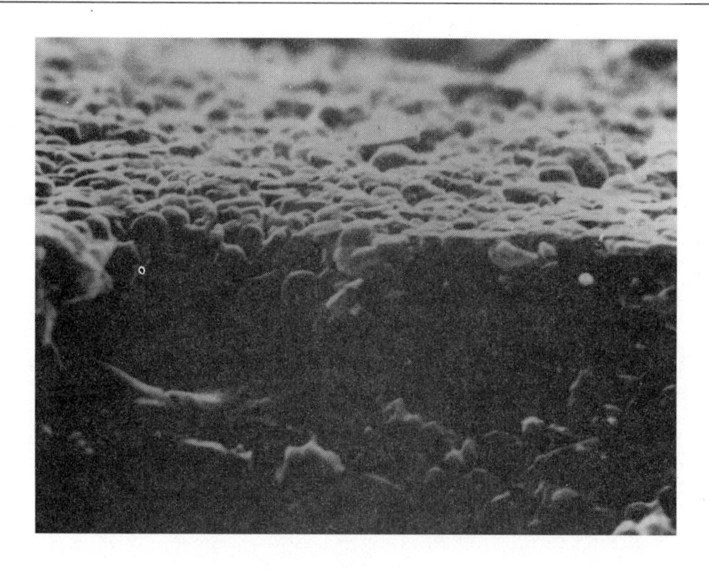

*Figure 9-3 Supercalendered Coating Containing a Hollow-Sphere Plastic Pigment*

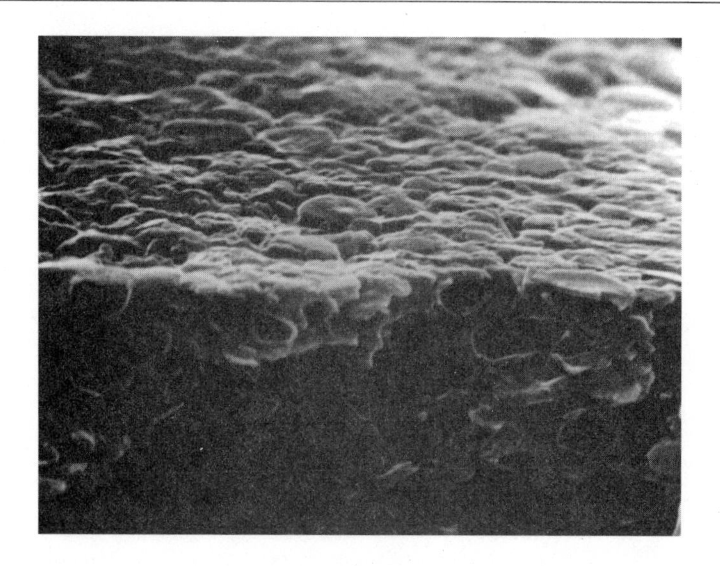

## Opacity

Proper selection of particle size for a plastic pigment also can lead to improved brightness and opacity, depending upon the particular coating formulation used. Opacity in a coating is produced as light is both scattered and absorbed as it passes through the coating. Light scatters or refracts as it passes from one medium to another as long as those media have differing refractive indices. With the exception of $TiO_2$, most commonly used mineral pigments have a refractive index of about 1.5-1.6. This is also true of most synthetic binders. Therefore, not much scattering of light occurs at the pigment-binder boundaries. Most of the light is scattered as the light passes from pigment or binder to air (refractive index of 1.0) and then back again. Pigmented paper coatings are usually prepared at a pigment volume concentration in excess of 70%, and often greater than 80%. Since the critical pigment volume concentration of most pigments is in the range of 50% to 60%, pigmented paper coatings possess a large amount of interstitial air. The spherical particles of plastic pigments can have an effect on particle packing. This, in turn, can change the size and distribution of the interstitial air voids, which can lead to increased opacity in pigmented paper coatings. When hollow-sphere plastic pigments are used this effect is enhanced. The encapsulated air voids within each particle increase the number of light-scattering sites. Figures 9-2 and 9-3 also illustrate the mechanism for opacity development.

## Brightness

Plastic pigments as a class have low absorption of electromagnetic radiation from 300 nm to 1500 nm. In other words, they are quite reflective of light from the near-UV region through the visible region. Consequently, plastic pigments are exceptionally bright (TAPPI brightness of >98%). An additional consequence of low absorption in the near-UV region is that plastic pigments will not interfere with the performance of optical brighteners. These expensive additives absorb UV light and then re-emit it as visible light to enhance brightness.

When plastic pigments are included in a mineral pigment formulation in place of some of the clay, the shade of the coating moves towards a more bluish-white tint, so the levels of the tinting pigments used must be adjusted if the same shade is to be maintained.

## Bulk

Plastic pigments contribute exceptional bulk to pigmented paper coatings. The density of the pigments range as low as 0.5 in the case of hollow-sphere pigments to approximately 1.05 for solid beads. In either case, the density of the plastic pigments are far below those of mineral pigments (**Table 9-2**). An additional bulk contribution can result when using plastic pigments because they are finishing aids. Thus, when replacing a portion of the mineral pigments, less intense calendering is required to achieve the target gloss. Since lower calender pressure or higher speeds can be used to achieve gloss, less compaction of the sheet takes place resulting in a stiffer, bulkier sheet.

*Table 9-2 Specific Gravity and Refractive Index for Some Common Binders and Pigments*

| Material | Specific Gravity | Refractive Index |
|---|---|---|
| Kaolin Clay | 2.58 | 1.57 |
| Calcium Carbonate (PPT) | 2.55 | 1.66 |
| Titanium Dioxide (Rutile) | 4.20 | 2.76 |
| Starch | 1.50 | 1.53 |
| Styrene-Butadiene Latex Binder | 1.02 | 1.57 |
| Polyvinyl Acetate Latex Binder | 1.20 | 1.47 |
| Acrylic Latex Binder | 1.07 | 1.47 |
| Polystyrene (Solid-Bead Plastic Pigment) | 1.05 | 1.59 |
| Hollow-Sphere Pigment | 0.50–0.85 | 1.0 (void)–1.59 (shell) |

# Analytical Procedures

## Critical Properties and Specifications

The properties most commonly measured and reported for quality assurance are pH, Brookfield viscosity, and solids content. In addition, manufacturers may measure and report particle size, surface tension, and void volume (where applicable).

## Measurement Methods and Techniques

One common method for determining the total pigment content in paper, whether coated or uncoated, is the ash test (TAPPI Test Method T 211, T 413, and UM 496). Plastic pigments are organic and thus will be burnt off during ashing along with the binders and other organic additives. Therefore, in using the ash method to determine coat weight, the plastic pigment should be treated as binder. Currently there are no analytical techniques that will distinguish the styrene in the plastic pigment from the styrene in the SBR binder. However, thermogravimetric analysis and scanning electron microscopy can help in estimating plastic pigment content when SBR is present in the binder system.

# Economic and Market Factors

Since plastic pigments use raw materials and processes similar to those used in the manufacture of synthetic binders, the economics are similar when the products are compared on an equal volume basis. Because the mechanism of performance is more dependent on volume than weight, it is more relevant to compare economics on this basis. The lower the density of the plastic pigment the greater the cost on a dry weight basis, while cost is similar on a volume basis. This is due to the fact that kettle cost allocation is usually based on through-put of product on a dry basis. This is much the same as machine time is allocated to the manufacture of paper. Compared to heavier weights of paper, lightweight paper production costs more per ton but less per ream.

The value of plastic pigment to paper is highly dependent on the specific application. In a mill that is bottle-necked at the supercalenders, mill capacity can be increased by using plastic pigment. Calendering response is increased, and the supercalenders can be run faster while still achieving the gloss targets. This reduces the need for capital expenditure and can be of great value. In the case of hollow-sphere pigments, value is further enhanced when titanium dioxide is present, either in the wet end or the coating. The significant opacity contribution from the encapsulated air void allows for significant contribution to value through $TiO_2$ reduction.

Plastic pigments of one form or another have found uses in many grades of coated paper and paperboard. In lightweight coated and ultralightweight coated they contribute to gloss, bulk, opacity, and printability. In premium and intermediate grades they are used to enhance sheet gloss development and improve print performance. In coated SBS board they are used to enhance response on gloss calenders and brushes. In most cases they are used to enhance the value of the paper in which they are used, rather than reduce raw material costs.

Plastic pigments are used throughout the world with all types of pigments, binders, and base stocks. They are used in groundwood-containing as well as wood-free papers, both acid and alkaline. Wherever an aid to finishing is desired, plastic pigments are of potential use.

# Future Outlook

## Market Trends and Forecast

There are at least three significant trends in coated paper markets that impact the future of plastic pigments:

1. **Mailing costs will continue to rise.**
   This produces increasing demands for lighter basis weights in weekly publications as publishers attempt to decrease magazine weight while maintaining the number of pages. Low-density plastic pigments are especially useful in achieving lower basis weights without sacrificing performance.

2. **There continues to be market pressure to increase the quality of printing.**
   There will be a continuing value in increased sheet gloss and printed gloss. This is a primary benefit to using plastic pigments.
3. **The paper industry continues to use higher and higher levels of post-consumer waste.**
   This tends to produce papers that are lower in both strength and brightness. Depending upon grade, plastic pigments can help offset both of these deficiencies. The low density of plastic pigments can assist in coat-weight reduction without loss of properties. This allows a greater fiber-to-coating ratio to be used, which can lead to fewer breaks and better production efficiencies.

## Impact of Developing Technologies

The wider use of plastic pigments in coated paper and paperboard has facilitated the quest for continual improvement in optical and print performance. As performance levels have been raised, greater opportunities for new pigments and binders have also become evident. The manufacturers of mineral pigments are playing a part in this evolution. The degree to which they are successful in developing new, gloss enhancing, bulking pigments will have an impact on the continued growth in the use of plastic pigments. However, plastic-pigment technology is still in a state of evolution and differentiated, higher performance products should be expected over at least the next decade.

Several plastic pigments have been available for some time and others have been introduced recently. Variables include polymeric composition, particle size, morphology, and percent void volume. Research and development continues and should provide even greater performance benefits or improved cost effectiveness. Most plastic pigments are listed in the *TAPPI Specialty Pigments Index*; however, check with suppliers of plastic pigments for updated information.

## Literature Cited


1. Heiser, E. J. and Shad, A. *TAPPI* 56(1): 70(1973).
2. Heiser, E. J. *TAPPI*, 48(8), 80A(1965).
3. Alince, B. and Lepoutre P., *TAPPI* 63(5): 49(1980).
4. Alince, B. and Lepoutre P., *TAPPI* 64(5): 67(1981).
5. Hagymassey, J. and Haynes, J. U., Jr., *TAPPI* 60(7): 126(1977).
6. Brown, J. T., *TAPPI 1991 Coating Conference Proceedings*, TAPPI PRESS, Atlanta, pp. 113-122.
7. Brown, J. T. and Latimer, J. J., *TAPPI 1992 Coating Conference Proceedings*, TAPPI PRESS, Atlanta, pp. 77-89.

# 10.

# Talcs

*Nikhil C. Trivedi*

The use of talc in papermaking in North America is somewhat limited; however, the worldwide usage is great. In fact, globally, the paper industry is the largest consumer of talc *(1)*. In the Far East and in Finland, talc is currently the preferred filler pigment for both economic and political reasons. Filler pigments are generally selected on a cost-performance basis. Each paper grade and production location will have an influence on which fillers are selected and the quantities of each to be used.

During the last decade, considerably more talc has been utilized in paper coating than had been used in the past. The amount of talc consumed is relatively small compared to kaolin clays and is used for special functions. As might be expected, the requirements for coating grades are much more stringent than for filler uses.

The development of fine grinding techniques permitted production of high-purity talc suitable as a pitch adsorbent for use in pitch control. Further refinement of such products using beneficiation followed by micronizing has resulted in a product that has value as an extender for titanium dioxide or as a higher-brightness pigment with good reflectance in the ultraviolet (UV) range.

In mineralogy, the term "talc" refers to a specific form of very pure hydrous magnesium silicate. In industry, the term talc is commonly used to cover a wide range of minerals and mineral mixtures containing talc in varying proportions, some of which, in fact, contain little or no talc at all. The term "industrial talc" would be a better description of such minerals. Because of the various and complex geological ways in which talc deposits were formed, it is common to find a number of other minerals closely associated with talc. Such associated minerals can include anthophyllite, antigorite, calcite, chlorite, diopside, dolomite, magnesite, quartz, serpentine, and tremolite.

In recent years, the discovery and development of relatively pure talc deposits and the use of beneficiation processes on less pure ore deposits have provided a plentiful source of true talc mineral for industrial use. The adaptability of talc to ultra-fine grinding, the platelike nature of the fine talc particles, and the inherent softness of talc have resulted in the mineral becoming more and more important and interesting to the paper industry.

## Properties

Pure talc refers to a hydrous magnesium silicate having a theoretical molecular composition of $3MgO{\cdot}4SiO_2{\cdot}H_2O$ and containing 31.7% MgO, 63.5% $SiO_2$, and 4.8% $H_2O$. The mineral occurs naturally in both foliated (platy) and massive (blocky) compact form. In the latter form, the mineral is sometimes called "steatite" (**Fig. 10-1**).

*Figure 10-1 Scanning Electron Micrographs of Blocky Talc (left) and Platy Talc (right)*

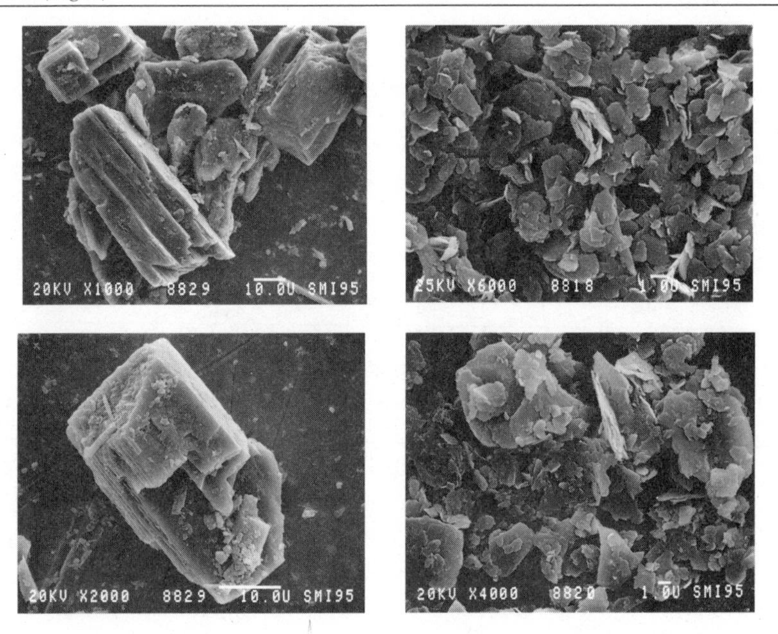


Upon fine grinding, talc fractures to form tiny platelike particles of irregular outline. This is the type of talc preferred for papermaking purposes. On rare occasions, a small portion of pure talc in fibrous form may be detected and can be mistakenly identified as tremolite or other asbestiform mineral. Absolutely pure talc is rare indeed, and the degree to which impurities occur determines the brightness and the hardness of the final ground product.

Platy talc consists of a layered structure in which a brucite sheet [$Mg(OH)_2$] is sandwiched between two silica ($SiO_2$) sheets. The theoretical breadth of this combination is infinite in expanse, with a theoretical thickness of 9.4 nm. The schematic design of the platy talc form is shown in **Fig. 10-2**. These plates are held together by van der Waals forces of the London type *(2)*. The weakness of these forces accounts for the ease with which talc is delaminated in the ultra-fine grinding process. This also accounts for the characteristic slipperiness and consequent lubricant capacity of talc in coating colors.

*Figure 10-2 Molecular Structure of Pure Talc Mineral*

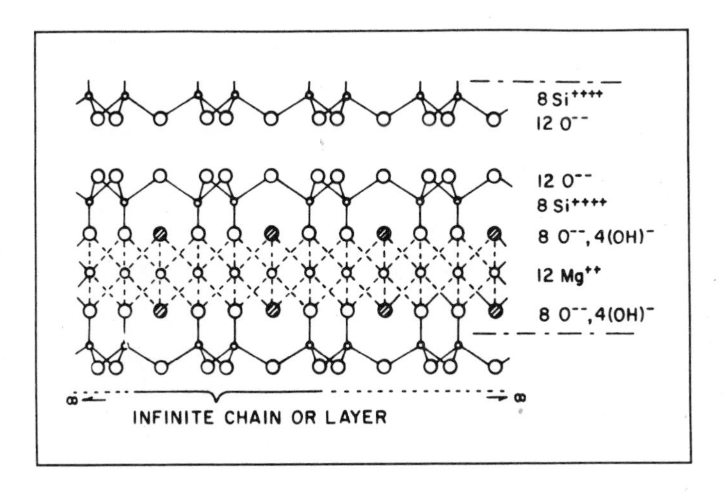


Talc is chemically inert throughout the papermaking process, although it exhibits a marked alkaline pH. The cation exchange capacity is very low, on the order of 2.4 meq/100 g; thus, its effect on overall system pH is small *(3)*. The flat surface of the platy talc is hydrophobic and organophilic, the effect of which will be discussed in detail later. The edge surface is hydrophilic, thus allowing dispersion in a hydrous system.

The index of refraction of talc is 1.54-1.59; its specific gravity is 2.75. Paper grades of ultra-fine ground talcs vary in ISO brightness between 85% and 88%. The preferred grades indicate low wire abrasion levels; however, impure talc grades can be more abrasive. Typical properties of talcs from several sources are shown in **Table 10-1**.

*Table 10-1 Typical Chemical Analyses of Talc from Various North American Sources (4, 5)*

| | Pure Talc, % (Theoretical) | Vermont Talc, % | Montana Talc, % | New York State Talc, % | Texas Talc, % |
|---|---|---|---|---|---|
| $SiO_2$ | 63.36 | 59.15 | 62.64 | 58.80 | 54.92 |
| MgO | 31.89 | 31.14 | 30.21 | 27.45 | 27.40 |
| $Fe_2O_3$ | ... | 3.28 | 1.51 | 0.05 | 0.46 |
| $TiO_2$ | ... | ... | ... | ... | ... |
| $Al_2O_3$ | ... | 0.26 | 0.31 | 0.57 | 0.32 |
| CaO | ... | 0.15 | Trace | 6.66 | 5.76 |
| $K_2O$ | ... | ... | 0.05 | ... | ... |
| $Na_2O$ | ... | ... | 0.15 | ... | ... |
| MnO | ... | ... | ... | 0.39 | ... |
| NiO | ... | ... | ... | ... | ... |
| $Cr_2O_3$ | ... | ... | ... | ... | ... |
| CoO | ... | ... | ... | ... | ... |
| FeO | ... | ... | ... | 0.15 | 0.38 |
| $P_2O_3$ | ... | ... | ... | ... | ... |
| LOI | 4.75 | 6.02 | 5.12 | 5.93 | 10.76 |
| Total, % | 100.00 | 100.00 | 100.00 | 100.00 | 100.00 |

Talc purity can best be analyzed through X-ray diffraction techniques, as illustrated in **Fig. 10-3**. These scans not only indicate the presence of talc, but also can be used to identify impurities and degree of impurity. The scan is a normal diffraction pattern within the range of 5 to 42 degrees of two-theta for copper K radiation. The peaks at 9.45, 19.0, 19.5, 28.6, 34.1, 34.5, and 36.2 degrees characterize the diffraction pattern for talc.

*Figure 10-3 X-ray Diffraction Pattern of Pure Talc (top) and DTA/TGA Curves for Pure Talc (bottom)*

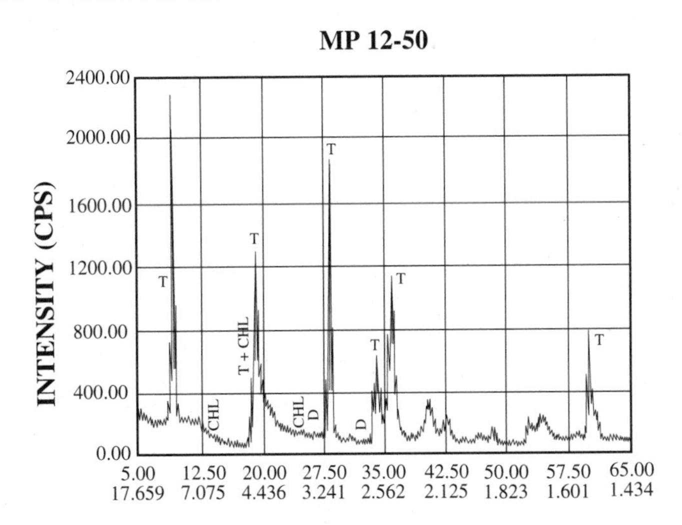


TWO-THETA/D-SPACING

T = TALC D = DOLOMITE

CHL = CHLORITE Q = QUARTZ

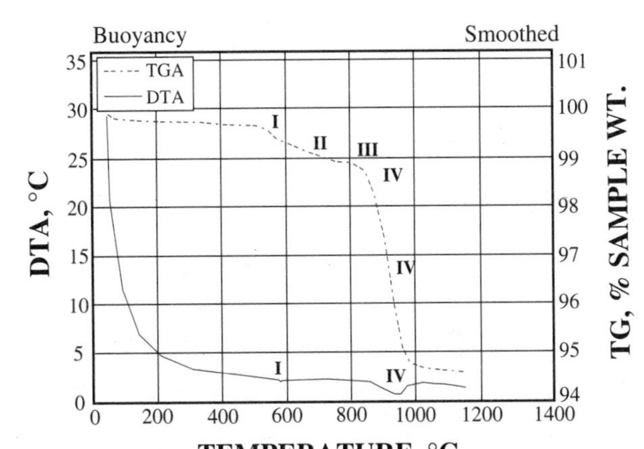


TEMPERATURE, °C

I. First dehydroxylation of Chlorite

II. Decarboxylation of Dolomite

III. Second dehydroxylation of Chlorite

IV. Dehydroxylation of Talc

Pask and Warner *(6)* describe the differential thermal analysis (DTA) method of talc investigation. A relatively pure talc sample is illustrated by the DTA curve shown in Fig. 10-3. The predominant endothermic peak at about 1776°F (980°C) is caused by the breakdown of the talc molecule and the evolution of the chemically bound water. Carbonate impurities generally show sharp endothermic peaks between 1112°F and 1652°F (600°C and 900°C). For instance, a sharp peak at about 1472-1580°F (800-860°C) can indicate the presence of calcite as the impurity. Peaks above 1776°F (980°C) could indicate the presence of tremolite, as an example. Thermal gravimetric analysis used in conjunction with DTA further expands the information available via this form of analysis. The degree of weight change corresponding to the temperature ranges help identify the impurity indicated.

One of the most important tools in the investigation of talcs, however, is the electron microscope. Both the transmission- and scanning-type microscopes are employed, depending on the final information desired. With the scanning microscope, it is quicker and easier to obtain a picture and to gain general information as to size and shape of the talc particles. It is preferable to use the transmission electron microscope (TEM) when more detailed investigations are needed, due to the ability of the TEM to produce greater magnification.  An example of a near theoretical purity, Montana talc, is illustrated in **Fig. 10-4**. Optical microscopy is of limited value with ultra-fine ground talcs, even with oil immersion techniques, because the major portion of the particles are too minute for clear definition.

*Figure 10-4  Transmission (left) and Scanning (right) Electron Micrographs of High-Purity Talc*

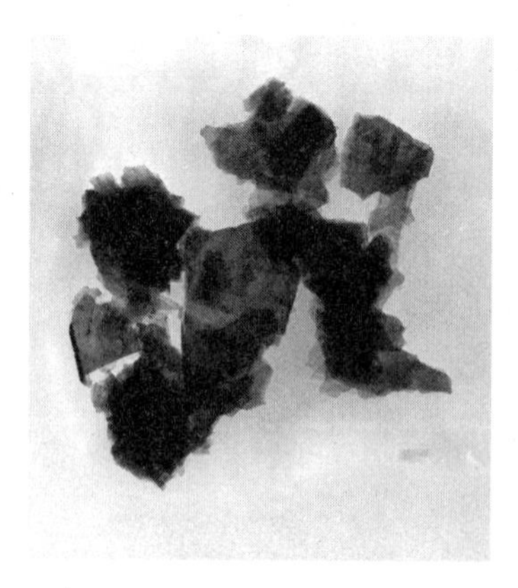

## Occurrence

Talc is a relatively common mineral; however, deposits of high purity are rare. The United States is the largest producer of high-quality talc in the world, with the major volume produced in the states of Montana, Vermont, Texas, and New York. The talcs found in New York contain large amounts of tremolite, and therefore have found little application in the paper industry. Vermont talcs are relatively impure, and thus require special processing for applications demanding high quality. Since the Vermont talc is of nominal brightness and high iron content, it also has limited use in paper manufacture. Texas talcs are contaminated with carbon and dolomite, so ceramics are their major application.

Montana talcs are of excellent purity and are characterized by their high whiteness and platy crystallinity. Because of this purity, the ultra-fine grinding process produces a large degree of total delamination, which results in the near transparency of portions of the exposed plates.

On a global basis, Finland, France, Austria, Italy, and Spain have well-developed talc deposits, supplying thousands of tons of talc to the European paper industry. China, India, and Korea also produce significant quantities of talcs for various end uses including papermaking.

## Methods of Manufacture

Talcs prepared for use as regular wet-end fillers are ground to a top size of 45 µm via roller mills or ball mills. Those prepared for coating, for high brightness, and for extender use must be ultra-fine ground. That used for pitch control ultimately appears in the finished sheet as part of the filler system.

The ore is removed from the deposit, in most cases, via normal drill-blast-shovel types of open pit quarrying techniques. This ore is crushed in jaw or gyratory crushers, dried, and milled with roller- or ball-mill-design equipment. Air classification is used in conjunction with the milling operation to select the feed material for the ultra-fine grinding devices.

The two methods of ultra-fine grinding dominant in the talc industry at this time are the fluid-energy-type of equipment, using superheated steam, and high-speed vertical hammer mills. The fluid-energy mills tend to produce a greater percentage of very small particles as compared to the vertical mills. Two ultra-fine talcs ground to the same maximum particle size may produce widely different total surface areas. A typical fluid-energy-prepared talc will show a surface area in the range of 16 $m_2/g$ to 17 $m^2/g$ by BET-$N_2$ adsorption *(7)*. **Figure 10-5** shows the particle-size distribution curve for such a material. Note that maximum particle size is about 12 µm; nearly 50% are less than 2 µm. These talcs are presently being used as coating pigments with good success.

*Figure 10-5 Particle-Size Distribution Curve for a Typical Fluid Energy Milled Talc*

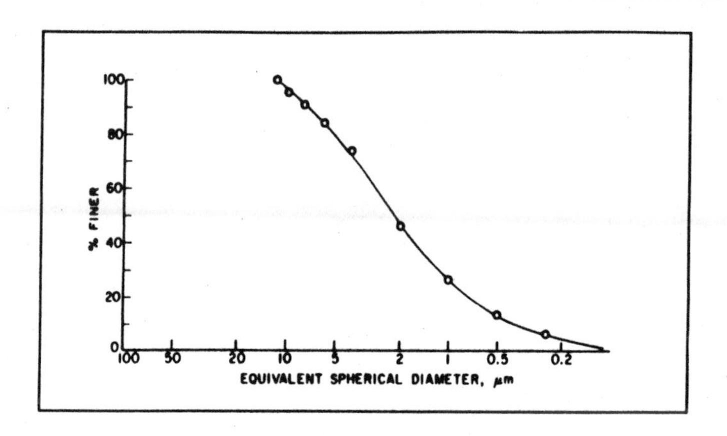


Beneficiation, when required, usually consists of flotation to improve purity (or reduce contaminant levels) and, sometimes, acid leaching or bleaching to improve color.

## Paper Filling

The choice of filler in a finished sheet of paper is a combination of the desired final characteristics and the cost-effectiveness of the filler. In North America, where both air-float and water-washed kaolin is very inexpensive, and precipitated and ground calcium carbonates are cost effective, papermakers have many non-talc filler choices.

There are no suitable kaolin deposits in the Far East; thus, all kaolin consumed must be imported from the United States, Brazil, or the United Kingdom. This makes kaolin very expensive, so none is used for filling, except by secondary occurrence through coated broke recycle. Talc occurs in abundance in both mainland China and Korea, so this is the main filler choice in Japan, the world's third largest paper producer. For instance, during 1994, the Japanese industry consumed 350,000 tons of talc filler, and is increasing consumption at an annual rate of 3% to 5%. The average 1994 price of paper-grade talc in Japan was 22 Yen/kg.

Necessity also lead to invention in Finland, where it was decreed that no raw material can be imported whose function could be fulfilled by a domestic product. Thus, the kaolin formerly used by the Finnish paper industry is now replaced by talc fillers mined in Finland. The 1994 consumption of talc for paper filling in Finland is estimated at 300,000 tons. The 1994 price of paper grade talc in Finland was about 700 FMk/ton.

The talc used as a papermaking additive must be of fairly high purity, containing less than 1% quartz. A higher quartz level is extremely abrasive to papermaking equipment. The general filler products are ground to approximately 99% finer than 325-mesh (-44 μm). The ISO brightness is usually 80+% and is blue-white in tint.

## General Talc Fillers

To ensure that the talc is thoroughly wet out, 325-mesh talcs are generally added dry directly to the hydropulpers during the pulp charging. It can also be slurried to 25-30% solids and added either at the hydropulper or at the machine chest, if there is adequate agitation. In an integrated mill, the chest addition would be the preferred method. Ordinarily, the talc slurry solids would be kept low in solids and no dispersants used to keep the first-pass retention as high as possible. Due to the relatively large particle size as compared to kaolin, there is less interference with hydrogen bonding of the cellulose, allowing higher filler additions than with kaolin.

Pilot paper machine comparative testing indicates that retention of the coarser-grade talc fillers is about equal to that of water-washed clay at low levels of loading, with a higher degree of retention at high levels of loading. Kaolin fillers produce greater opacity at equal filler loadings, which is to be expected due to the much finer particle-size distribution of the clay. Talc-filled sheets are more easily alkaline sized than clay-filled sheets but operate about the same under alum/rosin sizing conditions.

One of the applications where general talc filler is especially well suited is in supercalendered, uncoated, groundwood specialties. High filler contents of 30% to 35% talc give a very high smoothness on supercalendering and make an outstanding rotogravure sheet with improved print quality.

Starting about 1980, there has been considerable interest in using talc in very high-ash-bearing sheets, especially those manufactured in an alum/rosin sizing system.

## Ultra-Fine Ground Talc Fillers

The ultra-fine ground talcs find specialized application in high-brightness filling and as titanium dioxide extenders. **Figure 10-6** illustrates the basic differences between the ultra-fine ground particle size and the less fine general filler grade. The degree of fineness of the ultra-fine ground will contribute greatly to the opacifying ability of this type of filler.

*Figure 10-6 Particle-Size Distribution: General Talc Filler Average Particle Size = 10 μm; Ultra-Fine Talc Filler = 1.5 μm.*

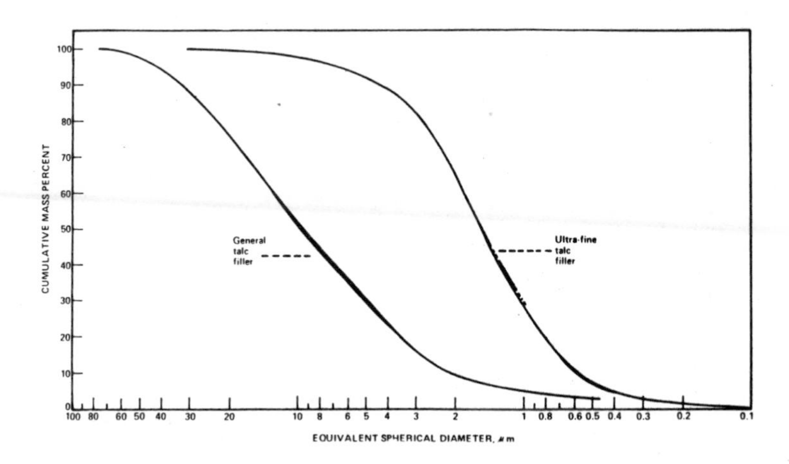


Scanning electron photomicrographs indicate that the fine talc particles appear to agglomerate with titanium dioxide particles, preventing the titanium dioxide from agglomerating with itself. In this manner, a substitution of up to 40% of the titanium dioxide by ultra-fine ground talcs can result in equal opacities in the finished sheet. Experience has shown that the blending of a predispersed talc slurry with a predispersed slurry of titanium dioxide can, in some cases, result in a greater extension than adding the two slurries separately. Care must be taken to satisfy the organophilicity of the talc slurry to prevent agglomerating the titanium dioxide slurry. Details of this process will be found in the coating preparation section of this chapter. **Table 10-2** shows handsheet data comparing performance of talc with ground calcium carbonate and kaolin.

*Table 10-2 Representative Sheet Properties of Filled Test Paper*

| | Talc | | Natural Calcium Carbonate | | Kaolin | |
|---|---|---|---|---|---|---|
| | 15% | 30% | 15% | 30% | 15% | 30% |
| Basis Weight, g/m² | 42.0 | 41.9 | 41.3 | 41.9 | 41.6 | 41.8 |
| Thickness, μm | 91 | 93 | 92 | 96 | 87 | 85 |
| Density, g/cm³ | 0.46 | 0.45 | 0.45 | 0.44 | 0.48 | 0.49 |
| Ash, % | 7.01 | 14.1 | 8.76 | 16.9 | 8.02 | 15.4 |
| First-pass Retention, % | 53.7 | 61.1 | 67.2 | 73.2 | 61.4 | 66.7 |
| Permeability, s | 19.0 | 16.0 | 12.0 | 6.0 | 16.9 | 14.1 |
| Tensile Strength, kg/cm² | 2.97 | 2.58 | 2.81 | 2.36 | 2.78 | 2.34 |
| Breaking Length, km | 4.71 | 4.11 | 4.54 | 3.75 | 4.46 | 3.73 |
| Bursting Strength, kg/cm² | 1.44 | 1.09 | 1.36 | 1.01 | 1.25 | 0.99 |
| Burst Factor | 3.43 | 2.61 | 3.29 | 2.41 | 3.00 | 2.37 |
| Brightness, % | 80.5 | 82.4 | 82.4 | 84.6 | 82.2 | 83.4 |
| Opacity, % | 78.5 | 81.5 | 81.9 | 83.2 | 79.4 | 81.9 |

While most ultra-fine ground talcs average only slightly above 85% ISO brightness, their blue-white tint tends to reflect most of the ultraviolet (UV) band of light. Because of this, they excite fluorescent dyes and make them more efficient. This characteristic has been frequently employed in greeting-card stock.

Although some talc grades are utilized basically as pitch control agents, their addition rate should be taken into consideration as a component of the filler system. Especially in the case of an integrated sulfite mill using green wood, the talc dosage to control depositable pitch may reach as high as 3-4%, which will end up as a 2-3% ash in the finished sheet. This is a premium filler that may well reduce the need for more expensive fillers; it should be used in the calculation of the cost-effectiveness of the talc as a pitch control agent.

## Coating Properties

There are several important properties that differentiate talc from other commonly used coating pigments, e.g., clay and calcium carbonate. **Table 10-3** provides a comparison of talc with these other pigments. Talc is hydrophobic, has a platelike morphology, and has a narrow particle-size distribution. Its hydrophobicity makes wetting or dispersion of talc difficult. The platy nature and lack of fine particles result in high slurry viscosity, air entrapment (foaming), and dilatancy.

*Table 10-3 Properties of Talc in Comparision with Other Coating Pigments*

| | Talc | Clay | Ground Calcium Carbonate |
|---|---|---|---|
| Density, $kg/m^3$ | 2750 | 2650 | 2700 |
| Refractive Index | 1.56 | 1.56 | 1.56 |
| Brightness, % ISO | 85 | 85 | 92 |
| Acid Solubility | Insoluble | Insoluble | Soluble |
| Surface Energy, $J/cm^2$ | 68-70 | 550-600 | 75-80 |
| Avg. Aspect Ratio | 30 | 20 | 2 |
| pH of Slurry | 9.0 | 6.5 | 9.2 |
| Solids Content of Slurry, % | 66.5-67.0 | 64.9 | 73.0 |

Ultra-fine ground talc is presently being used as a portion of the pigment content, principally in the area of rotogravure, label, and impact printing grades. The most important reason for the use of talc in rotogravure coating is improved printability without sacrificing gloss *(8)*. It also appears to have acquired application in offset and letterpress sheets. Pigmented size-press coatings are probably the major area of application, especially when the talc is used as the sole pigment.

It has been reported that a 10% to 40% addition of talc improves the print smoothness of rotogravure. The somewhat limper sheet produced with the higher percentage addition of the talc results in the better overall print quality. Talc is also known to improve rollability of the reels.

With both label grades and pigmented size-press coatings, the ability of talc to help improve gloss with calendering is the most important single consideration. Care in this area is necessary, as sheet brightness loss due to calender blackening is possible. In terms of the so-called impact printing-type sheets, the talc imparts release characteristics to the finished sheet as well, and ensures more even coatings. Rowe *(9)* describes this function of talc in the coating component dispersion in addition to its value in preventing smudging and blockage.

The use of talc as an additive pigment to matte finish coatings results in a finish that is less prone to marking during the printing process. This protective ability is also exploited in the manufacture of some types of encapsulated coatings.

# Handling and Dispersion

Because talc is highly hydrophobic and organophilic, it is difficult to properly disperse. If good-quality coating colors are to be prepared, care must be taken to ensure that the wetting of the talc particle is complete.

Ultra-fine grinding of talc leaves a layer of air on the surface of each particle, which results in dry packing containing as much as 97% air. In order to get pigment suspensions that are stable regarding flow characteristics, it is necessary to dispel this air completely. Care must be taken to ensure that this entrapped air does not remain as finely divided bubbles, which tend to become a stable foam until such time as mechanical shear is exerted on the coating system. This condition may lead to uneven coat weights, microsurface craters, and poor print quality.

To ensure the complete dispersion of talc, a combination of additives is necessary, as opposed to a single dispersing agent for hydrophilic pigments such as calcium carbonates and clay. The hydrophobic surface of the platelets of ultra-fine ground talc must first be satisfied by the addition of a wetting agent. If the surface of the talc is not completely adsorbed, the residual activity will rob the latex of its emulsifier when the pigment slurry is added to the binder portion of the coating color. Incomplete wetting will also lower the efficiency of the dispersing agent, resulting in higher viscosities and increased dilatancy of the talc slurry.

Lamar's discussion of the use of nonionic agents of the polyoxyethylene/ polyoxyproplyene type remains the most complete treatment of this phase of the pigment dispersion system *(10)*. Experience has indicated that the lower-molecular-weight combinations of these wetting agents are preferred because of their easier handling, lower level of foam forming, and better availability in a paper mill situation. Additions in the range of 2.5% of the nonionic wetting agent, based on the weight of the dry pigment, are considered to be normal for an ultra-fine ground talc of 12-16 $m^2/g$ surface area.

The final percentage addition needed for complete wetting will vary with the actual talc used in the coating formulation; however, deviations from this addition level will be found to be minimal. The precision of addition level is much less critical if the binder system does not contain a latex emulsion.

In addition to the wetting agent, a normal dispersing agent of the polyphosphate type is recommended. Potassium tripolyphosphate ($K_5P_3O_{10}$) appears to be the most efficient disperser, in terms of obtaining the lowest slurry viscosity and having the least tendency to overflocculate. Sodium hexametaphosphate ($Na_6P_6O_{18}$) comes very close to producing the same level of viscosity, but the dispersion curves show an earlier increase in viscosity in case of overflocculation. Tetrasodium pyrophosphate ($Na_4P_2O_7$) produces a slurry of somewhat higher viscosity than do either of the other two dispersants, and has a very sharp minimum viscosity point.

The optimum usage of potassium tripolyphosphate is approximately 1.3%.

Although the combination of 2.5% of nonionic wetting agent and about 1.3% potassium tripolyphosphate appears to be near ideal for latex-bearing coating colors, other dispersion means may be used when latex is not present in the binder systems.

The use of coploymers of styrene and maleic anhydride resins (SMA) for the dispersion of ultra-fine ground talc has found some application in the area of starch-talc coating colors. These resins are hydrolyzed with ammonia and made water soluble. In the hydrolyzed state, they become good pigment dispersants. In addition, the resin reverts to its insoluble form during the drying process when the ammonia is driven off, and becomes a part of the binder system. Although the full range of SMA resins will perform as dispersants, it appears that the longer-chain materials are most effective.

Developments discussed by Eklund *(11, 12)* indicate that CMC may be used to produce a protective colloidal suspension of talc with excellent stability. When this type of dispersion is based with latices, the earlier discussed satisfaction of the organophilic surface of the talc must be included in the formulation, as was the case with phosphate-type dispersants. This system appears to offer promise of higher-solids coating colors of good runnability.

## Formulation and Coating

As the later work with ultra-fine ground talcs indicates, the binder requirements are about equal to those of fine-particle-size kaolin, and the talcs can be substituted 1:1 in standard starch adhesive coating colors. Coating colors containing latices of various types need proper modification of the talc pigment surface, as discussed earlier, but do not need any adjustment of binder level. Coating colors containing either soya protein or casein need no special attention other than the normal pH precautions.

In practically every case where ultra-fine ground talc is being used in a coating formulation, it is used as a small portion of the overall pigment content. Application methods and final desired coat characteristics dictate the percentage addition rates. The tendency to dilatancy keeps the percentage relatively low when high solids are demanded, such as the case with blade-type coaters. Air knife and rod-type applicators allow greater addition rates with expected increases in ink receptivity and gloss over that of a straight clay pigment-content coating color. **Figure 10-7** shows the comparison between a 100% clay pigment content vs. 100% ultra-fine ground talc pigment content in terms of K&N ink receptivity. A low binder level was maintained to minimize its effect.

*Figure 10-7 Comparison Between a 100% Clay Pigment Content vs. 100% Ultra-Fine Ground Talc Pigment*

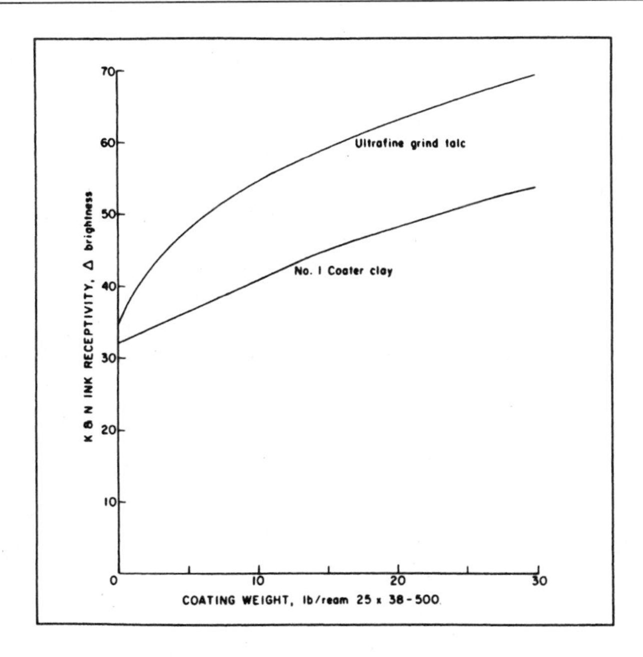


# Economic Considerations and Future Outlook

Ultra-fine ground talcs are somewhat more expensive than either clay or calcium carbonate. They are priced at about US$ 120-150/metric ton in Europe and US$ 200/ton in North America. Although they are normally shipped in 50-lb multiwall paper bags, they are available in both densified and compacted forms in approximately one-ton semi-bulk containers *(13)*.

The future of these types of talcs will expand as the trend to higher-aspect-ratio pigments gains momentum. A considerable amount of research effort is being expended in developing additional areas of value contribution for specialty pigments. These include such areas as special grinding techniques, surface treatments, and brightness improvements, which will lead to greater penetration into the overall coating industry market *(14)*.

In the manufacture of carbonless paper, talc can play a role in the production and coating of coated back (CB) microcapsules. Additionally, it can be an organic scavenger for the removal of unreactive monomers. It can also be a lubricant in the CB coating.

Another area of growth in the use of talc in paper-related application is deinking. Talc has been found to be an effective absorber of ink, and its usage in deinking of recycled paper is expected to grow worldwide. In Europe, it is mostly used in the deinking of tissue and newsprint. High surface area is an obvious need for this application, where dry brightness is of relatively little importance.

## Literature Cited


1. *The Economics of Talc and Pyrophyllite*, 3rd edn., Roskill Information Service, London, 1989.
2. Baak, T. and Gill, G. J., *Paperi ja Puu* 8: 450(1971).
3. Mulryan, H. T., *Encyclopedia of Chemical Technology*, 3rd edn., Vol. 22, "Talc", John Wiley & Sons, New York, 1983, p. 523.
4. Piniazkiewicz, R. J., McCarthy, E. F., and Genco, N. A., *Industrial Minerals and Rocks* (D. D. Carr, Ed.), 6th edn., "Talc", AIME, New York, 1994, pp. 1049-1069.
5. Trivedi, N. C. and Hagemeyer, R. W., *Industrial Minerals and Rocks* (D. D. Carr, Ed.), 6th edn., "Fillers and Coatings", AIME, New York, 1994, pp. 483-495.
6. Pask, J. A. and Warner, M. F., *J. Amer. Ceram. Soc.* 37(3): 118(1954).
7. "Mistron Frost Pigmentation of Starch Paper Coatings," Technical Report 57 T, Cyprus Industrial Minerals Co., Englewood, CO, June 1964.
8. Ahonen, P., *Tappi J.* 68(11): 92-97(1985).
9. Rowe, E. L., U.S. pat. 3,336,155 (Aug. 15, 1967).
10. Lamar, R. S. and Warner, M. F., *TAPPI 1965 Coating Conference Proceedings*, TAPPI PRESS, Atlanta.
11. Eklund, D., *Wochenbl. Papierfabr.* 102(5): 151(1974).
12. Eklund, D. and Teirfolk, J-E. *Tappi J.* 64(5): 63(1981).
13. Schober, W., *Pulp & Paper* (5): 117-119(1991).
14. Schober, W., *Pulp & Paper* (3): 62-64(1991).

# 11.

# Alumina Trihydrate

*David V. Healy and Dr. Klaus Kramer*

Alumina trihydrate (ATH) was first used in the papermaking process more than 50 years ago. Consumption in North America reached an all-time high of 25,000 tons in the 1970s. When two U.S. producers vacated the market in 1989, production figures stabilized at around 10,000 tons/yr. Product modifications and new applications for both paper and board have stimulated new interest in ATH as a filler and coating pigment.

## Origin

Sometimes known as aluminum hydroxide, ATH is sourced from bauxite. Bauxite is a reddish brown ore which is a mixture of various mineral forms of aluminum hydrates plus silica, iron oxide ($Fe_2O_3$), titanium dioxide, clay, and other impurities.

Besides the conversion of ATH to aluminum oxide ($Al_2O_3$) for aluminum metal production, large quantities of specially prepared ATH are used as raw material for chemicals, for flame retardant plastics and rubber, and also as a pigment and filler for paper and board.

Most bauxite for ATH filler and coating applications is supplied by Australia and the African nation of Guinea, which together account for 44% of the world's bauxite reserves and supply about 46% of annual production. Other producers of nonmetallic-grade bauxite are Guyana, Surinam, Greece, and China.

## Manufacturing Process

The production of ATH requires the solubilization of the aluminum content in bauxite and the separating out of other minerals. This is accomplished through the Bayer process.

Soluble aluminum compounds are leaded out in sodium hydroxide, and the insoluble impurities, i.e., iron oxides and silicates, are removed from the solution by sedimentation and filtration.

After final filtration, a clear liquor of sodium aluminate is cooled and seeded with specially prepared fine crystals of ATH. The dissolved alumina in the aluminate liquor crystallizes out on the seed crystals, which are then separated by filtration and washed.

During this precipitation step it is possible to vary the size of the particle from 0.5 µm to 100 µm. Particle size can be affected by various process conditions, including the preparation of the seed crystal. ATH can be precipitated as a final product or as an intermediate product. As an intermediate product it can be ground to a specified particle size or redissolved and reprecipitated for certain processing conditions.

The precipitated ATH is filtered and washed several times to remove soluble impurities. The filtrate is also recycled as make-up for incoming raw materials. The filter cake is either dried or reslurried with dispersant for slurry shipments. It is possible to spray-dry the slurry to produce a predispersed product.

## Crystal Structure

Fine and coarse precipitated alumina trihydrates have a chemical formula of $Al(OH)_3$ and are in a crystalline, not an amorphous, form of aluminum hydroxide. Alumina trihydrates are platelet, nonhydroscopic, chemically stable, nontoxic, and very white. These characteristics make ATH an ideal filler and coating pigment for the paper industry.

### Chemical Properties

A typical chemical analysis for ATH is presented in **Table 11-1**.

*Table 11-1 Typical Chemical Analysis of ATH*

| Chemical | Percent |
|---|---|
| $Al_2O_3$ | 65.20 |
| $SiO_2$ | 0.02 |
| $Na_2O$ | 0.30 |
| $Fe_2O_3$ | 0.01 |
| Moisture | 0.30 |
| Chemical Bound Water | 34.10 |

## Physical Properties

**Table 11-2** shows the physical and optical properties of alumina trihydrate.

*Table 11-2 ATH Physical and Optical Properties*

| | |
|---|---|
| TAPPI Brightness | 95-100% |
| Index of Refraction | 1.58 |
| Moh's Hardness | 2.5 |
| Einlehner Abrasion | 1-3 mg |
| pH of 20% slurry | 9.8 |
| Avg. Particle Size (laser scattering) | 0.9-1.1 μm |
| Screen Residue at 325-mesh | 0.05% |
| Solubility in Acids and Alkalis | Inert Between pH 3.5 and 10.5 |

Alumina trihydrates are either cationic or anionic, if a dispersant is added. ATH is naturally cationic and remains so if the filter cake is dried in its original form. Dispersants contribute to both ease of handling and drying.

## Rheological Behavior

Fine precipitated trihydrates can be slurried to 70% solids with the proper dispersant, pH, and mixing equipment.

Because of their chemical and physical composition, ATH pigment particles are layered with a film of water. As a result, ATH dispersions of 50% or more without dispersants form pastes and are not usable. With the use of dispersants, the viscosity of the pigment can be reduced and the solids increased.

Aqueous ATH dispersions without the proper dispersing agent and proper addition levels will produce thixotropic liquids or show pronounced dilatancy. Under the correct conditions, slurries will be produced that will behave like a Newtonian liquid.

Most effective dispersants are sodium polyacrylates, but polyphosphates and a blend of the two dispersants can be used (**Figure 11-1**).

Optimum dispersant pH is as important as dispersant use. Every dispersing agent has a pH value at which it is optimally effective (**Figure 11-1**).

*Figure 11-1 Viscosity curve of ATH slurry 63% solid content-0.5% dispersant: sodium-polyacrylate*

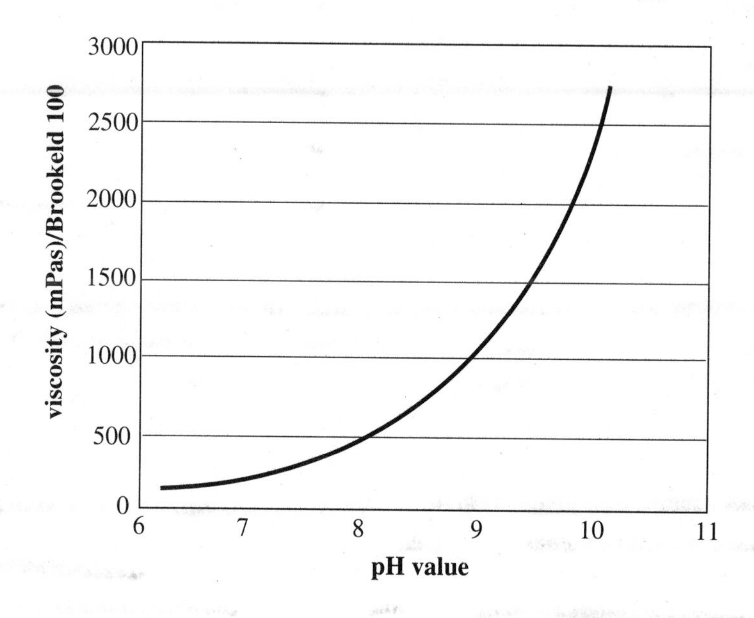


Where high-solids slurries or coating colors are involved, it is necessary to understand the importance of dispersing agents or blends, pH, temperature (less than 60°C), and high-shear mixers.

## Formulation

In most coating formulations where ATH is used, the amount of ATH will vary from 10% to 40% of the pigment. Some size-press coatings have used 100% ATH as the pigment, but it is usually in the 20-30% range. Properly dispersed ATH is commonly compatible with most other pigments, adhesives, and additives.

## Coating Applications

ATH is used in coatings for brightness, gloss, ink gloss, printability, and smoothness. It is compatible with grades of coated paper where optical brighteners are needed, where ink gloss is important, and where sharpness of the printed image is required.

Its high brightness and whiteness characteristics are used to improve the brightness of clay or carbonate-containing coatings. With 95% reflectance over the entire UV-spectrum, ATH does not interfere with the function of optical brighteners. ATH can improve brightness by several points (**Figs. 11-2 and 11-3**).

*Figure 11-2 Coating trials on opacity charts (13g/m² coating weight)*

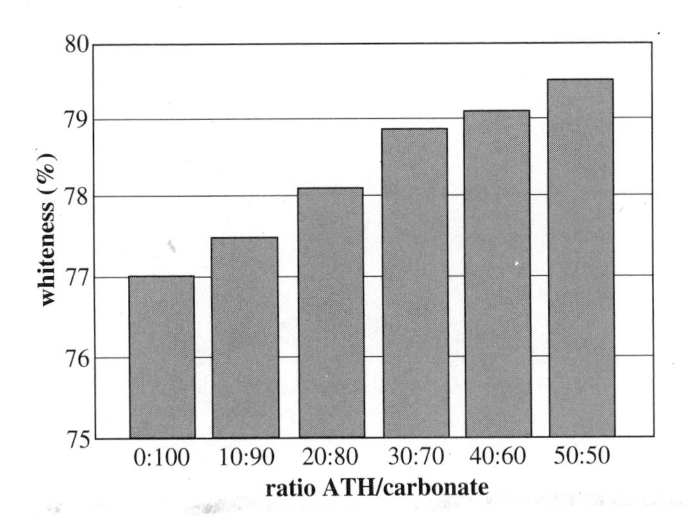


*Figure 11-3 Coating trials on opacity charts (13g/m² coating weight)*

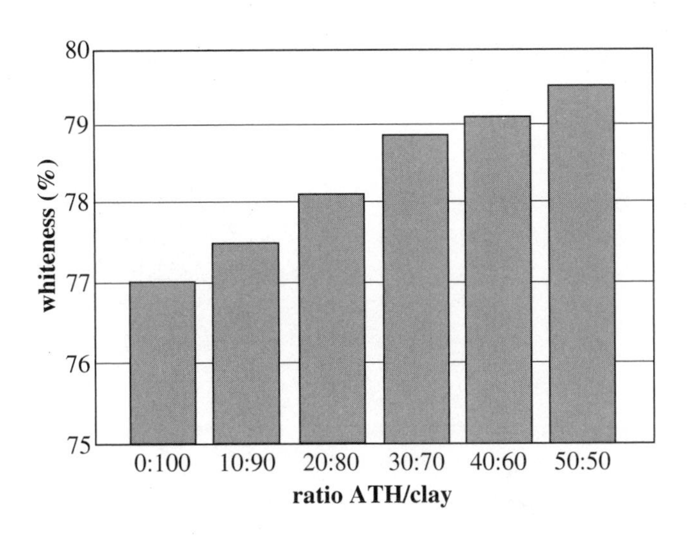

*Figure 11-4 Coating trials on opacity charts (13g/m² coating weight)*

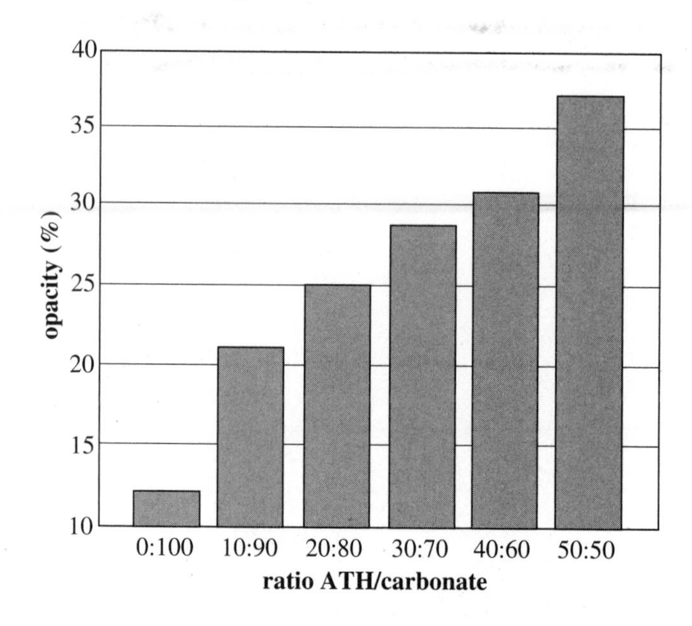


Opacity of clay and carbonate coatings can also be improved. ATH has a scattering coefficient of approximately 2000 cin²/g, which is greater than either clay or carbonate (**Figs. 11-4 and 11-5**).

*Figure 11-5 Coating trials on opacity charts (13g/m² coating weight)*

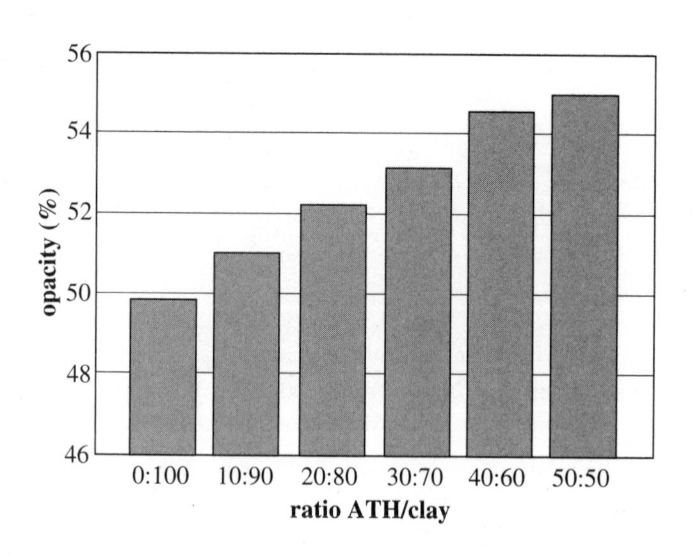

*Figure 11-6 Improvements of a clay-coated-paper with increasing amounts of ATH in the coating colour. Binder: Casein-latex-coating weight: 17 g/m². Measured values without glazing.*

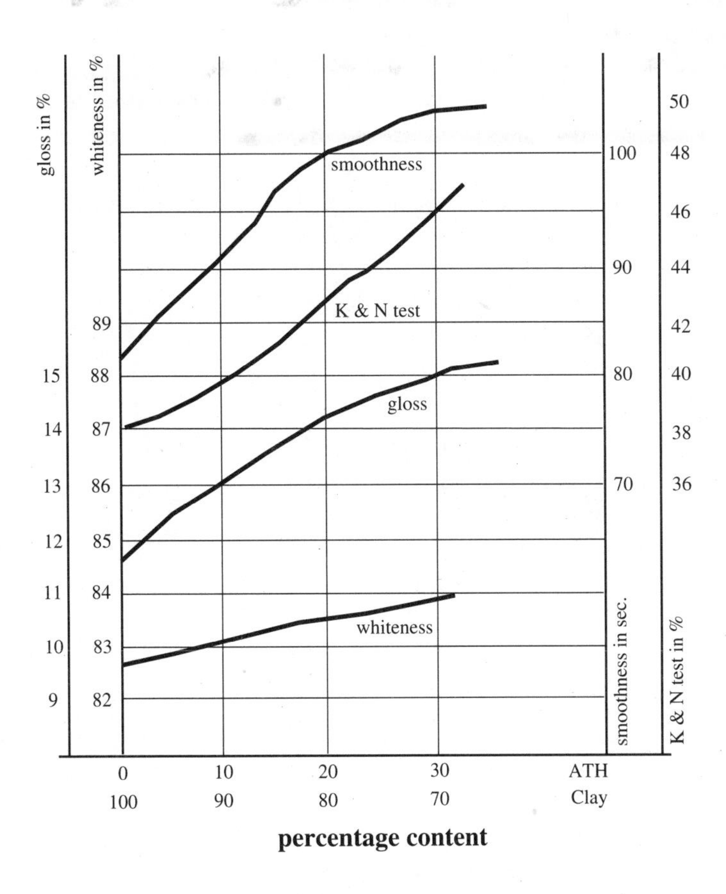


Printability is greatly improved with the use of ATH. Due to its platelet structure, ATH produces a more closed coating than other pigments, preventing the ink from penetrating into the coated surface, which can cause mottling. ATH also has a very high absorption capacity and prevents ink feathering and image shortness. Ink absorption in accordance with the K&N or Larocque test is high compared with other pigment composition.

ATH also demonstrates a uniform acceptance of ink over large areas, with freedom from dusting. Ink gloss is also improved because the ATH absorbs the ink at the surface, so it is possible to design a coated paper with lower paper gloss and to maintain ink gloss.

The platelet crystals of ATH are parallel to the surface of the laminate-like structure. At low calendering pressure, its roughness values are equivalent to those achieved with other pigments at much higher pressure. The smooth surface achieved with ATH allows for improved light refection and gives a higher gloss (**Fig. 11-7**). In supercalendered sheets containing alumina trihydrate, equal gloss is routinely achieved with 30% less supercalendering pressure when compared with competitive pigments. This reduction in pressure also results in an appreciable increase in tear strength.

*Figure 11-7 Properties of Aluminum Trihydrate (1.0 μm) extended coatings*

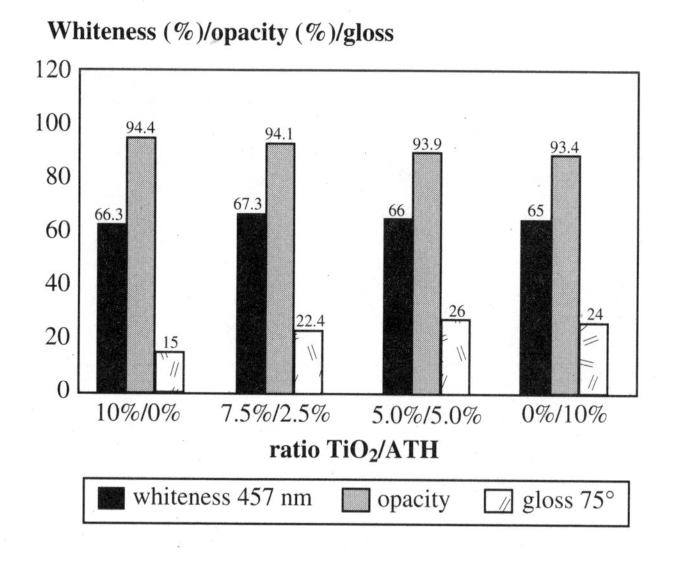


## ATH as an Extender

ATH can be used as an extender for $TiO_2$ while maintaining equal brightness and opacity. Usually one-third of the $TiO_2$ can be replaced by twice as much ATH for improved economics. With the use of ATH as an extender it is possible to improve ink gloss, especially in paperboard coatings (**Table 11-3**).

*Table 11-3 Properties of Alumina Trihydrate (1.0 um) Extended Coatings*

| % Clay | % Ti)2 | % ATH | Br. gain | Op. gain | 75° Gloss gain | Smoothness gain sec. | Larocque printability |
|---|---|---|---|---|---|---|---|
| 90 | 10.0 | 0 | 14.0 | 5.3 | 15.0 | 132 | 92.0 |
| 90 | 7.5 | 2.5 | 15.0 | 5.0 | 22.4 | 148 | 92.2 |
| 90 | 5.0 | 5.0 | 13.7 | 4.8 | 26.0 | 150 | 92.8 |
| 90 | 0 | 10.1 | 12.7 | 4.3 | 24.0 | 156 | 92.7 |

ATH also can be successfully used in precoats or size-press coatings with or without optical brighteners to improve brightness as compared to $TiO_2$ (**Fig. 11-8**).

*Figure 11-8 Points brightness increase over unsized control of size press drawdowns (all coatings contain 8% starch).*

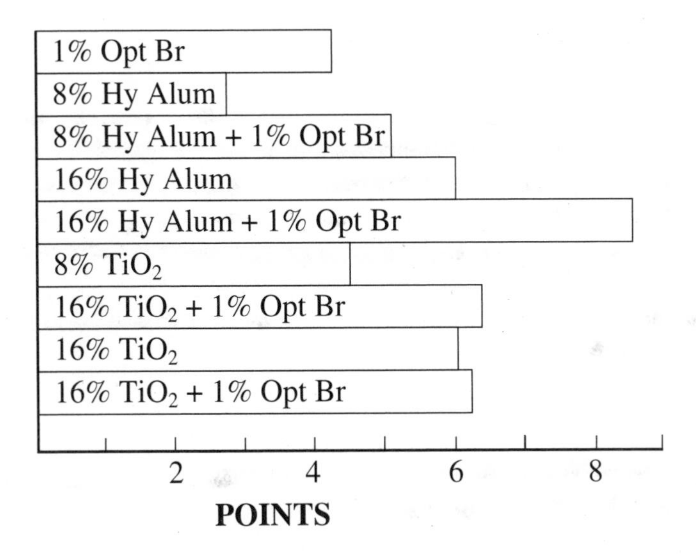


ATH can be used to improve several grades of paper:

- **Coated Board/Paper**
  — Improved whiteness, gloss, and opacity
  — Improved printability
  — Low-price extender for $TiO_2$

- **LWC Paper**
  — Improved whiteness and smoothness
  — Same gloss with lower calendering pressure
  — Improved printability
- **Carbonless Paper**
  — Improved whiteness and printability of CF layer
  — Improved long-term stability
  — Auxiliary pigment in color forming
- **Thermal Paper**
  — Improved print image
  — Reduced abrasion on thermal head
  — Good heat transfer to sheet
  — High transfer rates possible.

# ATH as a Filler

Alumina trihydrate is used as a filler to extend $TiO_2$ and to increase brightness in the papermaking process. It offers several advantages for wet-end applications.

## Brightness

A prime reason for using ATH is its effect on brightness, whiteness, and shade. It is comparable to $TiO_2$ at various filler levels when used alone or with other pigments. In fact, ATH outperforms $TiO_2$ when used in conjunction with optical brighteners because it has a 95% reflectance over the wavelength spectrum of 400-700 nm ($TiO_2$ reflectance decreases to 50% in the blue end of the visible spectrum).

ATH has proved particularly effective in improving shade in recycled and deinked papers, as well as under certain alkaline conditions.

## Retention

Fine precipitated ATH filler is cationic over a wide pH range and offers excellent retention to papermakers. When used with $TiO_2$ and kaolin it not only improves overall retention levels, but the retention levels of the co-fillers as well (**Fig. 11-9**).

*Figure 11-9 Filler retention woodfree paper 200 g/m²*

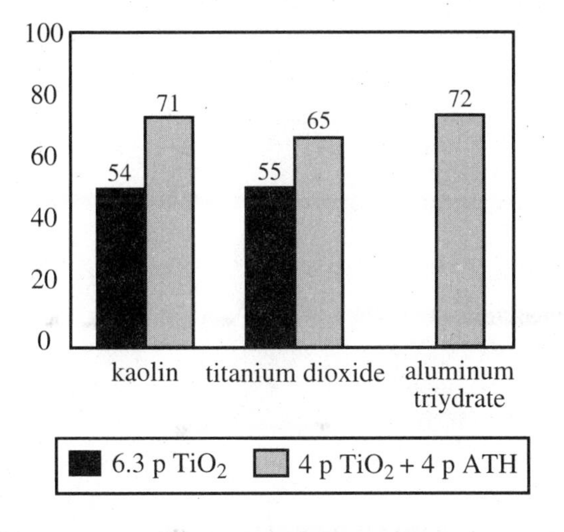


## Opacity

ATH can be used as an extender for $TiO_2$ with comparable results. Usually, to achieve this goal, one-third to one-half of the $TiO_2$ in the formulation is replaced with a blend of two parts ATH to one part $TiO_2$. This is made possible by the retention characteristics of finely precipitated ATH.

## Printability

ATH offers excellent printing properties. Its relatively rapid ink absorption reduces feathering in ink jet papers, while providing good relationship to ink penetration and strike-through.

Alumina trihydrate pigment also provides uniform ink absorption over large areas and very low abrasiveness.

Experience has shown that ATH must be used in certain quantities to achieve the desired effects as a filler. A minimum of three parts replacement of a like amount of filler is required in the furnish to achieve distinct and measurable quality improvements.

# Analytical Procedures

The percentage of alumina trihydrate in paper can be determined by ashing the paper according to TAPPI Test Method T 413 and fusing the ash in a mixture of two parts potassium carbonate and one part boric acid in a platinum crucible. The fused mass is put into a solution with hydrochloric acid, and the percentage of $Al_2O_3$, $TiO_2$, CaO, etc. in the solution is determined by atomic absorption.

The percentage of $Al_2O_3$ present from clay can be calculated from the concentration of $SiO_2$. The percentage of $Al_2O_3$ from clay is subtracted from total $Al_2O_3$ present to determine the percentage of $Al_2O_3$ from alumina trihydrate. The percentage of $Al_2O_3$ divided by 0.65 equals the percentage of alumina trihydrate.

Other ways of determining ATH in filled or coated sheets include TGA and X-ray diffraction or X-ray fluorescence methods.

## Handling and Packaging

ATH is supplied in white repulpable bags, semibulk bags, and slurry. Actual bag weight will vary depending on the supplier. Small bags are generally either 20 kg or 50 lb. The semibulk bags are 500 kg, 900 kg, or 2000 lb. Slurry ATH is available in tank cars or trucks at 65-70% solids.

In mill applications, slurries can be sourced from small bags or semibulk bags either as a separate slurry or co-blended with other pigments. For filler applications, white repulpable bags can be added directly to the pulper. In some filler applications it is desirable to prepare an ATH slurry and pump it to the addition point.

## Future Outlook

There is a growing interest in ATH where brightness is an issue, such as in recycled papers for deinked stock. Ink jet papers are also a promising application with their need for ink adsorption and reduction of ink feathering. New ATH products are being developed to improve gloss and extend or replace plastic pigments. Slurry systems are available to improve the handling of ATH.

# 12.

# High-Structure Amorphous Silica Pigments in Paper

*George E. Alderfer and Roger A. Crawford*

High-structure amorphous silica pigments are used by the paper industry as a partial or complete replacement for titanium dioxide and as a specialty pigment added to a furnish or coating formulation to give improved ink receptivity, porosity, bulk, increased coefficient of friction, and oil and water absorption to various grades of paper. High-structure amorphous silicas have unique structures, and there still exists a degree of art in synthesizing the various structures that are commercially available.

## Silica Technology *(1, 2)*

### Polymerization and Stabilization of Silica Sols

The term silica sol refers to a stable dispersion of discrete particles of amorphous silica. Stable concentrated sols have been available since the 1940s. Silica sols are prepared by polymerizing monomeric silica, usually silicic acid, such that siloxane linkages are maximized and uncondensed silanol groups are minimized (**Fig. 12-1**). Polymerization proceeds through the monomer, dimer, oligomer, and finally to the discrete particle. The spherical units, or ultimate particles, aggregate into larger particles, called primary aggregates. Precipitation conditions determine whether the individual particles develop into a three-dimensional gel or a larger individual aggregate. This is shown in **Fig. 12-2**, which also shows the various sol structures that can be developed depending on conditions. When salts are present, all forms polymerize to a gel structure.

*Figure 12-1 Types of Silica/Oxygen Bonds*

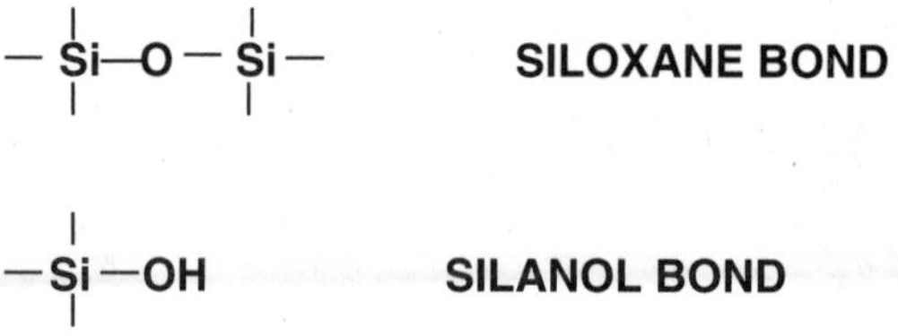

$-\overset{|}{\underset{|}{Si}}-O-\overset{|}{\underset{|}{Si}}-$ SILOXANE BOND

$-\overset{|}{\underset{|}{Si}}-OH$ SILANOL BOND

*Figure 12-2 Polymerization Behavior of Silica*

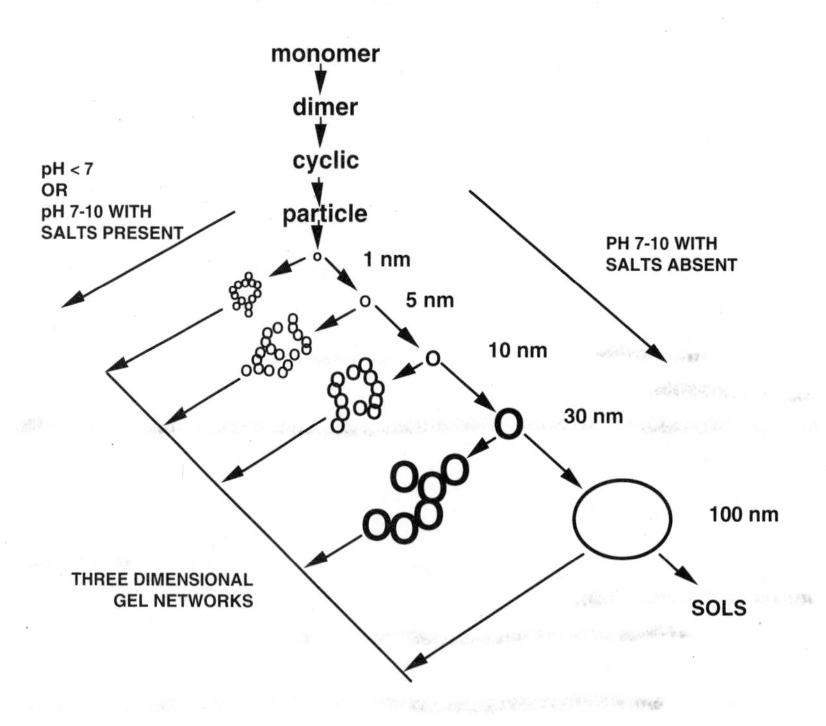


Silica ultimates have particle diameters in the range of 10 nm to 90 nm. In 1940, Carman *(3)* proposed a model in which the interior silicon atoms in the sol particle are joined by siloxane linkages, but the surface of the three-dimensional polymer is terminated in silanol groups. An idealized sol particle is show in **Fig. 12-3**. The surface silanols give amorphous, aggregated silicas their high degree of hydrophilicity and rapid dispersion in water during makedown.

*Figure 12-3 Carman Model*

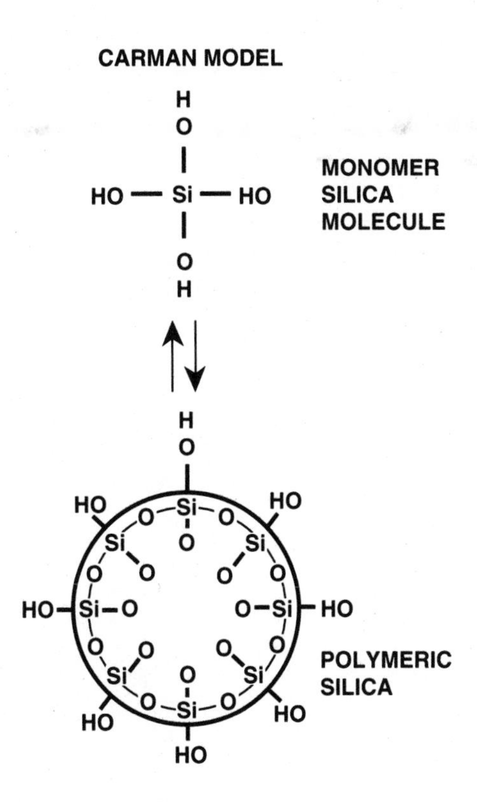


The process of aggregation and gelling in the silica system is unique. Unlike most metal oxides, silicon dioxide remains amorphous during polymerization and generally is in equilibrium with the monomer. While the "sol is being converted to the gel, the growing aggregates contain the same concentration of silicic acid and water as in the surrounding sol region" *(4)*. Hence, there is a relatively small change in viscosity until the "gel point" is reached, and then the viscosity increases rapidly. Sols have excellent temporary stability and slow gel time around pH 1.5-3, but very little stability and a rapid gel time in the pH 5 to pH 6 range. Above pH 7, the particles are strongly negative and only particle growth occurs. Above pH 10.5, dissolution of silica occurs.

The isoelectric point of a silica sol is pH 2, so one anticipates flocculation because of particle collisions. However, aggregation does not occur because the rate of condensation of silanols to siloxanes is a minimum at this pH. The condensation reaction occurs via an ionic mechanism; below pH 2 it depends on the $H^+$ ion while above pH 2 the reaction depends on the $OH^-$ ion concentration.

The sol particles maintain a slight negative charge to neutral pH, so particle collisions continue. In the pH 5 to pH 6 range, condensation and reverse hydrolysis proceed more rapidly and gelation occurs. Reverse hydrolysis occurs when a hydrogen from a silanol group reacts with a $SiO^-$ to produce a siloxane bond and hydroxyl ion.

Above pH 7, the surface negative charge increases so mutual repulsion occurs and the sol is stabilized. These variations in stability are shown in **Fig. 12-4**. The effect salts and hydrofluoric acid have on stability also are shown in Fig. 12-4. The gelling of silica will not be discussed further, but additional information is in Iler's *The Chemistry of Silica (5).*

*Figure 12-4 Effect of pH on Stability of Silica Sols*

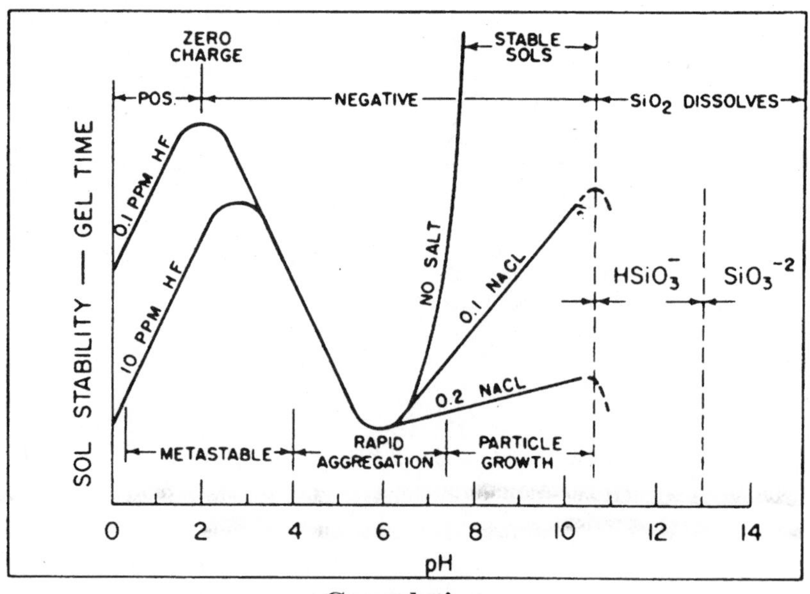


## Coagulation

The coagulation of silica uses a different mechanism than gelation but both utilize the same variables. In gelling, the sol suspension is homogeneous during cross-linking, so the mixture remains quite clear as the viscosity increases and the mass becomes rigid. Coagulation or aggregation results in an increase in particle size. As the particles grow, they begin to be large enough to interact with light, so the slurry becomes turbid as the precipitate forms. Coagulation occurs because of van der Waal forces, as shown in **Fig. 12-5**. In the pH range of 7 to 10, the $OH^-$ ion concentration gives the sol a more negative surface; hence, the particles remain separated (Fig. 12-5A). At low salt levels, the particles remain separated, and the sol is stable. However, at salt levels of 0.1 M or higher, sufficient numbers of hydrated sodium ions are available to cause flocculation of the silica aggregate. One theory is that when a hydrated sodium ion approaches a negative sol, the sodium loses a water molecule from its hydration sphere and becomes electrostatically attached to the negative sol (Fig. 12-5B). When another negative sol approaches the sol-sodium ion complex, the sodium ion loses another water molecule, and the negative sol becomes attached to the sol-sodium complex. The aggregate continues to build using this mechanism (Fig. 12-5C).

*Figure 12-5 Proposed Bonding Scheme to Form Primary Aggregates*

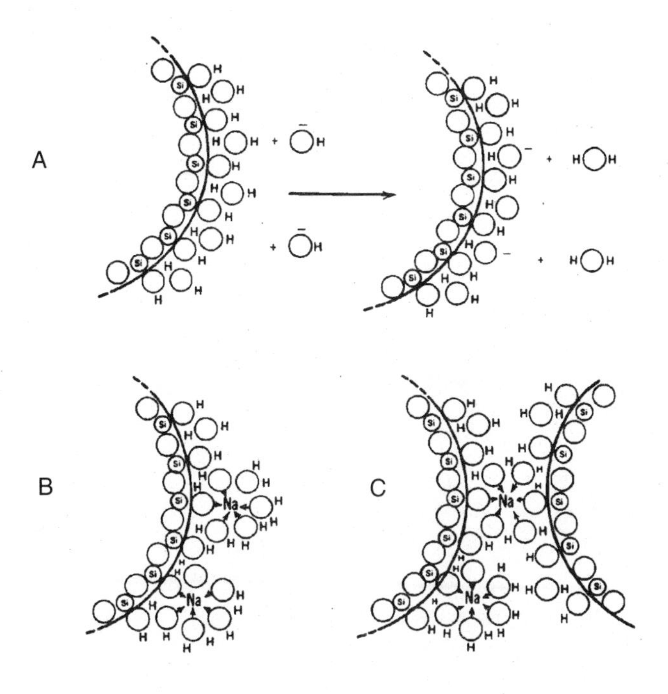


The basic differences between gelation and aggregation have been elucidated. In both cases, colloidal particles become "bonded" together to form a three-dimensional structure. The three forms just discussed are shown in **Fig. 12-6**. The upper left (Fig. 12-6A) shows sol particles dispersed due to the high negative charge on the sol surface. A large, three-dimensional gel network is shown in the upper right (Fig. 12-6B). The interstices are excellent sinks for water molecules, which is why gels are rigid at such a low percent solids. The bottom drawing represents a pigmentary, aggregated silica (Fig. 12-6C).

*Figure 12-6 Comparison of Sol, Gel, and Pigmentary Silica*

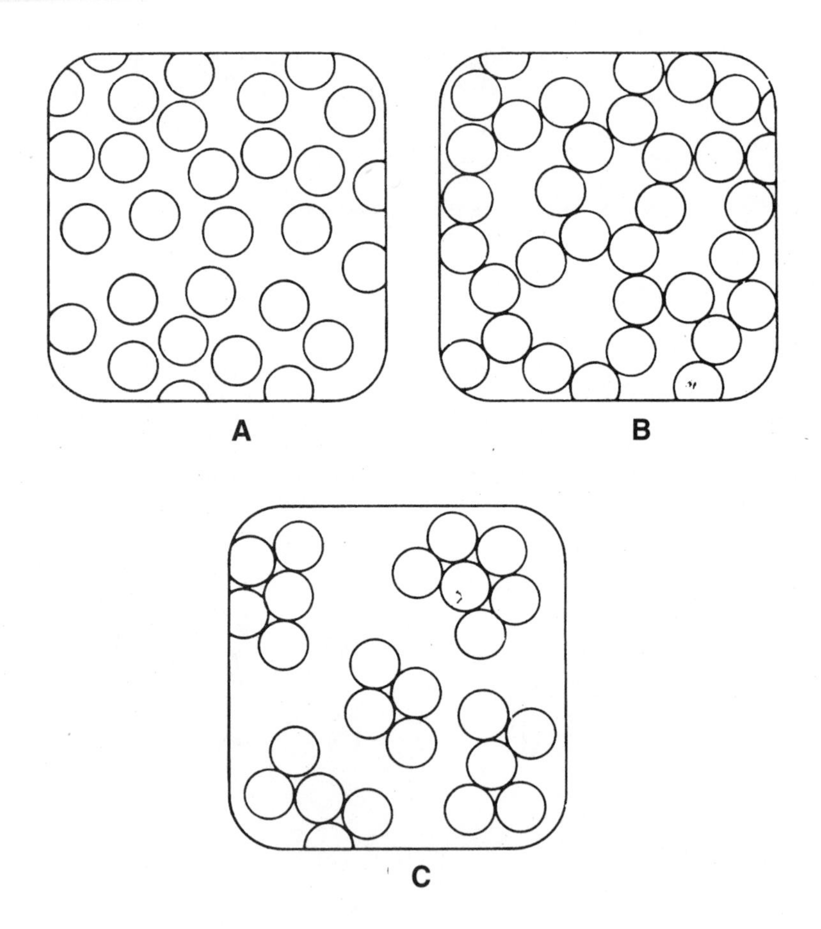


The diameters of individual sol particles are in the 10 nm to 90 nm range (0.010-0.090 μm), and primary aggregates range from 100 nm to 300 nm.

Flocculation of primary aggregates gives rise to the amorphous pigmentary silicas used in the paper industry. Pigmentary silicas have mean particle sizes from 1 μm to 30 μm, depending on the method of precipitation and finishing techniques. This secondary aggregation, or agglomeration, results from hydrogen bonding and is elaborated later in this chapter.

Two main differences betwen gel and pigmentary silica particles are the surface area and the oil absorption. Gel surface areas are usually between 300 $m^2/g$ and 700 $m^2/g$, while high-structure amorphous silicas have surface areas from 30 $m^2/g$ to 400 $m^2/g$. The second difference is developed during drying. The structure of the gel collapses, so oil absorptions are around 100 mL/100 g gel; pigmentary silicas with similar surface areas have oil absorptions greater than 300 mL/100 g gel.

## High-Structure Amorphous Silicas

The high-structure amorphous silicas are pigmentary particles and have unique chemical and physical properties. The paper industry uses silicas in wet-end and coating applications where high brightness, opacity, bulk, ink receptivity, porosity, reduced show-through, high coefficient of friction, and improved oil and water absorptivity are important factors.

Pigmentary amorphous silicas are prepared as shown in **Fig. 12-7**. The sodium silicate is not neutralized via ion exchange to maintain low ionic strength but acidified using a mineral acid, carbon dioxide, or other acid source. As with silica sol synthesis, colloidal particles are formed first. However, the high ionic strength of the system causes the ultimate particles to form linear oligomeric pigmentary units or cross-link to form a gel structure. By properly controlling the manufacturing conditions, only pigmentary silicas are formed. **Figure 12-8** shows a typical ultimate particle. Ultimate particles bond together via hydrogen bonds to form primary aggregates, much like cellulose fibers bond together during the drying of paper. **Figure 12-9** depicts a primary aggregate with the "circles" representing ultimate silica particles as described by Carman *(3)*. Usually 15-35 ultimate particles bond together to form the primary aggregate. The aggregation step is one of the techniques that generates the high-structure and opacifying properties associated with amorphous silicas.

*Figure 12-7 Pigmentary Precipitation*

SODIUM
SILICATE
ULTIMATE
PARTICLE
SILICA
AGGREGATION
AGGLOMERATION
FLOCCULATION

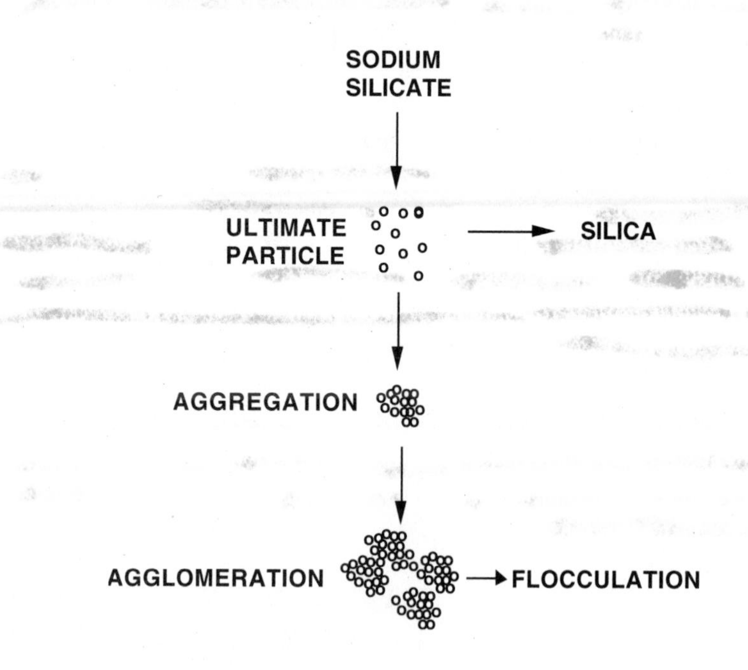

*Figure 12-8 Typical Silica Surface*

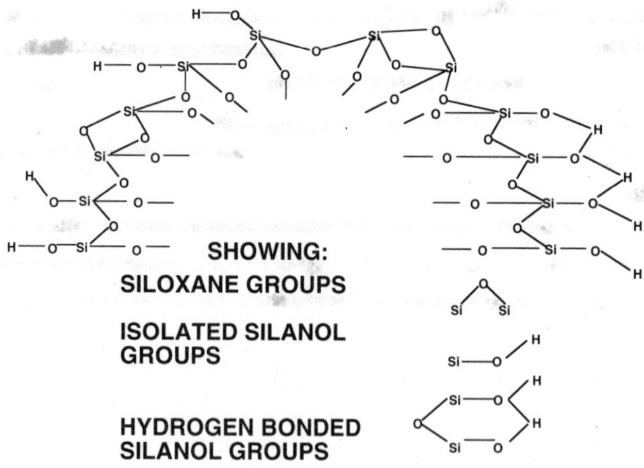

SHOWING:
SILOXANE GROUPS
ISOLATED SILANOL
GROUPS
HYDROGEN BONDED
SILANOL GROUPS

*Figure 12-9 Functional Silanol Groups*

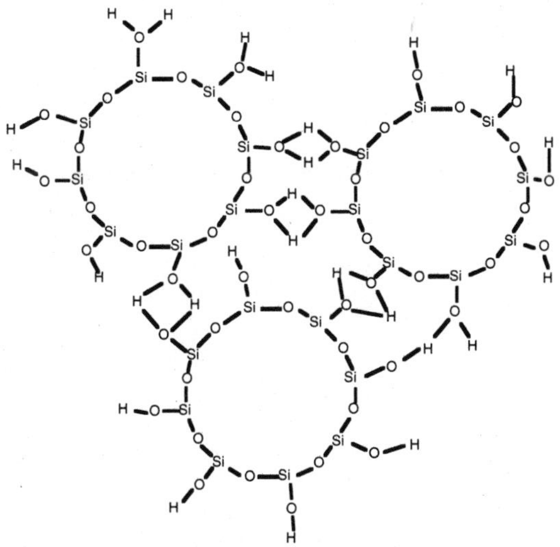

**SILICA TO SILICA HYDROGEN BONDING**

The aggregates agglomerate, also via hydrogen bonds, to form the high-structure amorphous silicas (**Fig. 12-10**). The circles represent primary aggregates which, as indicated in the last paragraph, are held together by hydrogen bonds. The hydrogen bonds between the primary aggregates are exaggerated to show the bonding mechanism. **Figure 12-11** is a 300,000 magnification transmission electron micrograph (TEM) of a high-structure amorphous silica pigment. The TEM shows ultimate particles (individual spheres), primary aggregates (a grape cluster), and agglomerate particles (a grape cluster of primary aggregates). A scanning electron micrograph (SEM) of an agglomerated silica is shown in **Fig. 12-12**. The agglomeration step develops solid-air interfaces that give high-structure amorphous silica pigments better opacifying properties than predicted by their refractive index. These synthetic pigments have pigment brightness in excess of 100 (Hunterlab D25A-Z percent), so they provide sheet brightness greater than that of most other pigments.

*Figure 12-10 Agglomeration of Silica Via Hydrogen Bonding*

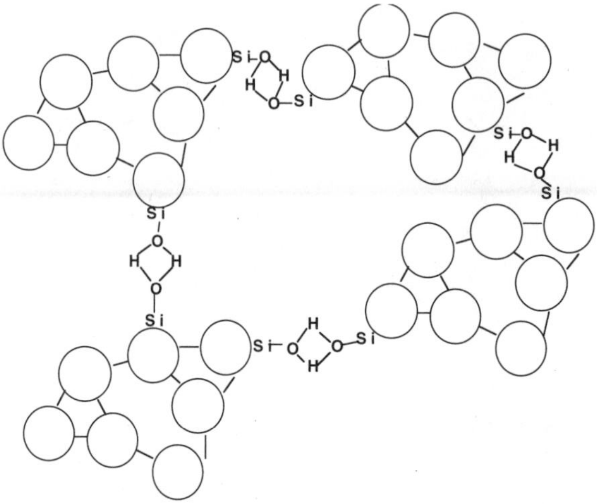

*Figure 12-11 TEM Phogtomicrograph of a Primary Aggregate of Amorphous Silica*

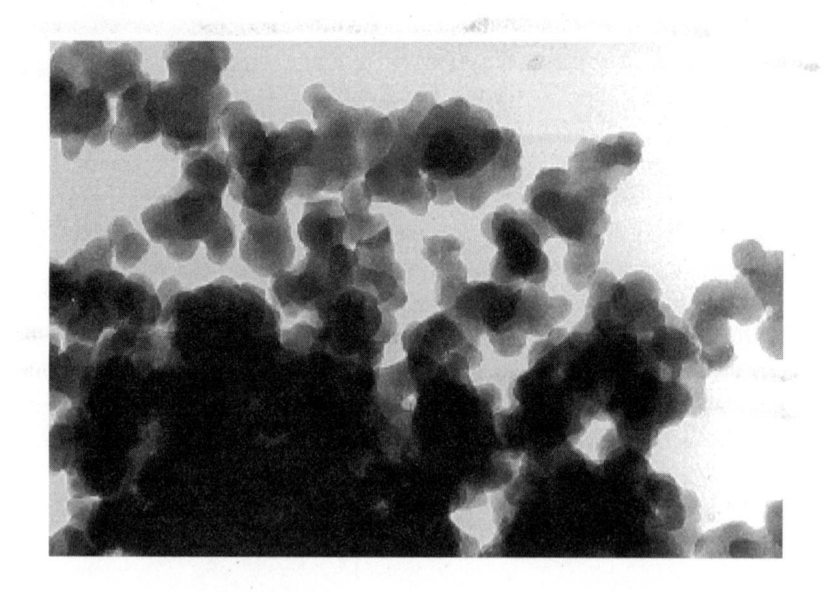

*Figure 12-12 SEM Phogtomicrograph of an Agglomerated Amorphous Silica*

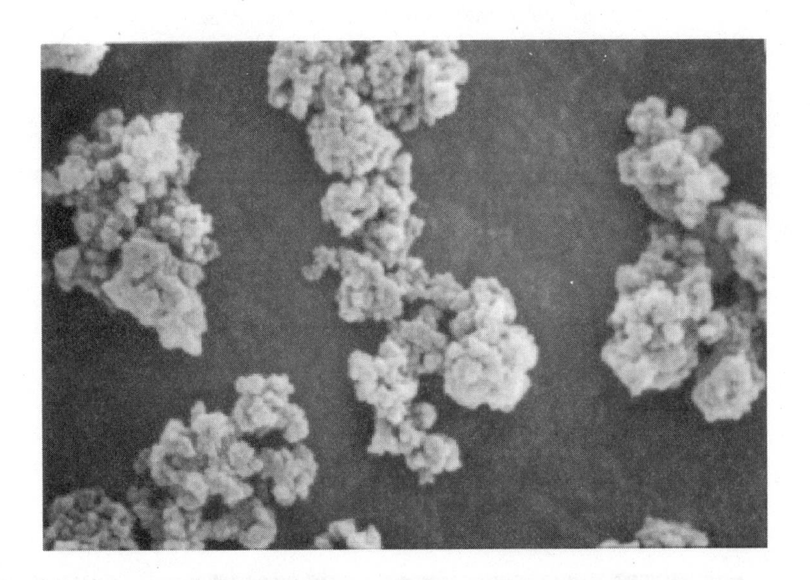

Therefore, high-structure amorphous silicas having a wide range of properties are produced by controlling (a) the size of the ultimate, (b) the degree of bonding during primary aggregate formation, and (c) the degree of bonding during agglomerate formation.

High-structure amorphous pigments, as they are normally produced, have zeta potentials greater than -40 mV and maintain that zeta potential throughout the pH range when mineral acids are used to adjust the pH *(6)*. Zeta potential versus pH for a typical high-structure amorphous silica pigment is shown in **Fig. 12-13**. Therefore, these pigmentary silicas are excellent anionic miniparticles, as described by Moberg *(7)*, and can be utilized in dual retention aid systems.

*Figure 12-13 Zeta Potential of Amorphous Silicas vs. Slurry pH*

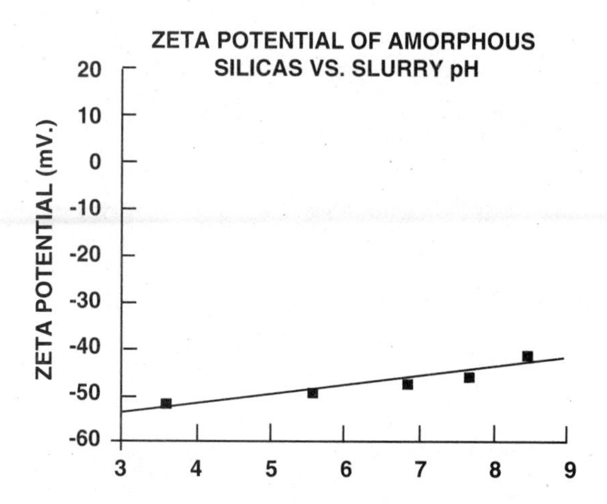


## Chemical and Physical Properties of High-Structure Amorphous Silicas

The high-structure amorphous silicas do not react with most components in a paper furnish; however, the surface silanols undergo some chemical reactions. Hydrogen bonds are formed with water, alcohols, and glycols. A unique reaction occurs between silanols on amorphous silicas and 1,2-dihydroxybenzene that is similar to the reaction between silica and alcohols. During the reaction a silicon atom is extracted from a tetrahedral silica oligomer and forms an octahedral dihydroxybenzene complex and a smaller silica ologomer. The smaller silica oligomer remaining reacts with more 1,2-dihydroxybenzene. This is a rare reaction that solubilizes silica in aqueous media. Under controlled conditions, silica reacts with alcohols to form hydrophobic silicic acid esters and with certain alkyl anhydrides to form alkyl-modified surfaces. Additional reactions are given in Iler *(8)*.

Silanols are not considered hydrogen donors but are electrophiles in the Lewis acid-base system and form stable compounds with Lewis bases. The $pK_a$ for the high-structure amorphous silica pigments described here range from -3.0 to 6.0, depending on the method of preparation. Therefore, the silica surfaces vary from moderately to mildly acidic.

Another unique property of pigmentary silicas is their low abrasivity. Typical results obtained from an Einlehner abrasion tester show high-structure amorphous silica pigments are slightly more abrasive than hydrous clays, with calcined clays, paper grade talc, and $TiO_2$ being at least an order of magnitude higher in abrasion (**Fig. 12-14**).

*Figure 12-14 Einlehner Abrasion Values (mg loss/100,000 rev) for Various Pigments*

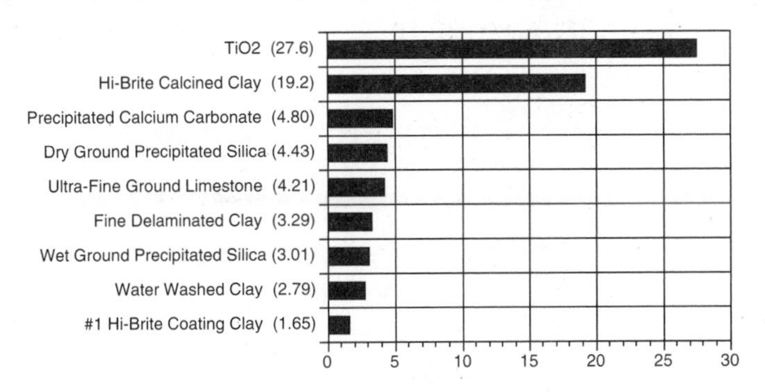


Pigmentary silica is also very effective at increasing sheet brightness. High-brightness bond and No. 1 premium grades of paper often add fluorescent whitening agents (FWA) to produce a sheet brightness above 96%. When high-structure amorphous silica pigments partially or completely replace $TiO_2$ in a coated or uncoated grade containing a FWA, brightness is significantly increased. FWAs absorb in the range of 340 nm to 370 nm and re-emit in the 420 nm to 470 nm range; hence the blue brightness of the sheet is increased both visually and as tested by TAPPI Test Methods. High-structure amorphous silica pigments reflect most of the UV light; therefore, nearly all the UV light is available to be absorbed by the FWA.

Titanium dioxide and clays are absorptive as well as reflective pigments. Part of the UV light is reflected as UV light; the rest is absorbed. Therefore, the efficiency of the FWA is reduced. The UV light absorbed by $TiO_2$ and clay is not re-emitted as visible light but becomes thermal energy; hence, these pigments reduce brightness by making less UV light available for the FWA. So, the silica pigments are better for high-brightness papers using fluorescent whitening agents. The UV absorption characteristics of the three pigments discussed are shown in **Fig. 12-15**.

*Figure 12-15 Pigment Absorbance vs. Wavelength*

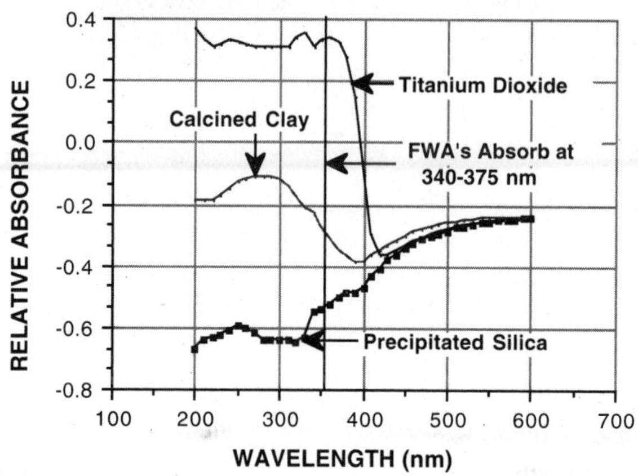


# Applications *(2)*

The high-structure amorphous silica pigments were designed for coating and wet-end paper applications. Due to precipitated amorphous silica's unique structure and surface chemistry, they have found application in a wide area of products from merchant and bond grades to very specialized grades such as laminate paper and specialized imaging papers.

## Coating Applications

The data from a laboratory trial in which a No. 5 merchant-grade base stock was coated on one side using a lightweight coating formulation were normalized to 6.5 lb coating per 3300 $ft^2$ per side (**Table 12-1**). The formulations using high-structure amorphous silica pigment show improved ink receptivity while brightness and gloss are equivalent to the control coated sheet. A small decrease in opacity occurred when all of the $TiO_2$ was replaced with high-structure silica pigments. The other small differences observed are within the experimental error of the data.

*Table 12-1 Laboratory Study A*

| Sample Sample | Parts $TiO_2$ | Parts Amorphous Silica | TAPPI Opacity, % | TAPPI Brightness, % | K&N Decrease, % | Gloss, % |
|---|---|---|---|---|---|---|
| 1 | 5 | 0 | 92.1 | 73.3 | 20.1 | 40 |
| 2 | 2 | 3 | 92.2 | 73.1 | 23.2 | 40 |
| 3 | 0 | 5 | 91.4 | 73.3 | 23.7 | 42 |

Lightweight coated sheet. Coating color: 95% clay and 5% white pigment. Coat weight 6.5 lb/3300 $ft^2$.

A second laboratory trial coated a No. 5 merchant-grade base sheet on one side using a different coating formulation. The data, normalized to 5.5 lb/3300 $ft^2$, are shown in **Table 12-2**. The brightness, Hunter color values, corrected TAPPI and printing opacities, smoothness, IGT pick, and print gloss for the coating containing the high-structure amorphous silica pigments are essentially the same as the $TiO_2$ control.

**Table 12-3** is a ladder study using a freesheet as the base stock. The data indicate that replacing 75% of the $TiO_2$ with high-structure amorphous silica gives equivalent opacity, brightness, Hunter values, and sheet gloss when compared to the $TiO_2$ control sheet.

**Table 12-4** shows results from a laboratory study that coated a No. 5 merchant-grade paper with 9.5 lb coating/3300 $ft^2$. This study was specifically designed to determine the level of brightness and opacity increase that may be obtained from high-structure amorphous silicas. Marginal increases in brightness and opacity were obtained when three parts $TiO_2$ were replaced with five parts of high-structure amorphous silica; however, when an additional five parts of silicas were added, the brightness increased by one point and opacity by one-half point.

Mill trial data also show optical properties remain unchanged when high-structure amorphous silica pigments replace $TiO_2$ in coating formulations. **Table 12-5** gives results from an extended lightweight coated (LWC) trial. The data show that when high-structure amorphous silica pigment replaces 30% of the $TiO_2$ in the coating formulation, the supercalendered brightness, opacity, gloss, and Parker Print-Surf of the sheet remain constant.

A mill trial using a wood-free sheet is shown in **Table 12-6**. These data, which are averages of several reels, show the opticals remain constant when high-structure amorphous silica pigments replace about 40% of the $TiO_2$ in the formulation. The average optical values given in Table 12-6 are equivalent when allowances are made for the differences in basesheet characteristics.

## Wet-End Applications

The high-structure amorphous silica pigments have been well received in the premium-grade bond market. These papers have high brightness and opacity, basis weights in excess of 50 lb/3300 $ft^2$, and require strength, durability, and permanence. Some of the properties are obtained using cotton fibers, bleached chemical wood pulps, or combinations of these, but additional properties are obtained using high-brightness and opacifying pigments. Ash contents often are 10% or higher.

Historically, titanium dioxide has been the pigment of choice in this market, but recently significant cost savings have been realized by replacing part or all of the titanium dioxide with high-structure amorphous silica pigments. Partial or complete replacement of $TiO_2$ with these silica pigments improves ink receptivity and printing characteristics while maintaining sheet brightness and opacity.

Many mills are converting to alkaline papermaking to reduce pigment costs, particularly $TiO_2$. Alkaline paper degrades significantly less with time than paper produced at low pH. This has given a boost to the precipitated calcium carbonate market, but calcium carbonate can only replace a finite amount of $TiO_2$ without a loss in sheet opacity. High-structure amorphous silica pigments can replace a significant amount of the remaining $TiO_2$ before any loss in opacity occurs.

Mill data show that replacing up to 55% of the $TiO_2$ in a standard 50-80-lb bond sheet maintains opacity, while slightly increasing brightness. Further, the Hunter b value decreases by as much as one-half point, indicating the paper has a slightly more bluish hue (less yellow), which should improve visual brightness.

# Other Specialty Applications

## Decorative Laminates

The decorative-laminate industry makes a large variety of end products using low- and high-pressure laminating technology. Typical of these products are counter and table tops (Formica), dresser and cupboard surfaces, etc. A decorative laminate contains many layers, but it is the resin-saturated decorative and overlay sheets where high-structure amorphous pigments are used.

Decorative papers use a special grade of $TiO_2$ to provide very high-saturated opacities and resistance to fade when exposed to UV light. Basis weights for most grades are in excess of 50 lb/3000 $ft_2$ ream, and ash levels are normally from 25% to 40%. Saturated opacities typically are greater than 95%.

Historically, this industry evaluated many pigments trying to reduce its dependence on $TiO_2$ but were never able to replace more than five percent without loss of opacity or fade resistance, or both. A high-structure silica specifically designed to replace substantial quantities of $TiO_2$ without any loss of opacity or brightness has been designed. Laboratory and mill data show that high-structure amorphous silica pigments can replace up to 20% of the $TiO_2$.

## Scrubable Wallpaper

Scrubable wallpaper places severe demands on the coating applied to the sheet. Because this product must be scrubable, the coating has a much higher binder level than most grades. This binder level with normal coating pigments results in a sheet with poor ink receptivity and severe mottling in the gravure printing operation. High-structure amorphous silica pigments in the coating open the structure enough to provide higher quality print without sacrificing scrubability.

## Thermal Printing Papers

Direct thermal-chemical printing media has a heat-sensitive recording layer on a paper substrate. The recording layer has a combination of a leuco dye and an activator, such as phenol. To produce an image the recording layer is activated by a heated recording head. Because of the intimate contact of the organic recording layer and the printing head, the coating layer can melt and adhere to the recording head. This "scum" and the associated sticking that it produces can be a severe defect in the paper. A number of pigments have been used to absorb the scum and clean the recording head, such as calcium carbonate, kaolin, and titanium dioxide. Amorphous precipitated silica originally could not be used in this manner. The high surface area of the silica provided a reaction site for the phenol and leuco dye to react. This caused "background fogging", a gray shade in the paper due to partially reacted dye.

The solution to this conundrum is to choose an amorphous silica that has high oil absorption, low surface area, and relatively small agglomerate size. The low surface area will minimize the background fogging, the control of the particle size will ensure controlled abrasion to clean the print head, and high oil absorption will keep the residue formed during heating away from the print head *(10)*.

## Ink Jet Paper

The ink used for ink jet printing is a water-soluble-dye based system. Most ink-jet inks are greater than 90% water; therefore, the paper must absorb water quickly to avoid wicking and maintain sharp edge acuity. This is compounded when a full four-color print is made. In this case, as much as four times the water that is used in monochrome printing may be added to the surface of the sheet to attain certain secondary colors and six times the ink for process black.

The highly absorbant, porous nature of high-structure amorphous silica pigments make them a natural choice for ink jet printing papers. These pigments quickly absorb the vehicle and sets the toner, which maintains edge acuity and proper color balance and saturation. The excellent water absorptivity of high-structure silicas minimizes the banding phenomenon caused by the receptivity of the paper for ink components relative to the reciprocal action of the printing head moving across the sheet. The high water absorptivity also decreases drying time for the print. Wet ink on the surface smears with normal handling.

The Jujo Paper Co. Ltd. patent *(11)* was one of the first patents to highlight the significant advantage of high-surface-area silicas for ink jet printing. This patent specifically claims the use of silica pigments with BET surface areas greater than 200 $M^2/g$. A year later, in a study by Lyne and Aspler *(12)*, 18 different papers were analyzed for use as ink jet papers. This study again concluded that those papers containing high-surface-area silicas in the coating performed best.

An ink jet sheet performs best when it has the right balance of absorptivity and sizing, has a surface area high enough for other printing methods such as offset printing or pencil, high surface smoothness, and high brightness. Silica helps improve absorptivity, smoothness, and brightness.

In general, the silica chosen for ink jet coating formulation should have the following properties:

- An agglomerate size of 3 μm or less
- High surface area (typically 150 $M^2/g$ or higher)
- High oil absorption
- Low refractive index.

These generalities will be adjusted as the formulation is developed. Higher-surface-area silicas tend to keep the ink at the surface of the paper. This can produce darker colors but can impair drying. High-surface-area silicas have smaller ultimate particle size. This can reduce the light scattering of the pigment because the particles are too small. Low light scattering improves the color of the printed image by not diluting the color as it penetrates into the sheet. Smaller particles make a smoother coating surface, therefore providing improved dot circularity. But smaller particles can decrease the pore volume of the coating, again affecting drying. As in all coating formulations, a balance is needed.

## Carbonless Paper

High-structure amorphous silica pigments are ideal for carbonless paper for many of the reasons just discussed for ink jet printing. The absorptive nature of silica keeps the print sharp. By quickly absorbing the dyes on the coated front from the coated back of the carbonless paper, the dye is prevented from migrating to adjacent areas. The high pigment brightness of the silica also adds contrast to the print.

## Mattes and Dulls

Another sector of merchant-grade papers are the low gloss, high quality printing papers known as mattes and dulls. These grades are difficult to produce because both high-quality printing and low sheet gloss are required. This dictates a very narrow region of surface roughness, optically rough but printably smooth. Therefore, sheet specifications require surface discontinuities of at least 5 µm but not so large that they cause printing defects.

High-structure amorphous silica pigments are precipitated so particle size and structure are tailored to fit requirements of the mattes and dulls. The agglomerated structure is strong enough to resist both scuffing (localized glossing due to handling) and calendering, which occurs during the manufacturing of the dull grades. The high pigment brightness and ink receptivity also assist in achieving the printing requirements for these grades.

## Summary

The silica precipitation conditions are modified to produce high-structure amorphous silica pigments having a wide range of properties. The ultimate particle size, the size and type of primary aggregates, the size and agglomeration of the final particles, and modifications in the surface chemistry are adjusted to produce silicas with specific properties.

High-structure amorphous silica pigments are used in wet-end and coating applications. The paper properties enhanced by these silica pigments are: brightness, ink receptivity, porosity, and opacity. Silicas are chemically inert to most common chemicals used in the paper industry, and the hydrophilic character of the surface makes dispersion in aqueous media easy and rapid. The surface charge on high-structure amorphous silica pigments does not change when mineral acids are used to adjust pH; therefore, they are used in acid and alkaline mills equally well. The exact amount of $TiO_2$ that can be replaced by these high-structure amorphous silica pigments depends on the application but usually ranges from 20% to 60%.

## Acknowledgement

Figures 12-2 and 12-4 through 12-6 *(4, 5, 8)* are reprinted by permission of John Wiley & Sons, Inc.

# Literature Cited

1. Crawford, R. A. and Alderfer, G. E., *TAPPI 1990 Neutral/Alkaline Papermaking Seminar Notes*, TAPPI PRESS, Atlanta, *Silica Use and Theory,* pg. 125.
2. Freis, R. E., Crawford, R. A., and Alderfer, G. E., paper presented at The Global Outlook for $TiO_2$ & $TiO_2$ Extenders/Replacements in Coatings, Paper, & Plastics, March 1990, Falmouth Associates, St. Louis.
3. Carman, P. C., *Trans. Faraday Soc.* 36: 964(1940).
4. Iler, R. K., *The Chemistry of Silica*, John Wiley & Sons, New York, 1979, p. 176.
5. Iler, R. K., *The Chemistry of Silica*, Chs. 3, 4, and 6, John Wiley & Sons, New York, 1979.
6. Crawford, R. A., unpublished internal results, PPG Industries.
7. Moberg, K., *TAPPI 1989 Retention and Drainage Short Course Notes*, TAPPI PRESS, Atlanta, p. 65.
8. Iler, R. K., *The Chemistry of Silica*, John Wiley & Sons, New York, 1979, p. 677.
9. Crawford, R. A. and Ewald, F., unpublished internal results, PPG Industries.
10. Usui, K., et al., U.S. pat. 4,509,064 (April 2, 1985).
11. Oshima, H., et al., U.S. pat. 4,478,910 (Oct. 23, 1984).
12. Lyne, M. B. and Aspler, J. S., *Tappi J.* 68(5): 106-110(1985).

# Index

# C

# D



# F



# G

# TAPPI's Vision Statement

**We** share the strengths of individuals
for the benefit of the industry.

**We** are a global community of
motivated individuals who lead
the technical advancement of the
paper and related industries.

**Together...**

**We** serve as an international forum
to exchange technical information
and promote research.

**We** provide outstanding educational
and professional growth opportunities
and recognize individual achievement.

**We** provide the public with sound scientific
information on industry related issues.

**We** create success by the quality,
timeliness and innovativeness of
our products and services.

**Integrity and fellowship
characterize our association.**